F
157
1969

S0-BBM-795

THE JOURNAL OF
CHARLES MASON AND JEREMIAH DIXON
1763-1768

MEMOIRS OF THE

AMERICAN PHILOSOPHICAL SOCIETY

Held at Philadelphia
For Promoting Useful Knowledge
VOLUME 76

FIG. 1. Stone marker (1766) on the Mason-Dixon Line in hedgerow west of road leading north from Rising Sun, Maryland. Photograph by Aubrey Bodine, by courtesy of *American Heritage*.

THE JOURNAL OF
CHARLES MASON
AND
JEREMIAH DIXON

Transcribed from the Original in the
United States National Archives
With an Introduction by

A. HUGHLETT MASON

University of Virginia

AMERICAN PHILOSOPHICAL SOCIETY
INDEPENDENCE SQUARE   PHILADELPHIA
1969

Copyright © 1969 by The American Philosophical Society
Library of Congress Catalog
Card Number 69-17273

Q
11
A512
v.76

PREFACE

When in 1860 the Journal of Charles Mason and Jeremiah Dixon, compiled in the field during their famous survey of the Maryland-Pennsylvania border, was found at Halifax, Nova Scotia, with it was Mason's certificate of election in 1768 to membership in the American Society of Philadelphia. In the next year after his election the American Society merged with another group, the American Philosophical Society, on whose roll his name was at once inscribed. It is therefore most appropriate that the Society, after two hundred years, should make the Journal available to historians of science, engineering, and colonial affairs by publishing it in full as faithfully transcribed and edited by Dr. A. Hughlett Mason.

The manuscript Journal is now in the United States National Archives. Its history before it came back to the United States is not fully documented. The final entry in the Journal, a letter written by Thomas Penn, in London, about two months after Mason departed from the colonies, suggests that Mason had taken the document to England in 1768. Nothing is heard of it after this for ninety-two years. The author of the biographical sketch of Charles Mason in the *Dictionary of National Biography,* Agnes Mary Clerke, states without citing the source of her information, that Mason's manuscript Journal and field notes "were found in 1860 at Halifax, Nova Scotia, flung amidst a pile of waste paper into a cellar of Government House." In 1861 a contributor to the *Historical Magazine,* Boston (vol. 5: pp. 119-202) signing himself P. C. Bliss, said that the manuscript Journal was then in the possession of a gentleman at Halifax, who had allowed him to see it and to publish a brief description with excerpts.

Bound with the Journal as it now exists are a few letters which explain the purchase of the Journal by the Department of State from Judge Alexander James of Halifax in 1877 for $500 in gold. Later it was transferred to the National Archives.

Dr. A. Hughlett Mason (who disclaims descent from Charles Mason) received in 1964 and 1965 grants from the American Philosophical Society's Penrose Fund to aid him in transcribing the Journal and Mason and Dixon's achievement in the light of his expert knowledge of geodetic theory and practical surveying. Earlier studies of the general history of the great survey have been published by the late Dr. Thomas D. Cope, Emeritus Professor of Physics in the University of Pennsylvania (who also had been aided by grants from the Penrose Fund). In a long series of papers from his own pen and two published jointly with H. W. Robinson, former Librarian of the British Museum, Dr. Cope brought together practically all that is known about the history of the great project that was finally completed by the two English surveyors—its historical origins, the political and administrative aspect of Mason and Dixon's employment, the nature and source of the instruments they employed. Those of Dr. Cope's studies which are directly relevant to the present undertaking are cited in the list of Sources following the Introduction.

Dr. Hughlett Mason, a former graduate student associated with Dr. Cope, now adds a practical explanation of Mason and Dixon's technical methods and a critique of their results. To his efforts, including the laborious and at times difficult transcription of the text of the Journal, all who are interested in the procedures of this brilliantly successful survey will be greatly indebted. Students of many phases of American colonial history also will appreciate the Journal's record of astronomical and meteorological phenomena, persons and places visited, and accounts of geographical features, natural history, and Indians both friendly and hostile.

GEORGE W. CORNER

CONTENTS

ILLUSTRATIONS

Redrawn versions of diagrams inserted by Charles Mason throughout the Journal appear on pages 212-228.

INTRODUCTION

I. THE MANUSCRIPT JOURNAL

The manuscript Journal is now in the National Archives, Washington, D. C., where it is in Record Group 59, General Records of the Department of State.

The following description is largely taken from an account prepared by the Department of State, with additional comment by the present editor. The volume is labeled on its backstrip as follows: "Mason & / Dixon's / Line. / Original / Journal / of the / Commissioners. / 1763."

The volume . . . is labeled on its backstrip as follows: "Mason & / Dixon's / Line. / Original / Journal / of the / Commissioners. / 1763."

The entries were probably made in a blank book with heavy paper covers, which are bound into the present volume. Later the leaves and covers of the blank book were cut apart and were glued to the "stubs" of a binder, to which various letters received were attached in the same manner. The manuscript was little damaged by these changes, though part of a word is occasionally concealed at the end of a line where the stub overlaps a sheet.

The journal is in a single hand throughout and is signed at the end "C: Mason." Most entries are in the first person plural, referring to the joint activities of Mason and Dixon; but others are in the first person singular, referring to events that occurred when Dixon was absent. From these facts it seems clear that the journalist is Mason. Slight variations in color of ink and slant of handwriting from one entry to another indicate that the journal is the original document, written from day to day, and not a smooth copy, prepared at a later time.

At the front of the volume, probably inserted when it was rebound by the Department of State, are copies of correspondence between the Secretary of State and George W. Childs, of Philadelphia, November 2, 1876-March 8, 1877, relating to the purchase of the journal by the United States Government from Judge Alexander James, of the Supreme Court of Nova Scotia. These copies are followed by several leaves of scattered notes, dated September 17,

1762; August 19-21, 1763; December 19-22 and 27-31, 1763; January 1-2, 1764; and April 1767. Bound at various points in the journal, in order of mention, are original letters received by Mason and Dixon from Richard Peters (Philadelphia, January 7, 1764), C. Morton (September 1, 1766), Hugh Hamersley (London, March 22, 1766), William Allen, Benjamin Chew, and John Ewing (Philadelphia, September 19, 1766), Thomas Penn (London, June 17, 1767), Nevil Maskelyne (Greenwich, February 24, 1767), Horatio Sharpe and others (Chester, June 18, 1767), Benjamin Chew (Philadelphia, December 10, 1767), Thomas Penn (London, June 17, 1767), Charles Thomson (April 15, 1768), and Thomas Penn (near Windsor [England], November 14, 1768).

A fair copy of the Journal in the same hand, that of Mason, is deposited in the Hall of Records of the State of Maryland, Annapolis.

An abridged copy of the Journal was printed under the title of "Field Notes and Astronomical Observations of Charles Mason and Jeremiah Dixon," in *Report of the Secretary of Internal Affairs of the Commonwealth of Pennsylvania, Containing Reports of the Surveys and Re-Surveys of the Boundary Lines of the Commonwealth, Accompanied with Maps of the Same* (Harrisburg, 1887), pp. 59-281.

The text of the Journal was reproduced by offset lithography directly from a typewritten transcript made under the editor's supervision. Brief explanatory statements added by the editor are introduced by the words "Editorial comment" or are enclosed in parentheses. Such parenthetical passages should be readily distinguishable from those appearing in the original document. Some abbreviations, as "do" for "ditto" and "So" for "South," have been spelled out. A few geographical and other terms have been modernized. A few abbreviated first names have been spelled out.

The background of the boundary controversy which waged between Pennsylvania and Maryland from 1681 to 1763 was of great scope and embraced numerous tedious considerations. Chief among these were questions of title resulting from exploration or conquest, interpretation of inadequate maps, and errors, ambiguities, and mathematical impossibilities in geographic delineation. Furthermore, the entire problem was badly complicated by the careless practice of English monarchs in making grants of land which had already been chartered by their predecessors. In addition to such well-founded difficulties, one can perceive throughout the entire contest a partisan desire to evade numerous clearly outlined specifications of the grants.

In consequence of the voyages of the Cabots in 1496-1497, England claimed by international law all of the Atlantic seaboard of North America from Nova Scotia to Cape Fear in present North Carolina. On the basis of such claims, King James I made the first two grants to the London and Plymouth Companies which respectively settled Jamestown in 1607 and Plymouth in 1620. The northernmost limit of the London Company in the third charter of 1611 was specified as the forty-first parallel of north latitude, and the southernmost limit of the Plymouth Company in 1620 was to be the thirty-eighth parallel. There was an obvious overlap here which included more than half of present Pennsylvania and New Jersey, all of Delaware and Maryland, and much of present Virginia. However, this overlap brought no controversy between Jamestown and Plymouth, as neither colony had early settlements within the area adversely assigned.

The colonization of Maryland may be traced to several events in the life of Sir George Calvert, subsequently the first Lord Baltimore, who was appointed to office in Ireland soon after the ascension to the throne of James I. His demonstrated ability and character gave rapid advancement to a position of influence and gained for him the esteem of the King. He was appointed Secretary of State in 1618 and was elevated to the peerage in 1625.

George Calvert's first attempt in establishing a colony was in Newfoundland in 1623, but he became discouraged in the undertaking on account of the severity of the climate and accordingly abandoned the project. For over a decade he had been a member of the Virginia Company of Planters which was interested in the settlement at Jamestown. When Virginia became a Royal Province in 1624, he was made a member of the provincial council in England. Still interested in colonization in the New World, he made a trip to Virginia and on his return petitioned King Charles I for a grant of land in that colony. At first George, Lord Baltimore,[1] requested territory south of the James River, but opposition was interposed and he subsequently requested and was granted land in northern Virginia. According to his charter, which did not pass the Great Seal until June 20, 1632, the colonial territory of Maryland was to be bounded on the north by the fortieth parallel of north latitude, on the south by the south bank of the Potomac River and by a parallel of latitude through Watkins Point on the Eastern Shore, on the east by the Atlantic Ocean, and on the west by a meridian through the source of the Potomac River. The charter specifically precluded the settlement of territory previously cultivated, i.e., "hactenus inculta." George, Lord Baltimore, died in England on April 15, 1632, before the granting of the charter. However, its provisions were awarded to his heir, Cecil, second Lord Baltimore, who in turn entrusted to his brother, Leonard Calvert, the carrying out of the initial details of colonization. He, with a company of about three hundred settlers, arrived on the lower Potomac on March 27, 1634, and established the first settlement in Maryland at St. Mary's City. The Calverts were Catholics at that time and the founding of Maryland was principally intended to provide a refuge in the New World for members of that faith who in England were without political or civil rights. However, as few Catholics came and as there was no discrimination against non-Catholics, the former soon numbered less than one-fourth of the colony.

As was earlier pointed out, the charter of Maryland provided for the colonization of land hitherto uncultivated. Settlements were thus prohibited where others

---

[1] The title of Lord Baltimore extends over a period of one hundred and forty-seven years, i.e., from 1624 to 1771. George Calvert, first Baron of Baltimore, was raised to the peerage by Charles I, and the title passed from father to son until it reached Frederick Calvert, sixth Lord Baltimore, who died in Naples in 1771 without an heir. It is so frequently used without specifying the individual that much confusion has resulted. In order to preserve clarity in this account, the names and dates of each are given below. The first year in each case is the date of accession, and the second is the date of death.

First Lord Baltimore: George Calvert, 1624-1632
Second Lord Baltimore: Cecil Calvert, 1632-1675
Third Lord Baltimore: Charles Calvert, 1675-1715
Fourth Lord Baltimore: Benedict Leonard Calvert, 1715-1715
Fifth Lord Baltimore: Charles Calvert, 1715-1751
Sixth Lord Baltimore: Frederick Calvert, 1751-1771

already were in possession. This gave rise to a minor territorial controversy with Virginia, which had earlier established outposts on Kent Island opposite Annapolis and Palmer's Island near Havre de Grace. Otherwise, no Maryland territory was settled by Caucasians at the time of the founding of Saint Mary's City in 1634.

Soon after the advent of the seventeenth century, Holland was anxious to establish a foothold in North America and needed some pretext to challenge the English claim of discovery. In great dynastic movements, adversaries usually attempt to interpret international law in their own behalf. In this instance it was argued that John Cabot had not touched sufficiently close to the North American mainland in the area of their interest to consider it an English possession. The Dutch claim was that the explorations of Henry Hudson in 1609 were more detailed, that he had carefully navigated the South (Delaware) River and North (Hudson) River, and that this geographical research transcended that of Cabot and was a basis for a better title. However, a study of the contemporary maps of this area revealed that both the Delaware and the Hudson Rivers were not unknown to explorers, and the British never admitted the validity of the Dutch title on the basis of discovery.

In conflict with English claims, the Dutch established a settlement in April, 1631, at a place variously denominated Swaanendael, Hoornkill, and Whorekill on the present Lewis Creek in Sussex County, Delaware. The attempt was unsuccessful, as the colony was destroyed by an Indian massacre the following year. This failure was followed by a second Dutch attempt in 1632 to which opposition was registered by the Virginians when the Governor (DeVries) visited Jamestown prior to proceeding up the Delaware. Although the good will of the Indians was gained, the settlement was abandoned the same year after failure of efforts at fishing and whaling.

Sweden became interested in colonial expansion at this time but, as with Holland, the question of legal title to territory on the Atlantic seaboard had to be faced. This dilemma they attempted to resolve by the device of purchasing territory from the natives. They planted a settlement at Paradise Point near Dover in March, 1638, in territory which earlier had been assigned by Charles I to Maryland. About two centuries later Chief Justice Marshall ruled that the predatory claims of discovery of land of natives (Indians) preempted the claims to title by purchase.

The Dutch were still entrenched on Manhattan and considered spurious the Swedish title of purchase from natives of land along the Delaware. In 1651 they invaded the Swedish settlement and erected Fort Casimir, the present New Castle. Three years later the Swedes retaliated and recaptured their stronghold. This somewhat bellicose proceeding was concluded two years later when the Dutch again invaded and recaptured Fort Casimir. The Swedes who remained in the contested territory eventually allied themselves with the English or Dutch.

By 1659 Cecil, second Lord Baltimore, found his charter rights very firmly challenged by the Hollanders, who were now uncontested in their settlement along the Delaware. Each side was soon making representations to the other claiming infringement of territory. The matter was referred by the Dutch to Governor Stuyvesant in Manhattan, while Lord Baltimore petitioned King Charles II for a confirmation of his charter which was granted in 1661. Matters had now reached an impasse. Not only was Maryland being populated by a hostile foreign power but northern and southern English colonies were severed by the Dutch stronghold on Manhattan and contiguous settlements. England became convinced that the Dutch must be dislodged.

In 1664 Charles II granted to his brother James, Duke of York, all the land between the Connecticut and Delaware Rivers. Acting as Lord High Admiral, he immediately launched a naval attack on Fort Amsterdam, which capitulated on September 8, 1664. Although the west side of Delaware Bay was not conveyed to the Duke of York, he, nevertheless, late in the same month appeared with his fleet before the Dutch settlement at New Amstel in Lord Baltimore's territory and reduced it to submission. After a brief success at re-conquest during disturbances in England in 1673, Holland finally ceded to the British in 1674 all of her possessions in North America. The theory had been held by the English that the Dutch never legally possessed land in North America, and on this assumption they could not surrender to the Duke of York what they did not actually possess. Therefore it would appear that Lord Baltimore should now have been in uncontested possession of his territory adjacent to the west side of Delaware Bay.

William Penn I had been a distinguished admiral in the British Navy and the family was highly esteemed by King Charles II and his brother James, Duke of York. He had loaned the King 16,000 pounds sterling. Young William Penn II had embraced the Quaker faith and desired to found in the New World a colony primarily for this religious sect. In lieu of the personal debt of the King to his father, he persuaded Charles II to grant him a charter to territory in the New World between Maryland and New York. This document was signed by the King on March 4, 1681. More specifically, the northern boundary of Pennsylvania was designated as the forty-third parallel of north latitude, and the western boundary as a meridian five degrees west of Delaware Bay. The southern boundary was more complex but was to extend eastward along the fortieth parallel of north latitude until it intersected a circle of twelve miles radius centered at some unspecified point in the settlement at New Castle, and the arc of the circle was to be the boundary from the point of intersection to Delaware Bay. This body of water was to be the eastern boundary. The carelessness with which such matters were handled in England will be obvious if one will take a map, draw a circle of twelve miles radius around New Castle courthouse, and observe that the fortieth parallel of north latitude passes about thirteen miles north of such a circle. Thus it is seen that the charter of Pennsylvania did not designate a closed figure. At this time began the boundary controversy between the Penns and the Calverts which was destined to persist for eighty-two years.

Charles, third Lord Baltimore, was in Maryland at the time of the granting of Penn's charter. He received notice thereof on April 2, 1681, and he was advised to confer with William Penn II to establish the boundaries between their two provinces. By letter from the King, they were required

to make a true division and separation of the said provinces of Maryland and Pennsylvania, according to the bounds and degrees of our said Letters Patent and fixing certain Land Marks where they shall appear to border upon each other for the preventing and avoiding all doubts and controversies that may otherwise happen concerning the same.

William Penn had selected a kinsman, William Markham, to act as deputy governor for him. He visited the third Lord Baltimore at the latter's home on the Patuxent River in August, 1681, but became ill and was cared for by his lordship for three weeks. Following his recovery, it was not considered that an unbiased conference could be held and they adjourned to meet again the following October. Other postponements took place on account of illness and difficulties of transportation, and negotiations were broken off for several months. During this interim, influential citizens in the northeastern counties of Maryland received letters from William Penn declaring that they were settled in Pennsylvania and that their tax payments to Maryland should discontinue. This led to bad relations in the area concerned. Observations for latitude were taken at several points on Delaware Bay between the present sites of New Castle and Chester and all seemed to indicate a value substantially under forty degrees. Finally in a conference between the second Lord Baltimore and Governor Markham near the present site of Chester, the former suggested that the two go up the Delaware River to the fortieth parallel. This was opposed by Governor Markham on the ground that William Penn's charter specified that his lower boundary should be no more than twelve miles north of New Castle. He furthermore asserted that, if the two patents overlapped, the matter would have to be resolved by the King. During this visit the third Lord Baltimore ordered the inhabitants of the surrounding area to pay no further taxes to Penn and stated that he would return later to collect his own.

At this time the third Lord Baltimore's title to the section later named the "Three Lower Counties" or the present State of Delaware began to be questioned. He had exercised considerable effort to establish settlements in this area but colonization proceeded slowly. When the Duke of York conquered the Dutch, he was actually left in possession of this territory, which he soon assigned to William Penn. It could hardly have escaped the attention of the Privy Council in England that such a situation would create further boundary complications, but as the Duke soon would ascend to the throne as King James II, it did not appear prudent to oppose him.

Previous negotiations between the third Lord Baltimore and Governor Markham had been attended with much hostility, and it seemed desirable to await the arrival of William Penn before considering further conferences. He arrived at New Castle on October 24, 1682, and took possession of the main body of his estate and also of the territory recently assigned to him by the Duke of York. Immediately he took steps to amalgamate the two areas.

This union having been accomplished, William Penn proceeded to southern Maryland, where in Anne Arundel County near Annapolis he conferred with Lord Baltimore on December 13, 1682. Here various impractical and unscientific procedures were proposed by Penn, some at the recommendation of the King, for locating the southern boundary of Pennsylvania, i.e., forty degrees north latitude. One method suggested was to measure northward from Cape Charles, Virginia, which was thought to be at the latitude of 37°05′, a figure now known to be only 1.5 minutes too small. Sixty statute miles was proposed as the measure of a degree, whereas actually in this zone 69.5 statute miles is much closer to the truth. Moreover, a route survey cannot be run very far north from Cape Charles without entering the Chesapeake Bay, as the Virginia portion of the Delmarva Peninsula runs northeasterly. Lord Baltimore's alternative suggestion that they go up the Delaware River with a sextant and locate the fortieth parallel of north latitude would have been much more practical.

It is believed that Penn knew from earlier reconnaissance that the fortieth parallel would lie above navigation on the Chesapeake. By using the measure of 60 miles per degree as the King recommended, he would have been able to gain about 28.5 miles in the measurement of about three degrees northward from Cape Charles. This would have assured him a port on the headwaters of the Bay. Of course, there most surely were able scientists in England at this period, particularly Newton, who knew the dimensions of the earth sufficiently well to advise the King of the approximate measure of a degree of latitude in statute miles much more precisely than the figure he proposed. One sees here a lack of perseverance and thoroughness.

Charles, Lord Baltimore, questioned Penn at this conference regarding the transfer of the "Three Lower

Counties" to the latter by the Duke of York. Penn stated that he would discuss this point as soon as the location of the northern boundary of Maryland was fixed. The following morning Lord Baltimore escorted William Penn to a Quaker settlement near Galesville, Maryland, about twelve miles south of Annapolis. After a meeting with the Quakers, Penn returned home by the Eastern Shore. Thus ended the first negotiations between William Penn and the third Lord Baltimore. Each proprietor had outlined his position, but no progress was made in adjusting their differences.

The following April, 1683, Penn communicated with Lord Baltimore and requested him to specify a place and time for a further discussion of their boundary issue. Arrangements were concluded for them to confer at New Castle later in the same month. The agenda included further discussion of the impractical procedure of making a linear measurement northward up the present Delmarva Peninsula, but the third Lord Baltimore disagreed with this and stated that all they needed was a latitude observation near the fortieth parallel. At this time Penn agreed to have the boundary established at Lord Baltimore's charter position if the latter would sell sufficient land adjacent to the headwaters of the Chesapeake Bay to insure his colony the access of incoming ships from England. But his lordship declined this proposal. The conference concluded without constructive results.

In 1682 two incidents occurred which may be evaluated as contributing heavily to the loss of the cause of Maryland. When Charles, third Lord Baltimore, returned from England after receiving his title, he was accompanied by his cousin, Colonel George Talbot. The latter appears to have been a man of much ability, destined to rise to a position of great prominence. He was granted an immense acreage near the headwaters of the Chesapeake Bay, probably to constitute a buffer area to fend off the migration of settlers from the territory over which Penn exercised dominion.

A sufficient number of astronomical observations had been made along the lower Susquehanna for the latitude to be fairly well established. Nevertheless, in the summer of 1682 Colonel Talbot ran a survey line from the mouth of Octoraro Creek in latitude 39°39′ to the mouth of Naaman Creek, latitude 39°48′, on the Delaware River about twelve miles northeast of New Castle. The length of this line was about forty-two miles and was run on a true bearing of about N73°E. On the average it was nineteen miles below the charter boundary of Maryland. This appears to have been a rough survey. No monuments were erected but some trees were blazed. Charles, Lord Baltimore, described this line as being "east-west" but too far south to his "disadvantage." However, one is constrained to inquire how an error of seventeen degrees in azimuth could have been made, as no such

magnetic variation is believed to have existed during the last several centuries in that region. This line immediately became the cause of much trouble. Penn maintained that Charles, Lord Baltimore, considered it the northern boundary of Maryland. Although there is little doubt that this view was taken by many Marylanders, there is ample documentation that it was not shared by the proprietor. The diplomacy was further complicated by a somewhat bizarre proceeding in late 1683 wherein the intrepid Colonel Talbot presented himself at Penn's residence on the Schuylkill River and demanded that the latter surrender to Lord Baltimore "all the Land upon the West Side of Delaware River and Bay, and the Seaboard side of fourtieth Degree of Northerly Latitude, and more particularly all that part thereof which lyeth to the Southward of the markt lyine aforesaid." The stalwart proprietor of Pennsylvania appears to have been somewhat hard put by the audacity of the Maryland colonel. He gave a lengthy reply in writing as to why he could not comply. It is believed that these two incidents had their impact in England, where in the inner circle of the King's Court William Penn already had superior standing.

The controversy now stood at a deadlock, and both sides realized that their conflicting demands would have to be referred to the Mother Country for adjudication. Such an arbitration of their interests was welcomed by Penn because of his high esteem in England and was favored by the Duke of York, the heir apparent to the throne. Conversely, the third Lord Baltimore abhorred such a proceeding, as he had been out of touch with the English court for many years. Additional causes which weakened his case were his action to obstruct the collection of the King's taxes in Maryland, the unfortunate incident of the Talbot survey line, and the demands of the impetuous Colonel Talbot on William Penn at his home. The case was first referred to the King and Privy Council. The King in turn referred it to the Board of Trade and Foreign Plantations. With reference to the territory along the Delaware, i.e., the "Three Lower Counties," Penn based his position on the claim that Lord Baltimore's charter rights were preempted by the fact that the Dutch and Swedes had settled that area prior to the granting of the charter of Maryland. The decision of the Board of Trade was that the present-day Delmarva Peninsula should be divided into two approximately equal portions north of Cape Henlopen and that the eastern portion should be assigned to Penn. The western portion would continue to be in Maryland. In the matter of the northern boundary, this appears to have been settled in favor of the third Lord Baltimore—the fortieth parallel of north latitude prevailed. This was known as the Decree of 1685. However, discussions concerning this issue continued and ultimately the boundary was located about nineteen miles below the charter parallel.

At the present time it is difficult to believe that

Charles I had intentionally inserted the cryptic Latin phrase "hactenus inculta," i.e., "hitherto uncultivated," specifically to give protection to the Dutch and Swedes, none of whom were settled in present-day Delaware at the time of the granting of the charter of Maryland. However, during the course of the proceeding the Duke of York succeeded to the throne as King James II. To have given a decision impugning the King's integrity would have been tantamount to political ruin. Specifically, the difficulty was that the Duke of York, now James II, had granted to William Penn the "Three Lower Counties" to which he held title only by conquest over the Dutch. Charles II had confirmed the Maryland charter as late as 1661. But a repetition at this time would have been to deny an earlier title of the King's—rather a sharp point. It is apparent that the northern border now reaffixed as forty degrees did not involve any act of James II.

If Lord Baltimore now had pressed for a survey, he might have been able to save all the territory later lost to Penn along his northern boundary. He surely had the charter specification within his grasp at this time. Nevertheless, there was dereliction in consummating his award of the fortieth parallel in this decision of 1685. A good survey conducted in conformity with the decree, and implemented with firm boundary markers at frequent intervals, would have set a precedent difficult to controvert. But he allowed his opportunity to slip.

For many years following the decision of 1685, matters were somewhat in a state of quiescence between the two proprietors. William and Mary succeeded James II in 1688. In 1690, because of what was considered too independent a spirit in Maryland, the control was taken from Lord Baltimore. The King assumed jurisdiction at that time and it became a royal province under a royal governor and remained in that status until 1715. The same fate was shared by William Penn, who lost control of his province in 1691, but his influence in England brought a return of his dominions to him in 1694. Charles, third Lord Baltimore, died in England in 1715, after an absence of thirty years. He was succeeded by his son, Benedict Leonard Calvert, fourth Lord Baltimore, who survived his father only a few months. Benedict was followed by his son, Charles, fifth Lord Baltimore, to whom the proprietorship of Maryland was restored. William Penn, who died in 1718, bequeathed his holdings in Pennsylvania to his wife, Hannah Penn, who in turn transferred her title to the province to her children, John, Thomas, Richard, and Dennis equally. This maneuver was inconsistent with the English law of inheritance whereby one-half of the estate should have been conveyed to William Penn, Jr., the founder's eldest son by an earlier marriage. The rapid changes in the proprietorship of Maryland and the contested title to Pennsylvania further contributed to set in abeyance the boundary controversy. The period, however, was not without one unsuccessful petition by Charles, fifth Lord Baltimore, to Queen Anne in 1709 to set aside the order of 1685 by which he had lost the "Three Lower Counties" although his northern boundary had been confirmed.

With the growth of population in the contested areas, taxes were difficult or impossible to collect and this meant loss of revenue to both proprietors. In 1731 Charles, fifth Lord Baltimore, petitioned King George II for an order requiring the proprietor of Pennsylvania to join with him in the demarcation of the boundaries. The matter was referred to the Committee for Trade and Plantations. Lord Baltimore and the Penns were present in England at the conferences. Another round of innuendoes resulted, mostly over the question of false geographical representations. But ultimately agreement was reached in 1732 authorizing the appointment of a commission to execute a boundary survey in accordance with terms in general determined upon in 1685. This called for the equal division of the Delmarva Peninsula from Cape Henlopen northward and for the northern boundary of Lord Baltimore's dominions to be fifteen miles south of the City of Philadelphia. The northern boundary of present Delaware was to be a circle "drawn at twelve miles distance" around the town of New Castle but the precise location of the center was not specified. Commissioners were ultimately appointed and their first meeting was at New Castle on October 17, 1732. As was usual, stalemates developed. The first concerned what point in New Castle was to be adopted as the center of the circle "at twelve miles distance." The only specification in the grant by Charles II to Penn was that the center should be at some point within the settlement of New Castle. The Pennsylvanians held that the instruction to conduct the survey carried within it the power to locate the center. The second basis for argument was the dimension of the circle. It is extremely doubtful that any mathematician or engineer would have thought of a circle "at twelve miles distance" otherwise than as a circle of twelve miles radius. The Marylanders disagreed as to the location of the center and also insisted upon a circle of twelve miles circumference (1.91 miles radius). Ultimately the commissioners signed a joint note declaring that they were unable to agree as to the basic instructions to the surveyors for delineating the boundaries of Pennsylvania, Maryland, and Delaware.

Border incidents had increased to the point that in 1738 the Governor and both houses of the Maryland legislature petitioned King George II, imploring his intercession. An edict was promptly forthcoming from the King forbidding disorders in areas of controversy and enjoining the proprietors from making grants therein. The King ordered two temporary lines to be run. One was to be 15.25 miles south of Philadelphia on the east side of the Susquehanna and the other 14.75 miles south of Philadelphia on the west side of the same river. An attempt was made to run these two lines under the supervision of both provinces, but the Marylanders were absent when the survey was to begin, and Penn hired two surveyors from New Jersey to lay down the lines. Their work was accepted as the boundary between Maryland and Pennsylvania until 1763.

The failure of the commissioners to proceed with the boundary survey as outlined in the agreement of 1732 finally led to "The Great Chancery Suit" which began in 1735. When the case was finally decided by Lord Hardwicke in 1750, it was decreed that the agreement of 1732 should be observed. Disputed points were detailed, though incompletely: the center of the circle should be the center of the town of New Castle; the circle was to be of twelve miles radius and the lower boundary of Delaware was specified as on a parallel of latitude through Cape Henlopen as shown on a map affixed to the Articles of Agreement.

Following the court's decision, another attempt was made to conduct a survey. Commissioners from Maryland and Pennsylvania met at New Castle on November 15, 1750, and decided upon the belfry of the courthouse as the center of New Castle. But then a controversy developed over the method of measuring the radius of the circle. The Marylanders insisted upon the distance being determined by chaining up hills and down valleys. The Pennsylvanians favored horizontal measure, which is the present legal method of conducting a survey. The termini of radii located by the former method obviously would not form a circle. Further argument ensued as to the method to be employed in locating additional points on the circle. It appears that the Pennsylvanians suggested the running of successive chords, each subtending one degree at the courthouse belfry. The Marylanders favored the running of radii centered at the belfry. This latter method would have required more than twelve hundred miles of linear chaining to locate each degree point along the circle, and the Christiana River would have had to be crossed over one hundred times. The argument over the location of Cape Henlopen had earlier been concluded by Lord Hardwicke and pursuant thereto the local surveyors were dispatched to that point and instructed to measure the length of a parallel of latitude, or possibly the arc of a great circle, across the Eastern Shore from the Atlantic to the Chesapeake and to locate its mid-point. At a distance of 66 miles from Cape Henlopen they came to the shore of Slaughter Creek, an estuary of the Bay. After chaining across the estuary and Taylor's Island (actually a peninsula separated from the mainland by the estuary), the eastern shore of the Chesapeake was reached at a distance of 69 miles 298 perches (rods) from the point of beginning on Fenwick Island. The surveyors' work was approved by the commissioners, but dissension arose among the latter regarding the distance to be divided by two for the purpose of locat-

ing the southwest corner of Delaware. The Maryland commissioners insisted upon the distance to Slaughter Creek but those from Pennsylvania pressed for the full measure to the Bay since Slaughter Creek was only two feet deep at low water. The lesser distance would have given Maryland a greater area. Another stalemate having developed, the commissioners adjourned to await further interpretation on this question and also those of the incomplete specification of the center of the town of New Castle and of slope chaining versus horizontal chaining.

In 1751 Charles, fifth Lord Baltimore, died in England. His eldest son Frederick, sixth and last Lord Baltimore, then a minor, inherited the title but his father devised his landed interests in Maryland to his daughter. This resulted in a court proceeding in which it was concluded that the land could not be separated from the title. An odd circumstance of Frederick's tenure was that on account of the marriage articles of his father he was not bound by any agreements between the previous Penns and Calverts or the legal decisions earlier rendered in England. He repudiated all of them and insisted upon a new deed, which was concluded and signed in July, 1760. However, it is to be observed that the boundary outlined in this instrument closely followed that of the agreement of 1732. The Lord High Chancellor finally ruled that the chaining should be horizontal, that the center of the town of New Castle should be the center of the belfry of the courthouse, and that the width of the Eastern Shore should be measured from the shore of the Atlantic to the shore of the Chesapeake. The position of Cape Henlopen, earlier contested, was definitely specified.

In 1760 commissioners were again appointed to see the survey through. As the matter now stood they were to locate the mid-point of the transpeninsular line and from this point run a line tangent to the circle of twelve miles radius about the belfry of New Castle courthouse. This circle had been laid out superficially by two surveyors in 1701 but in the location of the tangent point the circle in general was not of much importance. It was required to obtain a perpendicular intersection with the tangent line at the extremity of a twelve-mile radial line. Their procedure was to run a trial line along the meridian of the middle point until it was near the twelve-mile circle and then from the belfry of the courthouse at New Castle to run a radial line to its intersection point with the meridian line. When the field work was complete, it was found that the two shorter legs of the triangle were 79 miles 52 chains (79.65 miles) and 7 miles 39.97 chains (7.50 miles) and that the intersection angle was 113°36'. From these data a trigonometric calculation showed that the tangent line would make an angle of 3°32'05" westerly from the meridian line and that the radius from New Castle to the tangent point would make an angle of 19°03'55" northerly from the southwesterly radial line previously run. The commissioners instructed the surveyors to run the twelve-mile radial line on the course which had been calculated and to stake out the line at various points. At the conclusion of this assignment the field party discontinued work for the winter on December 2, 1761. In May of the following year they attempted to run the tangent line using the calculations referred to above. Over three months later an intersection was made at a distance of 81 miles 74 chains 65 links (81.933 miles) from the middle point and at a point 33 chains 76 links (0.422 mile) east of the extremity of the twelve-mile radial line. The angle of intersection was found to be 26 minutes larger than the required 90 degrees.

A second attempt now was made to run the tangent line. The surveyors were instructed to go to the end of the twelve-mile radial line and turn off an angle of 89°55'43" with the radius and in this direction to extend a line northward 157 feet 8 inches and to place a post at this point which was believed would be the tangent point. Later in the year they returned to the mid-point of the transpeninsular line and ran another trial tangent. This line, completed August 19, 1763, passed 5 chains 25 links to the west of the tangent point positioned as above described. A third calculation indicated that the true tangent line would run 2'45" east of the second trial line. However, the running of this line was never attempted. The technological problems were great and involved the application of much complex geodesy and astronomy, and the progress had been very slow. The Proprietors had earlier become convinced that the local surveyors needed assistance and had petitioned the Astronomer Royal to recommend scientists of ability to execute the work.

Charles Mason and Jeremiah Dixon were the nominees. Their competence had been adequately established. The former had a long record of distinguished service at the Royal Observatory, Greenwich, and the latter had established his reputation as an astronomer on eclipse and transit expeditions to determine the distance to the sun, i.e., solar parallax. A contract was prepared which was signed by Mason and Dixon and the Proprietors on August 4, 1763. They arrived in this country on the following November 15 and by highly scientific procedures over a period of fifty-eight months established the common boundaries of Pennsylvania, Delaware, Maryland, and Virginia. The excellence of their work has been attested to in more recent times by checks by such a prestigious organization as the U.S. Coast and Geodetic Survey.

One cannot read the account of the controversy between the Penns and the Calverts without amazement that such a conflict of interest could arise and remain unresolved for eighty-two years. Its causes were deep-rooted. One basic reason. earlier mentioned, was the careless practice of English royalty of assigning territorial rights that previously had been granted to oth-

ers. The situation was complicated by the lack of good maps but this could have been obviated by a little systematic cartographic work by the English government. Kings lacked competence in scientific matters and in the writing of their colonial charters made impossible geometrical specifications. As there were able scientists in England whose advice would have averted the resulting confusion, this defect in their official acts is difficult to excuse. An example is the specification of a "right line" on an ellipsoid of revolution. Adjudication was hampered by lack of rapid transportation. Frequently there was a tendency to argue matters to which a definite physical answer was easily available, as was the case with the location of the fortieth parallel of north latitude along the Delaware River, which was easily determinable by a competent surveyor. Again, there was the problem of impossible specifications, an example being the failure of a circle of twelve miles radius centered in the belfry of New Castle courthouse to reach the fortieth parallel of north latitude. There were also the untenable positions assumed by the respective disputants, examples being the arguments regarding the radius of the "circle at twelve miles distance" and also the disagreement over the distance from the Atlantic to the Chesapeake. Perhaps the most untenable of all these positions was the proposal by commissioners that linear distances be measured up hills and down valleys, which would have precluded any type of mathematical check on the work. A further source of trouble was that English courts did not appear consistent in their decisions and were given to political bias. For example, the cryptic Latin phrase "hactenus inculta" was interpreted as favoring Maryland in the matter of Virginia settlements but decided against Maryland in the matter of the Dutch and Swedes, who actually were not in that area at the date of the granting of its charter. To argue that King Charles I introduced this Latin phrase for the protection of the Dutch and Swedes requires the greatest elasticity of the imagination. The fact is that the English had been continually concerned lest their middle Atlantic seaboard would be permanently severed by these settlements. Then there seems to have been nothing final about the decrees of the English courts. At one time procrastination was plainly a cause of the third Lord Baltimore's difficulty, as he had his full forty degrees within his grasp but he failed to have a survey conducted.

The land areas lost by Maryland and Virginia (now West Virginia) to Pennsylvania were about 4,300 square miles and 1,100 square miles respectively. The southern boundary of Pennsylvania was actually placed 19.27 statute miles below the fortieth parallel of north latitude. As Delaware later became an autonomous jurisdiction, it is not here considered.

It is difficult to contravene the position of Maryland as having the earlier grant, but the position of the Penns seems to have been stronger in circles of English diplomacy.

Mason and Dixon arrived in Philadelphia from England on November 15, 1763. On the following day they attended a meeting of the Commissioners from Pennsylvania who had been appointed by the Penns to represent that colony and Delaware in the settlement of the boundary. They also dispatched a communication to His Excellency, Horatio Sharpe, Governor of Maryland, announcing their arrival. The astronomical and geodetic instruments were then landed and tested, and found to be undamaged. On November 30 the Commissioners appointed by Frederick, Lord Baltimore, to represent Maryland, arrived in Philadelphia.

December, 1763. A joint meeting of the Commissioners was held which lasted several days. The east-west boundary between Maryland and Pennsylvania was to follow a circle of latitude 15 miles south of the southernmost point of the City of Philadelphia. City officials agreed on the north wall of a house on the south side of Cedar Street, now called South Street, as being the southernmost point in the city and on the circle of latitude from which to measure the 15 miles southward. A temporary astronomical observatory was set up near this point and the two geodesists proceeded to make observations for latitude. The instrument they used was a type of astronomical transit which they called a "sector." Actually, the observatory was located 37.15 yards north of the point agreed upon as the southernmost point of the City of Philadelphia. This was taken as equal to 1.1 seconds of latitude. Making allowance for this small difference, the latitude of the southernmost point in Philadelphia was determined to be 39°56′29.1″ north. Modern observations find this to be in error by only 2.5 seconds.

January, 1764. The above-described determination was not concluded until the sixth, at which time the indicated latitude was submitted to the Commissioners from both provinces.

Mason and Dixon were required to move 15 miles south of this point to begin their border survey between Maryland and Pennsylvania. But actually this position would have been on the opposite side of the Delaware River, in New Jersey. To obviate this complication, it was decided to move westward along the circle of latitude of the southernmost point of Philadelphia to the Forks of the Brandywine River, about 31 miles distant. To guide them in this approximate determination of latitude, a navigator's quadrant was

utilized and a point arrived at very near the house of a Mr. John Harland. The observatory on Cedar Street in Philadelphia was disassembled and transported to this new position and later set up in the Harland yard. Extreme care was exercised in the transportation of the fragile instruments, which were placed on a featherbed in a wagon. It appears to have required a two-day trip by horse team to cover the 31 miles. The observatory not yet being ready, the astronomical transit or sector was promptly put in place in a tent, and a set of observations for latitude was begun on the fourteenth of the month. Later the instrument was moved to the observatory. The position of the sector in the tent was 9.5 yards north of its later position in the observatory; this necessitated a small correction of negative 0.3 second of latitude for observations in the tent. On the twenty-sixth a series of latitude observations was begun to determine the position of the observatory.

February, 1764. The observations were continued until the twenty-eighth. Four days prior to this date, wooden levels were brought for measuring the 15 statute miles horizontally. The mean of the latitude observations showed the observatory, i.e., the sector, to be 356.8 yards south of the parallel of latitude through the southernmost point in the City of Philadelphia. At this time Mason stated that, if the value of a degree, 69.5 miles, were later found to be slightly in error, the 356.8 yards would be adjusted accordingly. The reduction of the astronomical observations showed the latitude of the observatory in Mr. John Harland's yard in the Forks of the Brandywine River to be 39°56′18.9″, this being 10.2 seconds less than that of the southernmost point in the City of Philadelphia.

March, 1764. Progress during the first half of the month was much impeded by cloudy and falling weather which made astronomical observations impossible. On the fifth an observation for azimuth was made by observing Polaris at upper culmination and this direction was proved on the sixteenth. On the seventeenth an eclipse of the moon was observed to end at 8h21m59s apparent time. Mason remarked, "The edge of the sun's shadow was the best defined I ever saw, the air was so clear it was remarkably distinct from the penumbral shade."

About the middle of the month the survey party was enlarged by the employment of axmen to cut out a vista southward along a meridian from the observa-

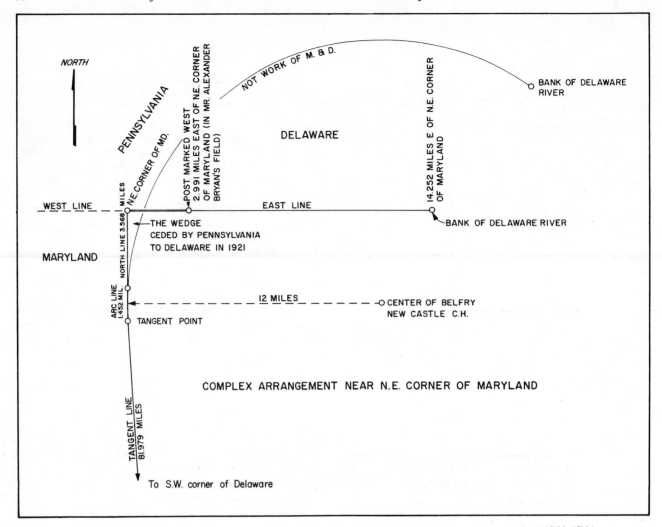

FIG. 2. Map illustrating the surveys of the Pennsylvania-Maryland-Delaware boundaries, 1730-1764.

tory on the Harland plantation until a point 15 miles south of the parallel of the southernmost point in Philadelphia had been reached.

April, 1764. Work was begun to measure accurately the required distance southward. This measurement was accomplished by the use of levels, i.e., wooden rods, 16.5 feet in length, evidently with a spirit level attached, whereby truly horizontal distances were assured. The path of chaining was, of course, the vista which the axmen had cut out in the direction of true south as earlier established by an astronomical observation on Polaris.

On the fifth a confirming observation was made, proving the first determination of the meridian to be very exact. A week later a point 15 miles south had been reached. In this chaining. allowance was made for the fact that the observatory in Brandywine was 10.5 seconds too far south. The following day the surveyors returned to Brandywine with the laborers, disassembled the observatory, and moved it and the as-

tronomical instruments and other equipment in four wagons to the end of the 15-mile line which was in a field of a Mr. Alexander Bryan. The next step was to assemble the observatory at that point.

At this time Mason and Dixon left for Philadelphia to inform the Commissioners of their arrival at the southern extremity of the 15-mile line. His Excellency, Horatio Sharpe, Governor of Maryland, also was informed. The field assistants had been furloughed and, the remaining five days of the month being inclement, nothing further was accomplished.

May, 1764. During the first twelve days the astronomers occupied themselves in making a latitude determination at the south end of the 15-mile line. Before reducing the observations, they decided to check the length of the line, and on the fourteenth of the month a remeasure running northward was started with the aid of five men. A small correction had to be made for slope distances measured on hills where the levels were not used. Allowing for this, the final posi-

1763	Stars Names	♄'s	nearest point on ♄ Sector	Revolutions & Seconds on ♄ Micromr	Diff	Apt. Zen. dist. Plane of ♄ Sector West	♄ No

Decr. 30.

Equal Altitudes
of Capella:
Time per Watch.

h. ' "	h. ' "
3. 50. 32	5. 55. 41
51. 35	56. 58
52. 54	58. 11

} Hence Capella pass'd the Merid." ♄ Transit
Instrument at 4.ʰ 54.ʹ 18ʺ and it was Obsd. to pass
the Vertical wire in the Sector at 4.ʰ 54.ʹ 7ʺ. —

31	α Lyræ	1. 20 + { 11. 45 ; 9. 28 }	2. 17	1. 22. 1, 0
	γ Androm:	1. 15 − { 6. 3 ; 5. 48½ } 0. 6, 5	1. 14. 13, 5

1764
January

☉ 1	γ Androm:	1. 15 − { 6. 19, 7 ; 6. 13, 3 } 0. 6, 4	1. 14. 53, 6
	β Persei	0. 5 + { 7. 22 ; 8. 1½ } 0. 31, 5	0. 5. 31, 5
	Capella	5. 50 − { 11. 28 ; 8. 35 } 2. 45, 0	5. 47. 31, 0
	β Aurigæ	4. 55 + { 8. 26+ ; 11. 13 } 2. 38, 7	4. 57. 22, 7
	Castor	7. 35 − { 11. 4 ; 13. 3 } 1. 51, 0	7. 33. 17, 0
	κ Urs: Majo:	8. 5 + { 12. 41 ; 15. 45− } 3. 3, 7	8. 7. 39, 7

2	γ Androm:	1. 15 − { 11. 33½ ; 11. 27 } 0. 6, 5	1. 14. 53, 5
	β Persei	0. 5 + { 10. 27½ ; 11. 5½ } 0. 30, 0	0. 5. 30, 0
	α Persei	9. 5 − { 13. 47 ; 12. 20 } 1. 27, 0	9. 3. 41, 0
	δ Persei	7. 5 − { 13. 22+ ; 12. 35 } 0. 39, 3	7. 4. 20, 7
	Capella	5. 50 − { 13. 5 ; 10. 11½ } 2. 45, 5	5. 47. 30, 5

FIG. 3. Table of stellar observations for latitude, December 31, 1763–January 1, 1764 (page 30 of Journal).

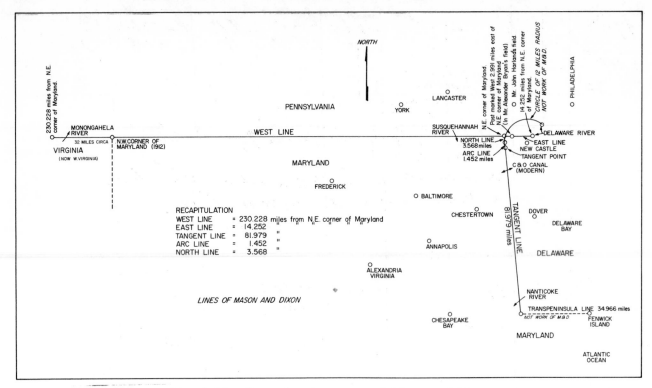

FIG. 4. Map illustrating the surveys of Mason and Dixon.

tion of the southern extremity of the 15-mile line was definitely settled upon. On the nineteenth the two geodesists attended a meeting of the Commissioners from both provinces at New Castle and, after their return to the observatory in Mr. Bryan's field, made additional stellar observations for latitude on two nights. On the twenty-first and twenty-second they were again in conference with the Commissioners at New Castle. Following this, Mason and Dixon made additional latitude (zenith distance) observations until the end of the month. There were several nights of cloudy weather during this period when no astronomical work could be accomplished.

June, 1764. Zenith distance readings were continued until the ninth of the month, at which time the scientists spent about four days in reducing all observations. The latitude of the southern extremity of the 15-mile line was found to be 39°43'17.4" north (page 103 of the Journal). This would be the geographic latitude of the West and East Lines of the Pennsylvania-Maryland border. The Commissioners had determined that the geodesists should now proceed to the "Middle Point" to run the Tangent Line. Specifically, the Middle Point was a position on the present-day Delmarva Peninsula supposedly midway on a great circle (starting at N90°W) between Cape Henlopen and the Chesapeake Bay. It subsequently came to mark the southwest corner of Delaware. The Tangent Line is a line running slightly northwesterly

(N3°43'30"W) from the Middle Point to a point of tangency with a circle of 12 miles radius around the belfry of New Castle courthouse. This line was to be the boundary between Maryland and Delaware (then included in the dominions of the Penns) along their respective eastern and western borders. Concurrently with this change in assignment, Mason and Dixon proceeded on the thirteenth of the month to pack up their scientific instruments and other equipment and make their way by wagons to New Castle, which was reached the following day. Axmen earlier furloughed were reemployed to assist in the new project. On the eighteenth the survey party left New Castle and arrived at Dover the following night. They encamped four nights later on the banks of the Nanticoke River, where tents were temporarily pitched. On the next day additional axmen were employed. The entire party, including a steward, tentkeepers, cooks, chain carriers, axmen, etc., now numbered thirty-nine persons—exceeding in size a present-day triangulation party of the Coast and Geodetic Survey. Equipment for travel included two wagons and eight horses. On the twenty-fifth the party with its equipment crossed the river in canoes, proceeded to the Middle Point, and began to run from thence a great circle arc in the northerly direction determined by geodetic calculations to give tangency to the circle of 12 miles radius. On the last day of the month they had again reached the Nanticoke. The river at this location is too wide to chain by usual procedures but the two scientists accurately determined its breadth by triangulation. A base line 8 chains in length was measured along the river shore. By determining two of the angles with a Hadley quadrant, a distance of 9 chains 4 links (596.6 feet) was found for the width of the stream at this point. Mileposts were accurately set at each mile point as the boundary survey progressed and at this location a distance from the Middle Point to the south bank of the Nanticoke was given as 6 miles 70 chains 25 links, i.e., 6.878 miles.

July, 1764. The line was pushed northward and at the end of the month the 48-mile point had been reached. The Choptank River was crossed near milepost forty-two. The stone marker which later replaced the temporary wooden marker now lies submerged behind a dam.

August, 1764. The line was continued northward until the twenty-fifth, at which time a distance of slightly over 81 miles from the Middle Point had been reached, at a point judged to be a little beyond the point of tangency with the 12-mile circle around New Castle courthouse. The sixty-ninth milepost had been set on the south side of the Bohemia River near the low water mark. On the eighteenth of the month, letters were sent to Horatio Sharpe, Esquire, Governor of Maryland, and to Mr. James Hamilton, Commissioner from Pennsylvania, stating that the line would reach the Tangent Point in eight or ten days. On the twenty-fifth of the month the Journal reports: "Set the 81st mile post and produced the Line till we judged we were past the Point settled before to be the Tangent Point in the circle round Newcastle of 12 Miles Radius." The next day a wagon was dispatched to Philadelphia to purchase additional tents. On the twenty-seventh of the month the radial line from the belfry of New Castle courthouse, earlier determined upon by colonial surveyors as running to the Tangent Point, was produced to the line which had just been run from the Middle Point. The distance between the actual intersection point and the point previously considered to be the Tangent Point was 22.51 chains (1485.66 feet). The length of the Tangent Line as just run to the point of intersection was 81 miles 78 chains 31 links (page 77). Mason comments: "The distance will be 81.78.25 when at right angles: and the Perpendicular to the 12 mile Post, 22.50 chains." He also comments: "The angle made by our line and the radius produced from New Castle is 89°50'—Measured by a Hadley's Quadrant."

September, 1764. Accurately establishing the Tangent Line now involved the preparation of tables of offsets, whereby the previous work was successively improved. They now proceeded to place temporary markers at the 5-mile points, working southward toward the Middle Point. On the tenth of the month

Mason records that the party was at a Mr. Twiford's on the bank of the Nanticoke River where they awaited for two days the arrival of the wagons with supplies.

Near the middle of the month Mason remarked that he went to see the Pocomoke Swamp and gave this description:

It's about 30 Miles in Length and 14 in breadth: (The West Line [Trans-peninsula] from the Sea to the Middle Point passes through it): There is the greatest quantity of Timber I ever saw: Above the Tallest Oak, Beech, Poplar, Hickory, Holly and Fir; Towers the lofty Cedar: (without a Branch), till its ever green conical top; seems to reach the clouds: The pleasing sight of which; renewed my wishes to see Mount Lebanon (page 81).

The great Pocomoke Swamp lies partly on both sides of the boundary line between Maryland and Delaware which runs west from Fenwick Island where Cape Henlopen lies and is roughly in the vicinity of Selbyville, Frankford, and Gumboro in Delaware and Whaleysville in Maryland. During the next twelve days, work was continued southward in measuring the offsets to improve the tangent until the Middle Point was reached on the twenty-fifth, when the scientists returned to Mr. Twiford's. The rest of the month was spent in still further improving the Tangent Line.

October, 1764. During this month additional effort was expended on further approximations to perfect the Tangent Line. This consisted of measuring offsets to the final position from points of predetermined error.

November, 1764. The work of improving the approximations was continued until on the twelfth Mason declared that the tangency was so nearly in agreement with mathematical requirements that it was the true Tangent Line in so far as any practical necessity was concerned. The required angle of 90° at the intersection was substantially met and the linear discrepancy seems to have been only about 26 inches. On the same day communications were dispatched to Governor Sharpe of Maryland and Mr. Joseph Hamilton, Commissioner from Pennsylvania, informing them of the completion of the work. The following week Mason and Dixon spent in waiting for the Commissioners from Pennsylvania and Maryland who assembled on the twenty-first at Christiana Bridge in New Castle County. At this time they were in agreement that the project of establishing the Tangent Line had been satisfactorily concluded. On the twenty-sixth of the month all survey helpers were furloughed for the winter season and Mason and Dixon returned to the home of Mr. John Harland at the Forks of the Brandywine.

December, 1764. This month was without activity except that a letter was written to the Proprietors to inform them that the Tangent Line had been established.

January, 1765. During this month no technical work was accomplished. A visit was made to Lancaster and Pechway, and they returned to Brandywine on the nineteenth.

February, 1765. Mason left Brandywine on the eleventh and proceeded to New York. He records that his horse was nearly lost in crossing the Delaware on ice. The route took him through Princeton. He commented that the college was the most elegantly constructed he had seen in America. The next four days were spent in New York, but then began his return by New Jersey and on the twenty-seventh he crossed the Delaware to New Castle and proceeded to Newark, Delaware.

March, 1765. Mason and Dixon now began preparations to run the "West Line," i.e., the line running westerly from the northeast corner of Maryland. Considerable time was spent in performing astronomical observations for azimuth to give the direction on which to start the first great circle arc of 10 minutes. (Journal, page 107 *et seq.*) As a consequence of inclement weather and other reasons not recorded, no further work was attempted until the twentieth. A deep snow followed the next day which the Journal entry gives as nearly three feet in depth on the level. No further technical work was accomplished this month.

April, 1765. On the fifth of the month Mason and Dixon proceeded to run the West Line, using for the first 10-minute arc of great circle a direction determined by calculations of spherical trigonometry and observations referred to above. Their measurements were from a "Post marked West" in Mr. Bryan's field, which in latitude was 15 miles south of the southernmost point in Philadelphia, and later turned out to be 2 miles 79 chains 27 links east of the northeast corner of Maryland. The survey proceeded westward, crossing Little Christiana Creek, Great Christiana Creek, and the Elk River. On the thirteenth a point had been reached near the end of the 10-minute arc of great circle, i.e., at 12 miles 25 chains from the point of beginning. At this time the scientists returned to the end of the line and came back with the astronomical transit or sector. The following day they set it up at the point reached on the thirteenth, to obtain a check on its latitude. The mean of the observations showed that the position of the sector was 1.29 seconds of arc north of the parallel through the Post marked West. A table of offsets was now prepared which took into consideration the distance from the great circle southward to the parallel and also the amount (129 feet) by which their line had erred from the desired great circle. The calculated offsets were measured off from the great circle by returning eastward and a temporary monument was placed at every mile point. The positions marked the true boundary between Maryland

and Pennsylvania. On the twenty-ninth of the month they proceeded to repeat the procedure, i.e., to run a second arc of great circle of 10-minute length. The following day they crossed the main branch of the North East River at a distance of 14 miles 2 chains from the Post marked West. At this time communications were dispatched to the Commissioners from Maryland and Pennsylvania to inform them that the survey would reach the Susquehanna River in twelve days.

May, 1765. The line was continued without interruption for nearly two weeks, during which time the route crossed the Octoraro River three times in quick succession. The river was very sinuous but each crossing was nearly perpendicular to its banks. The three crossings respectively began 20 miles 61 chains, 20 miles 71 chains, and 21 miles 25 chains, and the width of the river was recorded by Mason as about 50 yards. Conowingo Creek was crossed at 23 miles 67 chains, and at a distance of 25 miles 75 chains 57 links the end of the 10-minute arc of great circle was approximately reached. The sector was set up and latitude observations were made for two weeks. When the star positions had been reduced, a deviation from the standard parallel of 3.82 seconds of arc or 382 feet to the north was found. A table of offsets from the chord to the parallel was computed, from which the true boundary between Maryland and Pennsylvania could be staked out when the party began to move eastward. About this time the width of the Susquehanna River was determined by triangulation. Instead of employing a right triangle as is common practice among civil engineers, they apparently were forced into the device of using an oblique triangle, for which no reason is in evidence except that of necessary visibility between vertices. The calculated distance across the Susquehanna was 67 chains 68 links (0.846 mile). As in the case of the triangulation on the Nanticoke, the goniometry was carried out with a Hadley quadrant of 18 inches radius. A stake was placed on the west side of the Susquehanna River at a distance of 26 miles 72 chains 71 links from the Post marked West. The position was about 16 miles north of the headwaters of the Chesapeake Bay and about 57 miles southwesterly from Philadelphia. On the twenty-eighth the instruments were packed up and the survey party worked its way eastward while measuring the offsets at the mile points from the survey line to the true parallel of the Post marked West, thus marking the true boundary between Pennsylvania and Maryland.

June, 1765. On the first of June, Mason and Dixon returned to the Tangent Point not far from the Post marked West in Mr. Bryan's field. Here they made astronomical observations on Polaris and Alioth to establish the meridian which was necessary in order to run such a line due north from the Tangent Point, as required by the Commissioners. The North Line actually extended from the Tangent Point to the northeast corner of Maryland, intersecting the circle of 12 miles radius as a secant. The boundary between Maryland and Delaware in this part of the survey actually follows the circle, and the North Line at present is considered to extend from the point where it leaves the circle, to the northeast corner of Maryland. This line is short and the mission was quickly accomplished. On the third of the month Mason and Dixon sent communications to Annapolis and Philadelphia to inform the Commissioners that the North Line soon would be complete. Mathematical studies now were made to ascertain the length of the line as a secant, and this was found to be 1 mile 36 chains 10 links (1.451 miles) (page 131 and also page 133). Offsets on the segmental area of the circle of 12 miles radius were computed. These offsets were measured from the secant and were temporarily marked by wooden stakes. This locus of points was the Arc Line. The distance from the Tangent Point to the parallel through the Post marked West was measured as 5 miles 1 chain 50 links (5.019 miles) (page 134). The point of intersection of these two lines was the northeast corner of Maryland. The meridian from the Tangent Point crossed the required parallel 2 miles 79 chains 27 links (2.991 miles) west of the Post marked West. That is to say, the Post marked West was this distance east of the northeast corner of Maryland. In order that the permanent granite mileposts might stand at even miles from this latter point, all such markers were placed 73 links east of the temporary markers along the West Line. A post bearing a *W* on the west side and *N* on the north side was placed at the intersection point at the northeast corner of Maryland. The field work was completed on the seventh of the month. A delay of nine days now resulted, during which a meeting of the Commissioners was awaited, but on the seventeenth they met at Christiana Bridge in New Castle County. Seven permanent boundary stones were set as follows: one at the Tangent Point, four on the Arc Line above described, one on the North Line, and one at the intersection of the North Line with the main parallel, i.e., at the northeast corner of Maryland. The Commissioners now instructed the geodesists to extend the parallel westerly from the Susquehanna as far as the country was inhabited. Germane communications were dispatched to the Proprietors of Maryland and Pennsylvania. The party returned to the Susquehanna and after changing direction proceeded to extend the West Line from the point where work had been discontinued in order to establish the Arc Line and the North Line. At 28 miles 69 chains the route crossed the road leading from York to Rock Run. A schoolhouse was located one chain southward.

July, 1765. The line was continued during the first three days, at which time the surveyors had reached a point 37 miles 17 chains 98 links west of the Post marked West and believed they were again on the true parallel. A change in direction was made without latitude observations and the line was continued, crossing Deer Creek at 46 miles 40 chains. At a distance of 48 miles 64 chains 5 links they believed that the parallel again had been reached and made a series of observations which required about ten days. Reduction of the zenith distances showed them to be 0.56 second of arc or 56 feet south of the true parallel. A table of offsets was computed for the two previous 10-minute arcs, by which the distances to the boundary points could be measured. During the remaining week a new direction was laid off so as to intersect the parallel again at 10 minutes of great circle farther west. At 49 miles 7 chains the party crossed the "lower Road leading from York to Joppa and Baltimore," and at 52 miles 18 chains crossed the main branch of the Gunpowder River and at 60 miles 33 chains crossed the last branch, at which position on the thirtieth they believed they were again nearly on the parallel. No celestial observations were made but the direction was changed so as to intersect the parallel at 10 minutes westward.

August, 1765. The line was continued and crossed several creeks including the Codorus, Coniwago, and Piney, a branch of the Monocacy. At 71 miles 43 chains 19 links the surveyors believed they again had reached the parallel. On the seventh the astronomical transit was set up and a series of stars was observed for latitude. Mason recorded that a great hailstorm occurred at that time, one hailstone measuring 1.6 x 1.2 x 0.5 inches. Observations of zenith distance were continued through the eighteenth, following which about two days were spent in calculating the results, which showed the position of the sector to be 4.58 seconds north of the true parallel, the error amounting to 458 feet. A table of offsets from the great circle to the parallel was prepared for the previous two 10-minute arcs of great circle in order to stake out the boundary at a later date. The direction was now changed so as to intersect the parallel again at the end of a 10-minute arc of great circle. En route the survey crossed Piney Run, Monocacy Road, Willolloway Creek, Rock Creek, Mash Creek, and Middle Creek and at 83 miles 13 chains 96 links Mason and Dixon again believed they were on the true parallel. No latitude check was made. The direction was changed, so as to be near the parallel at the end of another 10-minute arc of great circle. At 86 miles 44 chains the foot of South Mountain was reached. On the thirtieth day of the month the party was at 88 miles 00 chains west of the Post marked West.

September, 1765. The line was continued and at 93 miles 63 chains and 94 miles 62 chains two springs were crossed running into Antietam Creek. The last spring was at the foot of South Mountain on the west side. At 94 miles 63 chains 10 links the astronomical transit was again set up and a series of latitude observations was carried out over a period of nine nights. Reduction of the observations showed the point of observation to be 0.56 second of arc or 56 feet south of the true parallel. A table of offsets was calculated to give the distances to be measured off at the various mile points west of the position where observations were made on the seventh of August at 71 miles 43 chains. The boundary points would be established later.

The running of the line was resumed on the twentieth in the direction to intersect the parallel at 10 minutes of great circle. At 95 miles 38 chains the line crossed a spring running into Antietam Creek. On Sunday, the twenty-second of September, Mason comments:

Went to see a cave (near the Mountain about 6 miles South of Mr. Shockey's). The entrance is an arch about 6 yards in length and four feet in height, when immediately there opens a room 45 yards in length, 40 in breadth and 7 or 8 in height. (Not one pillar to support nature's arch): There divine service is often (according to the Church of England) celebrated in the Winter Season. On the sidewalks are drawn by the Pencil of Time with the tears of the Rocks: The imitation of Organ, Pillar, Columns and Monuments of a Temple; which with the glimmering faint light; makes the whole an awful, solemn appearance: Striking its Visitants with a strong and melancholy reflection: that such is the abodes of the Dead: Thy inevitable doom, O Stranger; Soon to be numbered as one of them. From this room there is a narrow passage of about 100 yards at the end of which runs a fine river of water: On the sides of this passage are other rooms but not so large as the first (page 166).

Unfortunately, the cave, which was about 8 miles east of Hagerstown, near Cavetown, Maryland, has been destroyed by rock-quarrying in recent years. At 99 miles 35 chains the line crossed Antietam Creek and at 103 miles 69 chains it intersected a road leading to Swaddingem's Ferry on the Potomac. On the twenty-sixth, at 105 miles 78 chains 67 links, the direction was changed so as to be again on the parallel at the end of another 10-minute arc. No latitude check was made. The twenty-ninth being Sunday, Mason went south to the Potomac and forded to the Virginia side, where a log fort and a tavern were located. On the last day of the month the line crossed Conecocheague Creek at a distance of 109 miles 14 chains from the Post marked West.

October, 1765. The line was continued until on the seventh a distance of 117 miles 12 chains 97 links had been attained and at this point the sector was set up for a latitude check. For the next seventeen days the two astronomers were engaged in making zenith distance observations. The reduction of the readings showed the sector to be 8.47 seconds or 847 feet south of the parallel. From this information a table of offsets

was calculated for the last 22.373 miles. On Sunday, the twenty-seventh, Mason recorded: "From here we could see the Allegany Mountain for many miles, and judge it by its appearance to be about 50 Miles [in] distance, in the direction of our Line" (page 178). The two geodesists now set out, on the twenty-eighth, on their return eastward to the Susquehanna to measure off the offsets from the great circle arcs to the true parallel, thus marking the true boundary between Maryland and Pennsylvania. By the end of the month they had reached the seventy-fourth milepost.

November, 1765. The party continued moving easterly and measuring the distances from the great circle to the parallel and placing temporary posts at the mile points until the sixth of the month, at which time the twenty-seventh milepost near the west bank of the Susquehanna was reached. The following day the river was crossed at Peach Bottom Ferry. All help was furloughed for the winter season and on the eleventh Mason and Dixon left the Ferry for York to attend a meeting of the Commissioners which lasted four days. On the twenty-first they left York and proceeded to the Middle Point to set fifty permanent boundary markers in the Tangent Line, i.e., one at each mile point running northerly.

December, 1765. On the fifth the two scientists arrived at Mr. Twiford's on the Nanticoke and apparently remained there to await the arrival of the boundary stones from England. On the seventeenth, twenty such stones arrived on the Nanticoke and about the same time thirty arrived on the Choptank. At every 5 miles a stone was placed, bearing the coat of arms of the Penns on one side and that of the Baltimores on the reverse side. At intermediate mile points the markers were carved with a *P* on one side and an *M* on the reverse side.

January, 1766. Mason and Dixon left off for the winter season. There was no activity during this month except a trip to Philadelphia. On the sixth letters were written to the Proprietors of Pennsylvania and Maryland. Throughout the remainder of the month it appears they were at Mr. John Harland's home at the Forks of the Brandywine.

February, 1766. On the twenty-first of the month Mason "Left Brandywine and proceeded for curiosity to the Southward to see the Country" (page 180). From the text it does not appear that Dixon accompanied him. His route took him across the Susquehanna at Nelson's Ferry about 7 miles north of the Maryland border and from there to York, Pennsylvania; Frederick, Maryland; Alexandria, Dumfries, and Stafford Court House in Virginia. The latter town, about 40 miles south of Georgetown, Maryland, now a part of the City of Washington, D.C., was reached on the last day of the month.

March, 1766. Mason lodged near Port Royal on the Rappahannock River on the night of the first, and the next day crossed the river and remained for an additional day before proceeding on his route, which took him over the Pamunkey River and on to Williamsburg, described by him as the "Metropolis of Virginia," which he reached on the third. The following day he departed on his return by way of Port Royal and Hoe's Ferry on the Potomac, near the present Morgantown toll bridge, and lodged for the night at Port Tobacco, Maryland. On the eighth he was near Upper Marlboro and on the eleventh reached Annapolis, which he described as "the Metropolis of Maryland." Two days later he "compared with His Excellency, Horatio Sharpe, Esq., a copy of our Journal." On the fifteenth he left Annapolis and proceeded to North Mountain to continue the boundary survey. Two days later he had reached Frederick near South Mountain. On the eighteenth Dixon left Philadelphia to attend a meeting of the Commissioners on the twentieth at Chestertown on the Eastern Shore. The following day instructions were received to proceed with the line to the Allegheny Mountains. During the next three days the only activity was that the party furloughed in the early winter made rendezvous near Captain Shelby's at the foot of North Mountain.

April, 1766. The running of the line was now resumed. A direction to intersect the parallel in 10 minutes had been established the previous October. The head of Little Licking Creek running into Conecocheague was passed at 118 miles 63 chains. At 119 miles 18 chains the summit of North Mountain was reached. Fort Frederick was nearly 8 miles south and Fort Loudon near Parnel's Nob in Pennsylvania was about 11 miles north. With the exception of one day, operations were discontinued for twelve days, this being a period of inclement weather which also delayed the arrival of equipment. Operations were resumed on the seventeenth and at 122 miles 67 chains Great Licking Creek was crossed at the foot of North Mountain on the West Side and on the twenty-third at 129 miles 12 chains 04 links the direction was changed so as to intersect the parallel 10 minutes west. The next day, the twenty-fourth, the party appears to have reached a point on the meridian of the narrowest point in Maryland, close to Hancock. The Journal records as follows: "At 129¾ miles by estimation the Northernmost bend of the River Potowmack Bore South distant about a mile and a half. At 134 miles 54 chains the foot of Sidelong [Sideling] Hill was reached." On the twenty-ninth the end of the 10-minute arc was attained at a distance of 138 miles 50 chains. The sector, which had been left at Captain Shelby's was sent for in order to make a series of latitude observations.

May, 1766. On the fourth the sector was set up near the end of the 10-minute arc of great circle at a distance of 140 miles 15 chains 76 links from the Post marked West. Astronomical observations were made during the following twelve days. Reduction of the zenith distances showed the sector to be 0.20 second or 20 feet south of the true parallel. A table of offsets for the last two 10-minute arcs of great circle was now computed, but measurements of offsets were made at a later date. On Sunday, the eighteenth, the instruments were packed up and the party proceeded on the next 10-minute arc after having changed direction to intersect the parallel. At 143 miles 77 chains Fifteen Mile Creek was crossed. The summit of Great Warrior Mountain was reached at 151 miles 48 chains on the twenty-seventh. At this point direction was again changed so as to meet the parallel at 10 minutes west. On the last day of the month they crossed Wills Creek at 161 miles 25 chains from the Post marked West.

June, 1766. The line was continued until the ninth, when the end of the 10-minute arc of great circle was reached at a distance of 165 miles 54 chains 88 links from the Post marked West, at which position the sector was set up and latitude observations were made on clear nights until the fifteenth. The reduction of these zenith distances showed the position to be 2.41 seconds or 241 feet to the south of the true parallel. A table of offsets was computed for laying off the true boundary. Interesting notes in the Journal under the date of the fourteenth read in part: "From the solitary tops of these Mountains, the Eye gazes round with pleasure; filling the mind with adoration to that pervading spirit that made them." On the eighteenth the party proceeded to work backward toward the Post marked West and to lay off the calculated offsets from the great circle to the parallel. On Sunday, the twenty-second, a comment is observed that the route of General Braddock was crossed "which he cut through the Mountains to lead the Army under his command to the Westward in the year 1755, but fate; how hard: made through the desert a path, himself to pass; and never; never to return." On the twenty-eighth the marking of the positions for the boundary markers was complete as far as the milepost 154.

July, 1766. The marking of the boundary was continued by measuring the offsets from the great circle and on the fifth, milepost 140 was reached. On the sixth, Mason noted that he measured three leaves on one stem of a hickory tree, each of which was 17 inches in length and 12 inches in breadth. The following day he commented that he was able to observe the circle of latitude which had been cut out and that as viewed from the promontory of Sideling Hill it "formed the arch of a lesser circle very agreeable to the laws of a sphere." On the twenty-sixth the boundary points had been located eastward to milepost 107 and this effort was continued for the remainder of the month.

August, 1766. The work of measuring the offsets to the true boundary between Pennsylvania and Maryland was continued. On the fifth of the month an eclipse of the sun was observed which from the notation of Mason would appear to have been about 70 per cent total. It began about 11h20m and ended at 2h20m17s. On the ninth the line had been laid out to milepost 85 and on the sixteenth to milepost 73. On the twentieth an eclipse of the moon was observed which was recorded as about 50 per cent total. Measurements of the offsets were continued until the end of the month, at which time milepost 44 had been reached.

September, 1766. The work of measuring the offsets from the great circle to the parallel was continued and on the twelfth communications were sent to Annapolis and Philadelphia to acquaint the Commissioners that the marking of the West Line to the extent of the field work would be finished on the twenty-seventh of the month. Actually, on the twenty-fifth an intersection was made between the true parallel and the meridian through the Tangent Point extended northward, i.e., the northeast corner of Maryland. This fulfilled the surveyors' instructions to that date. On the same day Mason again commented that from any eminence where 15 or 20 miles of the marked parallel could be observed, the geometrical properties of the sphere were in evidence. He also noted that the total number of boundary posts set up to that time in the West Line was 303, or about one to each half mile. Intermediate positions evidently were interpolated as the offsets were calculated for only full-mile positions. A "Visto" about 8 yards wide was cut out along the border between the two provinces. On the twenty-seventh a letter was received from the Commissioners stating that they would meet the two geodesists at Christiana Bridge in New Castle County on the twenty-eighth of the next month. On the last day of the month the field party was furloughed.

October, 1766. On the first day of the month Mason and Dixon were in Newark in New Castle County. The above-mentioned letter conveyed the information that agreement had been reached in the matter of their

employing the interval of time to the 28th Instant, in executing our instructions from the Royal Society of London; towards determining the Length of a degree of Latitude (of which Instructions the Commissioners of both Provinces had received notice from the Honorable: the Proprietors: To whom we wrote in June 1765 for leave to use their Instruments; and the indulgence to do it in their Provinces). Accordingly from this information we this day set out with the Sector* etc. for the Middle Point, or South end of the Tangent Line; To execute the Instructions from the Royal Society.

* The telescope part, carried by three men.

The work of determining the dimensions of the earth on the Delmarva Peninsula was not considered to be closely related to the separation of the dominions of the Penns and the Calverts, and for that reason will be discussed in a separate chapter.

On the twentieth of October the instruments were packed up at the Middle Point and sent to Newark, Delaware, where Mason and Dixon arrived on the twenty-fourth. Instructions were received on the twenty-ninth that one hundred boundary stones were to be set on the Tangent Line, and on the West Line one at each mile point.

November, 1766. The above assignment apparently occupied their time during the first half of the month. On the eighteenth, nineteenth, and twentieth Mason and Dixon attended a meeting of the Commissioners at Christiana Bridge. The stones had all been set in the Tangent Line and for 65 miles on the West Line, i.e., the boundary between Maryland and Pennsylvania, but no stone was placed at the sixty-fourth-mile position from the northeast corner of Maryland. In the setting of the stones one of the Commissioners of each province was present. On the twenty-first Mason and Dixon attended a meeting of the Commissioners, when instruction was given that the parallel of latitude of the Pennsylvania-Maryland border should be extended eastward from the northeast corner of Maryland to the Delaware River. A complication was also to be resolved: Indian opposition had made hazardous the extension of the West Line beyond the point reached on June 9, 1766. This problem was referred to Sir William Johnson, His Majesty's Agent for Indian Affairs in the Colonies, who attempted to gain the consent of the Six Nations. On the twenty-fifth Mason and Dixon proceeded to extend the parallel of latitude eastward from the northeast corner of Maryland to Delaware Bay. The length of this line had to be determined in order that the 5 degrees of longitude along Pennsylvania's southern border could be measured from Delaware Bay. The usual method of running great circle arcs of ten minutes and measuring offsets was employed. On the twenty-fifth the small deflection was turned off at the Post marked West and the work proceeded eastward. The bank of the Delaware was reached on the thirtieth at a distance of 11 miles 20 chains 88 links east of the Post marked West. The offset at this point, not being at the extremity of a great circle arc, was actually 7 feet south thereof. No latitude observations were made.

December, 1766. The following day a wooden post was placed at the point referred to above, i.e., on the bank of the Delaware and in latitude 15 miles south of the southernmost point of the City of Philadelphia. Mason and Dixon again turned their attention to measuring the length of a degree of latitude in the region chosen for this purpose. On the fifth of the month they were again at Brandywine, where they set up the sector at Mr. John Harland's and made additional observations in the same parallel where similar work had earlier been done in January, 1764. Observations of zenith distance, for the determination of the length of a degree of latitude, occupied nearly all of the month.

January, 1767. Most of the month was taken up with standardizing the clocks in connection with the geodetic work of the Royal Society. This would appear to have been a very cold winter. On the first day of the month Mason reported a temperature of twenty-two degrees below zero F. and commented: "In rectifying the Instrument for the Equal Altitude; the immediate touch of the brass was like patting one's fingers against the points of Pins and Needles; the Cold was so intense."

February, 1767. Standardization work was continued. Some studies were made on the time of immersion and emersion of the satellites of Jupiter. This work was related only to the Royal Society's project.

March, 1767. During the first two and a half weeks numerous meteorological data were recorded. On the twenty-second the scientists left Brandywine for New Town (Chestertown) on the Chester River to attend a conference with the Commissioners on the twenty-fourth. But at the end of the next day the latter had not arrived and Mason and Dixon left for Annapolis where they were apprised by Governor Horatio Sharpe that the meeting had been postponed until the twenty-eighth of the following month. From there they returned to Brandywine.

April, 1767. The scientists left Brandywine on the seventh and were in Philadelphia on the eighth and ninth. Here they were informed by the Commissioners for Pennsylvania that no answer had been received from Sir William Johnson as to whether a further extension of the West Line would be permitted by the Indians. On the seventeenth they were again at Brandywine but left in about a week and about the twenty-fifth were in Philadelphia, where they were informed that arrangements with the Indians were still incomplete. They returned to Brandywine at the end of the month.

May, 1767. There was little activity on the boundary determination during this month. A meeting of the Commissioners proposed for the twentieth was postponed on account of lack of a report from Sir William Johnson. On the twenty-fourth a letter was received from Nevil Maskelyne, Astronomer Royal, in which he outlined the methods proposed for the study of the dimensions of the earth. Also included was an ephemeris for 1767. Acting on instructions in the let-

ter, Mason and Dixon sent the astronomical clock to Philadelphia. The letter of the Astronomer Royal appears on pages 279, 280, and 281 of the Journal.

June, 1767. A report on the rate of the clock was prepared and directed to the Reverend Nevil Maskelyne and Dr. Morton, Secretary of the Royal Society. A communication was received from Sir William Johnson stating that the Indians had agreed to the continuation of the West Line. The weather seems to have been very hot during the first half of the month. Mason reported temperatures of 95°F. on the fifth and sixth and 102°F. on the thirtieth at four in the afternoon. The scientists were in Philadelphia on the eleventh and twelfth and prepared instructions to the Proprietors of both provinces stating that they were arranging to return for the completion of the West Line to 5 degrees of longitude west of the Delaware River. In the middle of the month they sent their instruments by wagon to the westernmost point previously reached in June, 1766. At the same time they left Brandywine and went to New Town, now Chestertown, on the Chester River in Maryland to meet with the Commissioners.

July, 1767. On the seventh the equipment arrived at Fort Cumberland and the next day the geodesists were at the Allegheny frontier, where they had discontinued the boundary survey a year previous. A new direction was obtained on the thirteenth and a 10-minute arc of great circle was begun. At 168 miles 78 chains they reached the top of Savage Mountain, which Mason records as being the great dividing ridge of the Allegheny Mountains. Near the middle of the month the party was joined by fourteen Indian deputies, i.e., eleven Mohawks and three Onondagas, accompanied by an interpreter, Mr. Hugh Crawford. The direction was changed on the twenty-fifth at 177 miles 4 chains 45 links and another 10-minute arc of great circle was begun. No latitude observations were taken at this time. A small branch running into the Little Yochio Geni [Youghiogheny] was crossed on the thirtieth.

August, 1767. The line was continued. On the sixth at 188 miles 41 chains 65 links the direction was again changed, without latitude observations, so as to meet the parallel at 10 minutes west. At 189 miles 69 chains the old route of General Braddock leading from Fort Cumberland to Fort Pitt was crossed, and four days later on the eleventh the middle of a small island in the Big Youghiogheny was reached at a distance of 194 miles 28 chains 00 links. The water was reported to be about a foot deep. On the seventeenth, at a distance of 199 miles 63 chains 68 links from the Post marked West in Mr. Bryan's field, the sector, or astronomical transit, was set up and observations for latitude were made for seven days. The results showed that they were 9.9 seconds or 990 feet north of the parallel and this distance had to be laid off to the southward to reach the true boundary. At this station one of the Mohawk Chiefs, Mr. John Green, and his nephew left the party to "return to their own country." On the twenty-fifth several field assistants were appointed to work eastward and measure the offsets from the great circle to the true parallel and open up the "Visto" or true boundary between Maryland and Pennsylvania to the point where work had been resumed on the thirteenth of July. On the twenty-sixth Mason and Dixon changed direction at the point reached on the seventeenth and with the main body of the party continued westward. On the last day of the month they reached the 204-mile point and reported that Big Meadows was north about five miles.

September, 1767. The line was continued westward. At a distance of 219 miles 22 chains 25 links the east bank of Cheat River was reached. The line was reported to cross the river perpendicularly and the width was given as about 10 chains. The end of the 10-minute arc of great circle was reached at 222 miles 24 chains 12 links from the Post marked West. This station was at the "top of a very high steep bank at the foot of which is the River Monaungahela." The sector was set up on the nineteenth and latitude observations were made for nine nights. Reduction of the zenith distances showed the position of the sector to be 3.57 seconds or 357 feet south of the parallel. On the twenty-eighth Mason and Dixon began to open the "Visto" eastward on the true parallel in order to obtain a direction for the next 10-minute arc of great circle. On the twenty-ninth the party was badly depleted when twenty-six members deserted. Probably many were Indian deputies, who would not cross the Monongahela River for fear of attack by the Shawnee and Delaware Indians. However, fifteen axmen agreed to remain on duty to extend the line to the end of the 10-minute arc of great circle. Additional help was summoned on the thirtieth from nearby Redstone.

October, 1767. The work proceeded in continuing the boundary survey westward. A messenger was dispatched to Fort Cumberland to obtain additional helpers for the survey party and on the seventh the party was again fully staffed. The extension of the line continued and crossed an Indian war path at 231 miles 20 chains. This was near a town which had been burned and most of the inhabitants killed in an Indian massacre in 1755. On the ninth the chief of the Indians who were acting as deputies declared that the war path just reached "was the extent of his commission from the Chiefs of the Six Nations" and that he would proceed no farther. All the Indian deputies now began to protest against any additional extension of the line, but nevertheless, Mason and Dixon continued for nearly 2 more miles and concluded the

boundary demarcation at a distance of 233 miles 17 chains 48 links from the Post marked West. The sector was set up at a distance of 233 miles 13 chains 68 links and latitude observations were taken from the eleventh to the eighteenth. These showed that the sector was 2.23 seconds or 223 feet south of the parallel and this distance was measured off to the northward to reach the true boundary. A table of offsets for the last 10-minute arc of great circle was now computed and the remainder of the month was spent in measuring such offsets from the arc of great circle actually run.

November, 1767. The party continued to move eastward and to measure the offsets to the true boundary from the 10-minute arcs of great circle until the station 199 miles 63 chains 68 links was reached. Eastward, beyond this position, temporary markers had already been placed. Accordingly, there was now one continuous "Visto" along the boundary, extending entirely from the northeast corner of Maryland to the westernmost extent of the survey at 233 miles 17 chains 48 links from the Post marked West. On the fifth Mr. Hugh Crawford and the Indians and all helpers except thirteen retained to erect markers in the line left for their homes. These temporary markers were huge mounds of earth and stones piled around the wooden posts which had been placed at the mile points on the boundary. In the mountains in mid-November this task was beset by very severe weather and under such extreme conditions, with twenty-one inches of snow, the survey helpers declined to continue. On the twenty-ninth the demarcation was complete to Town Hill and the next day Sideling Hill was reached and the boundary markers, i.e., piles of stone, had been placed to milepost 135 from the Post marked West, moving eastward. East of this point cut stone markers had previously been placed. West of Sideling Hill they were not used on account of the difficulty of transportation.

As already stated, the distance to the northeast corner of Maryland from the Post marked West was 2 miles 79 chains 27 links measured westerly. This gives the position of the extreme point reached as 230 miles 18 chains 21 links from the northeast corner of Maryland, about 30 miles west of that, long afterward, in 1912, decreed by the U.S. Supreme Court to be the northeast corner of Maryland. In accordance with later findings, Lord Baltimore bore half the cost for a portion of the survey which did not concern his province—30 miles of demarcation between Pennsylvania and Virginia, now West Virginia.

December, 1767. Mason and Dixon were at Conecocheague on the fourth and from that point wrote to the Commissioners in Annapolis and Philadelphia to inform them that they would be in Philadelphia on the fifteenth of the month. The scientists were at Brandywine on the tenth. The following day they received a letter from Mr. Benjamin Chew, one of the Commissioners from Pennsylvania, stating that an official meeting would be held at Christiana Bridge on the twenty-third. Actually the meeting was held on the twenty-fourth, twenty-fifth, and twenty-sixth. At the conclusion of this conference the Commissioners gave instructions to Mason and Dixon to draw a plan of the boundary lines which they had marked.

January, 1768. The plans of the lines of demarcation were delivered to the Reverend Richard Peters, Commissioner from Maryland. This concluded the official responsibilities of Mason and Dixon in the boundary survey. They were to remain in the colonies until the following eleventh of September, occupied in research on the dimensions of the earth for the Royal Society.

IV. ASTRONOMICAL AND GEODETIC METHODS EMPLOYED BY MASON AND DIXON

1. SCIENTIFIC PROCEDURE OF MASON AND DIXON IN ESTABLISHING THE PARALLEL

The method employed by Mason and Dixon, now known as the secant method, basically consists of running arcs of great circle which intersect the desired parallel of latitude at predetermined intercepts. In the northern hemisphere the arc of the great circle always lies north of the arc of the parallel. The distance from the great circle to the parallel at the midpoint of the arc can be calculated by spherical trigonometry. At intermediate points the offsets from the great circle are determined by a parabolic variation. The locus of such points represents a parallel of latitude.

A second type of correction must always be made. It is never possible to run a long tangent or arc of great circle without some bearing error. The line inevitably will deviate to the right or left. This circumstance necessitates frequent latitude checks, usually at the end of each arc of great circle where the parallel should have been intersected. The latitude observations show the error in the running of the arc, and the distances between the intended arc and the arc as actually run are easily proportioned at desired points according to straight-line variation.

The latitude agreed upon for the boundary between Maryland and Pennsylvania was that of the "Post marked West," which was on a parallel 15 miles south of the southernmost point in Philadelphia. The latitude was found by Mason and Dixon to be 39°43'17.4" (page 103) and in moving west they always attempted to hold to this parallel. In the running of the boundary the length of the great circle arcs selected was 10 minutes, now known to equal 11.5151 statute miles.

A fundamental quantity which had to be predetermined was the bearing on which to run the various 10-minute arcs of great circle in order to intersect the parallel at their extremities. This was calculated from spherical trigonometry as follows:

Latitude of Post marked West = 39°43'17.4" (page 69)
Co-Latitude of
Post marked West   = 50°16'42.6" (page 69)

Length of
semi-arc of great circle   = 0°05'00.0"

The above data specify a right spherical triangle with sides as follows:

a. Extending from the pole of the earth to the intersection point of a circle of latitude with a 10-minute arc of great circle (50°16'42.6")
b. Extending from the pole of the earth to the midpoint of a 10-minute arc of great circle
c. The semi-arc of great circle = 0°05'00"

From the trigonometry of the right spherical triangle it is seen that

$$\text{Cosine Bearing} = \frac{\tan 0°05'00''}{\tan 50°16'42.6''} = \frac{.00145444}{1.20358657}$$
$$= .00120842 \quad (0° - 04' - 09'')$$
$$\text{Bearing} = \text{N}89°55'51''\text{W}$$

This shows that the deflection angle to be turned off at the extremity of each chord or 10-minute arc was 0°08'18".

These changes in direction at times were accomplished by astronomical procedures, but it appears that the angle was frequently turned off from the plate of the transit or was established by the method of offsets from the tangent.

2. STARS OBSERVED

The major portion of the astronomical work consisted of latitude observations to furnish control for the boundary demarcation between Pennsylvania and Maryland. For this purpose stars of low zenith distance were employed. Other work involved azimuth determinations such as were necessary to ascertain the direction of the Tangent Line at the Middle Point in connection with the subsequent study of the length of a degree of latitude for the Royal Society. Azimuth settings also were required for control of the directions of the numerous 10-minute chords of great circle from which the offsets to the boundary were measured.

In addition, it was necessary to establish the meridian in running the North Line and the line of 15 miles length between the stations at Mr. John Harland's and Mr. Alexander Bryan's. At other times observations were required in connection with the standardization of clocks for the Royal Society and the checking of occultations.

Following are two lists of stars used by Mason and Dixon for the purposes indicated:

Stars for Latitude

Gamma Andromedae (Almach)
Beta Aurigae (Menkalinan)
Gamma Cygni (Sadr)
Delta Cygni
Alpha Lyrae (Vega)
Alpha Persei (Marfak)
Beta Persei (Algol)
Alpha Aurigae (Capella)
Alpha Geminorum (Castor)

Time Stars and Azimuth Stars

Alpha Andromedae (Alpheratz)
Beta Andromedae (Mirach)
Alpha Arietis (Hamal)
Alpha Coronae Borealis (Alphecca)
Beta Draconis
Gamma Draconis
Gamma Geminorum
Alpha Leonis (Regulus)
Beta Leonis (Denebola)
Alpha Ophiuchi (Rasalhague)
Alpha Orionis (Betelgeuse)
Eta Tauri (Alcyone)
Beta Ursae Majoris (Merak)
Epsilon Ursae Majoris (Alioth)
Beta Ursae Minoris (Kochab)
Alpha Tauri (Aldebaran)
Alpha Scorpii (Antares)
Alpha Boötis (Arcturus)
Alpha Ursae Minoris (Polaris)
Beta Geminorum (Pollux)
Alpha Canis Minoris (Procyon)
Alpha Canis Majoris (Sirius)
Alpha Virginis (Spica)

3. OBSERVATIONS AND THEIR REDUCTION

In the latitude calculations the usual formula was followed, i.e.:

$$z = \phi - \delta$$

The declinations, δ, were taken from a then recent star catalogue by the Astronomer Royal, James Bradley, whose assistant Charles Mason had been from 1756 to 1760. Corrections to observed star positions were made for nutation, precession, annual aberration, and refrac-

tion. Proper motion corrections do not appear but as the star positions were of current date, this item probably was not important. Annual parallax had not yet been evaluated and hence does not appear in the list of corrections. Its influence is usually small.

When the survey line crossed a river, triangulation procedures were used to determine the unknown distance. Oblique triangles were used at times, an unusual practice which must be attributed to lack of a clear vista along the lines desired for sight. The angles were taken with a Hadley quadrant. Distances were measured horizontally and were recorded in miles, chains, and links.

In azimuth observations and in establishing the meridian, the method of taking stars at equal altitudes at premeridian and postmeridian transits was employed. Other methods were those of offsets from the tangent and the precalculation of the time at which a star would be on a desired azimuth.

4. THE SOUTHERN BORDER OF DELAWARE

The semi-Transpeninsular Line or southern border of Delaware was specified to extend from Cape Henlopen west to a point midway between the Atlantic Ocean and the Chesapeake Bay, i.e., the Middle Point. But as there is no record of astronomical control for latitude, it would appear that what the colonial surveyors did was actually to prolong a tangent which would have been an arc of a great circle. Eight monuments were placed. This was not the work of Mason and Dixon, having been accomplished by local surveyors in 1751.

5. THE FIVE LINES OF MASON AND DIXON

The border demarcations of the two geodesists may be summarized as follows:

a. The West Line, or border between Pennsylvania on the north and Maryland and Virginia (now West Virginia) on the south, which extends 230 miles 18 chains 21 links west from the northeast corner of Maryland.

b. The East Line, which extends as a secant through the northern portion of Delaware. The length from the northeast corner of Maryland to Delaware Bay is 14 miles 20 chains 15 links. This distance was desired in order to ascertain when 5 degrees of longitude west of Delaware Bay had been reached. The line was of no importance to Maryland though that colony sustained half of the expense of running it.

c. The Tangent Line, which extends from the Middle Point to the Tangent Point for a distance of 6558.31 chains or 81 miles 78 chains 31 links (page 269).

d. The Arc Line, which follows a part of the curve of the circle of 12 miles radius around New Castle courthouse. The subtended secant is 1.451 miles.

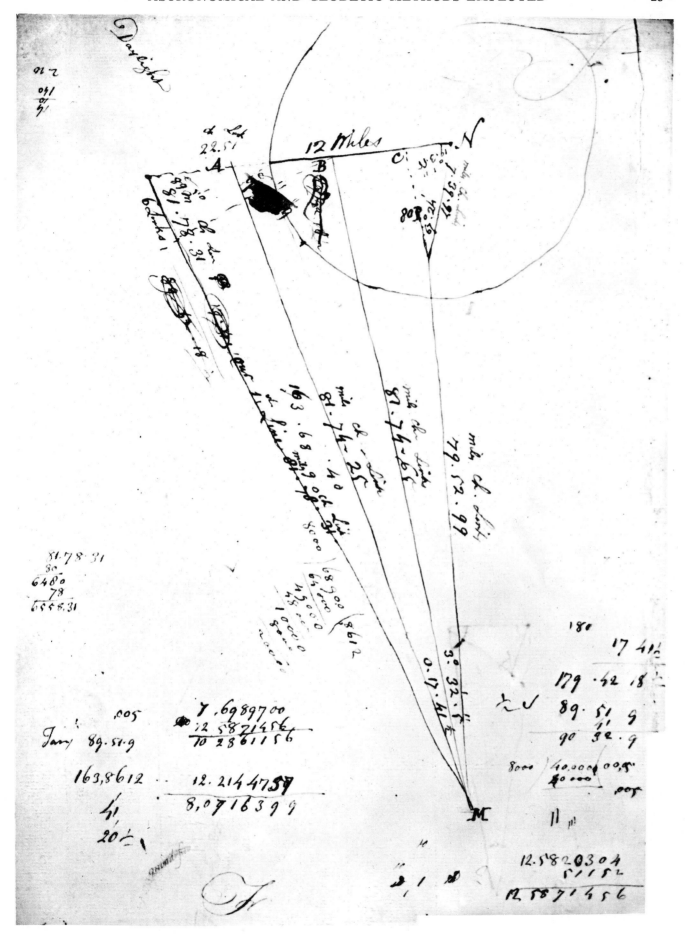

FIG. 5. Surveyors' diagram illustrating location of the Tangent Line (Journal, page 24).

This gives the length of the Arc Line as 1.452 miles.

e. The North Line, which is the distance from the Tangent Point to the northeast corner of Maryland less that portion of the line which is a secant to the circle of 12 miles radius. This equals 5.019 miles less 1.451 miles = 3.568 miles.

Some monuments were reset in 1849 with slight alterations in distance.

6. CORRECTIONS TO THE TANGENT LINE

The Tangent Line as established by colonial surveyors was somewhat imperfect. It is believed that in general the procedure employed by Mason and Dixon in ultimately obtaining a tangency was to determine the error at the Tangent Point, to reset the point accordingly, and to move all other markers on the line by a distance proportional to their distance from the Middle Point. However, statements in the Journal on this matter are obscure.

7. INSTRUMENTS AND EQUIPMENT USED

The principal item of equipment was an astronomical transit or "sector," as it was called. It is believed to have been similar to the zenith telescopes used until recent years by the U.S. Coast and Geodetic Survey.

The name evidently arose from the fact that the graduated arc for the reading of zenith distances actually was a sector of a circle. A micrometer made observations possible to a hundredth of a second of arc. Troughton and Simms of London were producing excellent instruments of this kind in 1849.

Other equipment consisted of a direction transit, a navigator's quadrant, chains of 66 feet (100 links per chain), an astronomical clock, wooden rods of 16.5 feet with spirit level, and other rods of 10 feet length. Also included were an up-to-date star catalogue by Dr. Bradley, adequate tables for astronomical corrections to observations, and seven-place logarithmic tables for numbers and sines and tangents. To these items may be added the other more common articles required by surveyors, camp equipment for thirty-nine men, and horses and wagons for transportation of personnel and gear.

At times Mason and Dixon worked under unusual and adverse circumstances, for example, on Christmas Day, and in snow two feet deep, and in temperatures as low as 22° below zero F. Their task was carried out in frontier country without benefit of modern methods and conveniences. But, after two hundred years, checks by the most refined methods of geodesy attest to the mathematical excellence of their accomplishment.

V. DETERMINATION OF THE LENGTH OF A DEGREE OF LATITUDE FOR THE ROYAL SOCIETY

The geometry involved in a preliminary evaluation of the circumference of the earth is indeed quite simple. Assuming a nearly spherical figure, it is obvious that the circumference may be approximately calculated from a knowledge of the length of one degree of latitude. If such a distance be represented by d, then the circumference C will be 360 d. To evaluate d, all one has to do is to measure the distance between two points on a meridional arc and obtain latitude observations at each point. Then d is the quotient of the total distance divided by the difference in latitude. The latitude follows from the well-known equation,

$$z = \phi - \delta$$

where z = zenith distance of a star at upper meridian transit

δ = declination of the star

ϕ = latitude of the point of observation.

Modern geodetic work may be considered to have started in 1617 with Willebrord Snell, also famed for having discovered the sine law of refraction. His method was to determine the length of the arc of a meridian by triangulation, but ultimately he reached a value which was about 3 per cent too small. Other similar attempts were made in the seventeenth and eighteenth centuries in France, Lapland, Peru, and South Africa.

A very desirable requirement in this type of geodetic research is terrain level enough to permit laying out a truly horizontal line. Mason and Dixon, having observed the smooth topography of what we now call the Delmarva Peninsula, in 1764 proposed to the Royal Society that it sponsor the measurement there of an arc of the meridian. The proposal met with enthusiastic response. Much germane correspondence may be seen in the Journal of Mason and Dixon, pages 209-221. Their work on this problem was principally accomplished after the completion of the boundary survey, but some progress was made during the winter furlough and in periods when instructions were awaited from the Commissioners.

Elaborate instruments were shipped by the Royal Society to be used in the research but as mentioned on page 213 of the Journal the equipment was lost with the missing ship "Egdon." However, Mason decided that the instruments which had been used in the boundary survey could be depended upon to give satisfactory results. The Penns and Lord Baltimore made available additional equipment of their own. Very detailed instructions sent over by Nevil Maskelyne, Astronomer Royal, appear on pages 213-218 of the Journal.

The procedure followed was to determine very precisely the latitude of the Middle Point, i.e., the southwest corner of Delaware, and also that of the north end of the 15-mile line where previous observations had been made in January, 1764, in the yard of Mr. John Harland at the Forks of the Brandywine. The difference in latitude between these two points would give the length in degrees of an arc along a meridian between the two circles of latitude on which they lie. In addition to the astronomical observations, it was necessary to obtain the distance in feet between the two parallels. This consisted of three components:

1. The 15-mile line from Mr. Harland's to Mr. Bryan's.
2. The North Line from the West Line to the Tangent Point.
3. The meridional component of the Tangent Line from the Tangent Point to the Middle Point. (The bearing of the line at the Middle Point is N3°43′30″W by astronomical observations.) (page 267)

Mason lists the following data as a basis for the necessary calculations:

1. Based on the entire line from Mr. Harland's to the Middle Point:
   a. Latitude at Mr. Harland's at Brandywine
      = 39°56′19″   (page 267)
   b. Latitude of the Middle Point
      = 38°27′34″   (page 267)
   c. Latitude at the mid-point of the arc
      = 39°11′56.5″
   d. Difference in latitude
      = 1°28′44.99″ = 5324.99″ = 1.47916389 degrees   (page 269)
   e. Distance between the points
      = 8132.933 chains   (page 271)
   f. Length of a degree of latitude
      = 8132.933 chains divided by 1.47916389 degrees
      = 5498.331 chains = 68 miles 58 chains 33 links   (page 271)
      = 68.7291 miles

The modern value based on the Clarke Spheroid of 1866 is 68.9833 miles (one second of arc = 30.838 meters). One meter = 39.370432 inches. Mason and Dixon's error was therefore 0.2542 mile, 0.368 per cent of the correct value.

2. Based on the line from Mr. Bryan's to the Middle Point:

a. Latitude at Mr. Bryan's
   = 39°43′23.45″   (page 272)
b. Latitude at the Middle Point
   = 38°27′34″   (page 267)
c. Latitude at the mid-point of the arc
   = 39°05′28.72″
d. Difference in latitude
   = 1°15′49.45″ = 4549.45″ = 1.26373611 degrees   (page 272)
e. Distance between the two points
   = 6956 chains 76 links   (page 272)
f. Length of a degree of latitude
   = 6956.76 chains divided by 1.26373611 degrees
   = 68 miles 64 chains 91 links   (page 272)
   = 68.8114 miles

The modern value based on the Clarke Spheroid of 1866 is 68.9810 miles (one second of arc = 30.837 meters). Mason and Dixon's error is 0.1696 mile, 0.246 per cent of the correct value.

The two arcs are sufficiently close in mid-point latitude for an average to appear justifiable. The mean value would be determined by 68.7291 and 68.8114, or 68.7702 miles. Assuming a spherical earth, the circumference would be 24757 miles. The radius then becomes $24757 \div 2\pi = 3940$ miles. Based on the Clarke Spheroid of 1866, the equatorial radius is 3963.34 miles and the polar radius is 3949.99 miles. Using the equatorial radius twice, the mean radius is 3959 miles. The error is seen to be 19 miles in radius or 0.48 per cent.[1]

Cavendish (1731-1810) reviewed the results of Mason and Dixon in association with the topography of the Atlantic Seaboard and Allegheny Mountains. He concluded that the excess of attraction from the mountains and the deficiency beyond the continental shelf could have produced a significant effect on the latitude observations. An examination of the behavior of the geoid in the concerned area discloses a very erratic condition.[2] To extrapolate known station errors for values at the three concerned points would not appear in consonance with the scientific approach and therefore will not be attempted. It would be necessary to connect the three stations occupied by Mason and Dixon with the North American Datum and ascertain the anomaly in latitude at each point.

At the time of Mason and Dixon the ellipticity of the earth was known (see correspondence from Maskelyne, Journal, page 218) but had not been mathematically evaluated. The basic information desired at that epoch was the circumference of the earth based

[1] *The Figure of the Earth,* Bulletin 78 of National Research Council.
[2] *Deflections of the Vertical in the United States* (Special Publication No. 229, U.S. Coast and Geodetic Survey).

FIG. 6. Map accompanying Charles Mason's report, "Observations for Determining the Length of a Degree of Latitude," *Philosophical Transactions of the Royal Society of London* **58** (1768): pp. 274-328.

on the assumption of a spherical figure. The refinements of Bessel, Clarke, and Hayford had to be awaited.

In all research, progress is by slow, successive advances, each discovery contributing its part to our precious heritage of knowledge. In the domain of world geodesy the names of Mason and Dixon will always be found in the roll of great scientists who with zeal and patience sought to advance knowledge of the figure of our earth.

VI. SOURCES AND TECHNICAL REFERENCES

BAYLIFF, W. H. 1959. The Maryland-Pennsylvania and the Maryland-Delaware Boundaries. Bulletin No. 4 (2nd ed.), Maryland Board of Natural Resources (Annapolis, Md.).

BURCHARD, EDWARD L., and EDWARD B. MATHEWS. 1908-1909. "Manuscripts and Publications Relating to the Mason and Dixon Line and Other lines in Pennsylvania, Maryland, and the Virginias." In: *Report of the Resurvey of the Maryland-Pennsylvania Boundary,* Secretary of Internal Affairs, Harrisburg, Pa., and Maryland Geological Survey, Special Publication VII (Baltimore, Md., Johns Hopkins Press).

COPE, THOMAS D. 1939. "The Stargazer's Stone." *Pennsylvania History* **6:** pp. 205-220.

—— 1944. "The Apprentice Years of Mason and Dixon." *Ibid.* **11:** pp. 155-170.

—— 1948. "Collecting Source Material about Charles Mason and Jeremiah Dixon." *Proc. Amer. Philos. Soc.* **92:** pp. 111-114.

—— 1949. "Mason and Dixon, English Men of Science." *Delaware Notes* (University of Delaware, Newark, Del., 22nd ser.), pp. 13-32.

—— 1951. "Some Contacts of Benjamin Franklin with Mason and Dixon and their Work." *Proc. Amer. Philos. Soc.* **95:** pp. 232-238.

—— 1953. "The Jersey Quadrant Used in Pennsylvania." *Ibid.* **97:** pp. 565-571.

—— 1955. "Some Local Scholars who Counseled the Proprietors and their Commissioners during the Border Surveys of the 1760's." *Ibid.* **99:** pp. 268-276.

—— 1956. "When the Stars Interrupted the Running of a Meridian Line Northward up the Delmarva Peninsula." *Ibid.* **100:** pp. 557-566.

COPE, THOMAS D., and H. W. ROBINSON. 1952. "The Astronomical Manuscripts which Charles Mason Gave to Provost the Reverend John Ewing during October 1786." *Ibid.* **96:** pp. 417-423.

COPE, THOMAS D., and H. W. ROBINSON. 1954. "When the Maryland-Pennsylvania Boundary Survey Changed from a Political and Legal Study into a Scientific and Technological Project." *Ibid.* **98:** pp. 432-441.

CUMMINS, HUBERTIS M. 1962. *The Mason and Dixon Line, Story for a Bicentenary, 1763-1963* (Harrisburg, Pa. Commonwealth of Pennsylvania, Department of Internal Affairs).

DOUGLAS, EDWARD M. 1932. "Boundaries, Areas, Geographic Centers, and Altitudes of the United States and the Several States." *U.S. Geological Survey, Bulletin No. 817* (Washington, Government Printing Office).

DUERKSEN, J. A. 1941. *Deflections of the Vertical in the United States.* U.S. Coast and Geodetic Survey, Special Publication No. 229 (U.S. Department of Commerce, Washington, D.C.).

DWIGHT, H. D. 1926. "The Mason and Dixon Line." *Yale Review,* n.s., **15:** pp. 687-702.

FOOTNER, HULBERT. 1944. *Rivers of the Eastern Shore* (New York, Farrar and Rinehart).

HOSKINSON, ALBERT J., and J. A. DUERKSEN. 1947. "Determination of Longitude, Latitude, and Azimuth." *Manual of Geodetic Astronomy,* U.S. Coast and Geodetic Survey, Special Publication No. 237 (Washington, Government Printing Office).

HOSMER, GEORGE L. 1930. *Geodesy* (2nd ed., New York, Wiley).

LAMBERT, W. D. *ca.* 1947. "Two Geodesists of the Eighteenth Century." Manuscript article in possession of A. Hughlett Mason.

MASON, CHARLES. 1768. "Observations for Determining the Length of a Degree of Latitude in the Provinces of Maryland and Pennsylvania, in North America." *Phil. Trans. Royal Society of London* **58:** pp. 274-328.

MASON, A. HUGHLETT, and WILLIAM F. SWINDLER. 1964. "Mason and Dixon, Their Line and Its Legend." *American Heritage* **15:** pp. 22-29, 93-96.

RUDY, G. T., *et al.* 1931. *Physics of the Earth. II, The Figure of the Earth* (Washington, D.C., National Research Council).

THE JOURNAL OF
CHARLES MASON AND JEREMIAH DIXON
1763-1768

The numbers, beginning with 25, appearing in the
right-hand margin indicate the last line on the corresponding pages in the Mason and Dixon Journal.

Redrawn versions of the freehand representations of
Charles Mason appear at the end of the transcript. The
figure numbers agree with the page numbers in the
Journal.

1763
November
8 15 Arrived at Philadelphia.

16 Attended a meeting of the Commissioners appointed by the
Proprietors of Pennsylvania to settle the boundaries of the Province

17 Wrote to his Excellency Horatio Sharpe Esqr. Governour of
Maryland, signifying our arrival at Philadelphia.

22 Landed the Instruments.

25 Set up the Sector } and found they had not receiv'd
28 Set up the Transit } any damage.

30 The Commissioners appointed by Lord Baltimore to settle the
Boundaries of Maryland came to Philadelphia.

1763
November
15 Arrived at Philadelphia
16 Attended a meeting of the Commissioners appointed by the
    Proprietors of Pennsylvania to settle the boundaries of the Province
17 Wrote to his Excellency Horatio Sharpe, Esquire, Governor of
    Maryland, signifying our arrival at Philadelphia.
22 Landed the Instruments
25 Set up the Sector and found it had not received any damage
28 Set up the Transit and found it had not received any damage
30 The Commissioners appointed by Lord Baltimore to settle the
    Boundaries of Maryland came to Philadelphia

December
1   Attended a meeting of the Commissioners of both Provinces,
    and set up the Compound Instrument of Lord Baltimore's
2   Attended a meeting of the Commissioners
3   Attended a meeting of the Commissioners
5   Attended a meeting of the Commissioners and directed a carpenter to build an observatory
    near the point settled by the Commissioners to be the South end of the
    City of Philadelphia
6   Set up a Sector brought by the Commissioners from Maryland
    and found the nonius (vernier) would not touch the middle part of the arch.
    Was sworn before the Commissioners.
7   Attended the Commissioners
8   Carried some of our Instruments in to the Observatory
9   Attended the Commissioners and received our Instructions
10-13 incl. Got the Observatory finished and fixed up our Instruments
    proper for observing.
14-15 incl. Rain and Snow

1763

December

16 Brought the Instrument into the Meridian by making several
   stars pass along the horizontal wire in the middle of the Telescope
   The method pursued in doing of this is as follows:
   Let HO be the horizontal, and NS be the
   vertical wire, Then we bring a Northern
   star (one as far north of the zenith as the limit of the Arch) to
   the Horizontal wire at a, and it will describe
   the arch of a circle as a b c, (the Telescope inverting).
   If a p be apparently equal to pc, it is truly
   in the Meridian, if not equal, we proceed by trial until they are equal;
   which may be done with four or five stars to great exactitude as we
   find by comparing the time of the stars passing the wire NS, with the
   time they transit the Meridian as found by Equal Altitudes

17 Cloudy

18 Cloudy. Sunday.

19   Plane of the Sector facing the E A S T

	Star Magnitudes	Star Names	Right Ascension		Nearest point on the Sector		Revolutions and Seconds on the Micrometer		Difference		Apparent Zenith Distance			
			h	m	o	'	R	"	R	"	o	'	"	
		Delta Persei			7	5 -	10	20	0	41.5	7	4	18.5	N
							11	9.5						
	0.2	Capella	4	59	5	50 -	2	39.5	3	6.5	5	47	17.5	
							5	46						
		Chi Ursae Majoris			8	5 +	5	26.5	2	45.2	8	7	29.2	
							2	33						
20	0.1	Alpha Lyrae	18	29	1	20 +	9	29.5	2	17.5	1	22	1.5	
							11	47						
	2.2	Gamma Androm.	1	49	1	15 -	7	32	0	9.0	1	14	51.0	
							7	41						
	2.0	Beta Persei	2	53	0	5 +	10	16.5	0	25.0	0	5	25.0	
							9	43.5						
		Delta Persei	3	26	7	5 -	8	43	0	43.5	7	4	16.5	
							9	34.5						
	0.2	Capella	4	59	5	50 -	16	24.5	3	0.0	5	47	24.0	
							9	24.5						Fig.
	2.0	Beta Aurigae	5	42	4	55 +	5	40.5	2	29.5	4	57	13.5	26
							3	11						
21		Alpha Cygni	2	34	4	30 +	8	36	0	16.0	4	30	16.0	N *
							8	20						
		Gamma Andromedae			1	15 -	7	48 +	0	10.7	1	14	49.3	N
							8	7						
		Beta Persei			0	5 +	8	33 +	0	26.3	0	5	26.3	N
							8	7						
		Delta Persei			7	5 -	6	45.5	0	44.5	7	4	15.5	N
							7	38						
		Capella			5	50 -	7	37.5	3	5.5	5	47	18.5	N
							10	43						
		Beta Aurigae			4	55 +	11	14.5	2	25.2	4	57	9.2	N
							8	41 +						
		Castor	7	19	7	35 -	8	9 -	1	46.2	7	33	21.8	S
							6	14.5						

* very faint

Star Magnitude	Star Names	Right Ascension h	m	Nearest point on the Sector o	'	Revolutions and Seconds on the Micrometer R	"	Difference R	"	Apparent Zenith Distance o	'	"	
22	Alpha Lyrae			1	20 +	7, 9	21.5, 43	2	21.5	1	22	5.5	S
	Alpha Cygni			4	30 +	11, 11	48, 32 +	0	15.7	4	30	15.7	*
	Capella			5	50 -	10, 13	43, 43.5	3	0.5	5	47	23.5	
	Castor			7	35 -	14, 12	33 -, 37	1	47.7	7	33	20.3	
	Chi Ursae Majoris			8	5 +	7, 4	15, 19.75	2	47.3	8	7	31.3	
23 Cloudy													
24 Cloudy													
25 Sunday	Gamma Andromedae			1	15 -	5, 6	45.5, 4	0	10.5	1	14	49.5	N
	Beta Persei			0	5 +	6, 5	21, 49	0	23.7	0	5	23.7	
	Delta Persei			7	5 -	7, 8	15.5, 9	0	45.5	7	4	14.5	
0.2	Capella			5	50 -	7, 10	36, 36	3	0.0	5	47	24.0	
2.0	Beta Aurigae			4	55 +	10, 7	17, 34	2	35.0	4	57	19.0	
1.6	Castor			7	35 -	7, 5	48, 50	1	49.7	7	33	18.3	

27

Equal Altitudes of Beta Aurigae on the Transit Instrument

Time of Watch h	m	s	h	m	s	Passed the Meridian h	m	s
4	23	15	----------------					
	24	22	6	59	16	5	41	49
	25	35	7	0	25	5	41	50

Hence Beta Aurigae passed the Meridian at 5h 41m 49.5s by the watch and it
was observed to pass the vertical or meridian wire in the Sector at
5h 41m 50s by the watch

Star Magnitude	Star Names	Right Ascension h	m	Nearest point on the Sector o	'	Revolutions and Seconds on the Micrometer R	"	Difference R	"	Apparent Zenith Distance o	'	"	
26 Cloudy													
27 0.1	Alpha Lyrae	18	29	1	20 +	4, 6	3, 25	2	22.0	1	22	6.0	S
2.2	Gamma Andromedae			1	15 -	4, 4	17, 29 -	0	11.7	1	14	48.3	N
0.2	Beta Persei			0	5 +	4, 3	19.5, 45	0	26.5	0	5	26.5	N
1.9	Alpha Persei			9	5 -	3, 5	31 -, 13 +	1	34.6	9	3	33.4	N
	Delta Persei			7	5 -	5, 6	16, 6 +	0	42.3	7	4	17.7	N
0.2	Capella			5	50 -	5, 8	22.5, 26	3	3.5	5	47	20.5	N
2.0	Beta Aurigae			4	55 +	8, 5	23 -, 45	2	29.7	4	57	13.7	N
1.6	Castor			7	35 -	6, 4	20 +, 24	1	48.3	7	33	19.7	S

28

* faint

Star Magnitude	Star Names	Right Ascension h	m	Nearest Point on the Sector °	'	Revolutions and Seconds on the Micrometer R	"	Difference R	"	Apparent Zenith Distance (Plane East) °	'	"
28 0.1	Alpha Lyrae	18	29	1	20+	11	5.5	2	20.2	1	22	4.2
						13	26-					

After Alpha Lyrae passed the Meridian we turned the Plane of the Sector
and brought it in the Meridian by Stars of the Evening, then took the following
Plane of the Sector facing the WEST

Star Magnitude	Star Names	Right Ascension h	m	Nearest Point on the Sector °	'	Revolutions and Seconds on the Micrometer R	"	Difference R	"	Apparent Zenith Distance (Plane East) °	'	"
28 0.2	Capella	4	59	5	50-	6	24.5	2	44.8	5	47	31.2
						3	32-					
2.0	Beta Aurigae	5	43	4	55+	4	13	2	39.5	4	57	23.5
						7	0.5					
1.6	Castor			7	35-	6	46-	2	1.7	7	33	14.3
						8	47.5					
	Chi Ursae Majoris			8	5+	4	46.5	3	4.2	8	7	40.2
						7	51-					

29 Cloudy

Star Magnitude	Star Names	Right Ascension h	m	Nearest Point on the Sector °	'	Revolutions and Seconds on the Micrometer R	"	Difference R	"	Apparent Zenith Distance (Plane East) °	'	"	
30 0.1	Alpha Lyrae	18	29	1	20+	3	36-	2	13.7	1	21	57.7	S
						1	22						
1.3	Alpha Cygni			4	30+	6	22-	0	13.3	4	30	13.3	N
						6	35						
	Gamma Andromedae			1	15-	6	16.5	0	5.8	1	14	54.2	N
						6	11-						
	Beta Persei			0	5+	5	47+	0	31.2	0	5	31.2	N
						6	26.5						
	Alpha Persei			9	5-	6	28	Not completed					
						5	7+						
	Delta Persei			7	5-	3	44+	0	39.8	7	4	20.2	N
						3	4.5						
	Capella			5	50-	3	42.3	2	49.3	5	47	26.7	N
						0	45						
	Beta Aurigae			4	55+	0	41	2	39.5	4	57	23.5	N
						3	28.5						
	Castor			7	35-	7	43.5	1	51.8	7	33	16.2	S
						9	43+						
	Chi Ursae Majoris			8	5+	9	47.4	3	4.6	8	7	40.6	
						13	0.0						29

Equal Altitudes of Capella
Time by the Watch

h	m	s	h	m	s
3	50	32	5	55	41
	51	35		56	58
	52	54		58	11

Hence Capella passed the Meridian of the Transit
Instrument at 4h 54m 18s and it was observed to
pass the Vertical Wire of the Sector at 4h 54m 7s

Star Magnitude	Star Names	Nearest Point on the Sector °	'	Revolutions and Seconds on the Micrometer R	"	Difference R	"	Apparent Zenith Distance (Plane East) °	'	"
31	Alpha Lyrae	1	20+	11	45	2	17	1	22	1.0
				9	28					
	Gamma Andromedae	1	15-	6	3	0	6.5	1	14	53.5
				5	48.5					

1764
January
1 Sun.

Star Magnitude	Star Names	Nearest Point on the Sector °	'	Revolutions and Seconds on the Micrometer R	"	Difference R	"	Apparent Zenith Distance (Plane East) °	'	"	
	Gamma Andromedae	1	15-	6	19.7	0	6.4	1	14	53.6	N
				6	13.3						
	Beta Persei	0	5+	7	22	0	31.5	0	5	31.5	
				8	1.5						
	Capella	5	50-	11	28	2	45.0	5	47	31.0	
				8	35						
	Beta Aurigae	4	55+	8	26+	2	38.7	4	57	22.7	
				11	13						
	Castor	7	35-	11	4	1	51.0	7	33	17.0	
				13	3						
	Chi Ursae Majoris	8	5+	12	41	3	3.7	8	7	39.7	
				15	45-						

Star Magnitude	Star Names	Right Ascension		Nearest point on the Sector		Revolutions and Seconds on the Micrometer		Difference		Apparent Zenith Distance (Plane West)		
		h	m	o	'	R	"	R	"	o	'	"
2	Gamma Andromedae	1	15-			11	33.5	0	6.5	1	14	53.5
						11	27					
	Beta Persei	0	5+			10	27.5	0	30.0	0	5	30.0
						11	5.5					
	Alpha Persei	9	5-			13	47	1	27.0	9	3	41.0
						12	20					
	Delta Persei	7	5-			13	22+	0	39.3	7	4	20.7
						12	35					
	Capella	5	50-			13	5	2	45.5	5	47	30.5
						10	11.5					
	Beta Aurigae	4	55+			10	39.5	2	38.5	4	57	22.5
						13	26					
	Castor	7	35-			11	39.5	1	50.5	7	33	17.5
						13	38					
3	Alpha Cygni	4	30+			8	7.5	0	14.0	4	30	14.0*
						8	21.5					
4	Alpha Lyrae	1	20+			8	29	2	17.5	1	22	1.5
						6	11.5					

For the Southing of the Southernmost point of the City of Philadelphia from the Sector in the Observatory. (NOTE: Angle notation supplied by editor)

log 10.3 = 1.01284
log 13.7 = 1.13672
Difference $\overline{9.87612-10}$ = log cos Angle HBC
Angle HBC = $41^{\circ}15'$
Angle BHC = $180^{\circ} - 2(41^{\circ}15') = 97^{\circ}30'$
Angle AHP = $97^{\circ}30' - 90^{\circ}00' = 7^{\circ}30'$
AP = 45.55 sin $7^{\circ}30'$
log 45.6 = 10.65896-10
log sin $7^{\circ}30'$= 9.11570-10
log AP = $\overline{9.77466-10}$
   AP = 5.95
   SH = $\underline{31.2}$
        37.15 = Yards the point is South of the Sector
        = 1.1" of latitude

In the above PH is on the South side of Cedar Street, P the point fixed on by the Commissioners to be the Southernmost point of the City of Philadelphia. S represents the Sector in the Observatory. (PA is the meridional distance that) H is South from the Sector.

30

Figure

31

* very faint

Apparent Zenith Distance, Plane of the Sector EAST

1763 December	Gamma Andromedae	Beta Persei	Alpha Persei	Delta Persei	Capella	Beta Aurigae	Castor
19	—	—	—	—	—	—	—
20	1 14 51.0	0 5 25.0	—	7 4 16.5	5 47 24.0	4 57 13.5	7 33 21.8
21	1 14 49.3	0 5 26.3	—	7 4 15.5	5 47 23.5	—	7 33 20.3
22	—	—	—	—	—	—	—
25 (Sun.)	1 14 49.5	0 5 23.7	—	7 4 14.5	5 47 24.0	—	7 33 18.3
27	1 14 48.3	0 5 26.5	9 3 33.4	7 4 17.7	5 47 20.5	4 57 13.7	7 33 19.7
Mean (Dec. 23)	1 14 49.5	0 5 25.4	9 3 33.4	7 4 16.05	5 47 23.0	4 57 13.6	7 33 20.0
Aberration	-11.8	- 9.5	-10.7	- 9.3	- 3.9	- 1.3	- 3.6
Deviation	- 3.1	- 5.5	- 6.0	- 6.5	- 8.7	- 9.2	+ 9.2
Refraction	+ 1.4	+ 0.1	+10.5	+ 8.3	+ 6.7	+ 5.8	+ 8.8
Mean Zenith Distance	1 14 36.0	0 5 10.5	9 3 27.2	7 4 8.5	5 47 17.1	4 57 8.9	7 33 34.4
Precession to Jan. 1,1764	+ 0.4	+ 0.4	+ 0.2	+ 0.3	+ 0.1	0.0	+ 0.2
Corrected Z.D.	1 14 36.4	0 5 10.9	9 3 27.4	7 4 8.8	5 47 17.2	4 57 8.9	7 33 34.6
Declination (Dr. Bradley)	—	—	—	47 0 39.7	45 43 52.9	44 53 44.8	32 22 56.7
Latitude (Plane East)	—	—	—	39 56 31.2	39 56 35.7	39 56 35.9	39 56 31.3

Plane of the Sector WEST

1763 December	Gamma Andromedae	Beta Persei	Alpha Persei	Delta Persei	Capella	Beta Aurigae	Castor
28	1 14 54.2	0 5 31.2	—	—	5 47 31.2	4 57 23.5	7 33 14.3
30	1 14 53.5	0 5 31.5	—	7 4 20.2	—	4 57 23.5	7 33 16.2
31	1 14 53.6	0 5 30.0	—	—	—	—	—
1764 1 Jan. (Sun.)	1 14 53.5	—	—	—	—	—	—
2	—	—	9 3 41.0	7 4 20.7	5 47 31.0	4 57 22.7	7 33 17.0
3	—	—	—	—	5 47 30.5	4 57 22.5	7 33 17.5
4	—	—	—	—	—	—	—
Mean, 1 Jan.	1 14 53.7	0 5 30.9	9 3 41.0	7 4 20.5	5 47 30.9	4 57 23.0	7 33 16.2
Abberation	-11.5	- 9.7	-11.0	- 9.9	- 5.0	- 2.4	- 3.1
Deviation	- 3.1	- 5.5	- 6.0	- 6.5	- 8.7	- 9.2	+ 9.2
Refraction	+ 1.4	+ 0.1	+10.5	+ 8.3	+ 6.7	+ 5.8	+ 8.8
Mean Zenith Distance	1 14 40.5	0 5 15.8	9 3 34.5	7 4 12.4	5 47 23.9	4 57 17.2	7 33 31.1
Declination (Dr. Bradley)	—	—	—	47 0 40.0	45 43 53.0	44 53 44.2	32 22 56.8
Latitude (Plane West)	—	—	—	39 56 27.6	39 56 29.1	39 56 27.0	39 56 27.9
Latitude (Plane East)	—	—	—	39 56 31.2	39 56 35.8	39 56 35.3	39 56 31.3
Mean Latitude	—	—	—	39 56 29.4	39 56 32.4	39 56 31.2	39 56 29.6

Mean Latitudes (Delta Persei column): 29.4, 32.4, 31.2, 29.6, 28.4

39 56 30.2 = Latitude of the observatory

Mean of all Latitudes

	Gamma Andromedae	Beta Persei	Alpha Persei	Delta Persei	Capella	Beta Aurigae	Castor
Mean Z. D. (East)	1 14 36.4	0 5 10.9	9 3 27.4	7 4 8.8	5 47 17.2	4 57 8.9	7 33 34.6
Mean Z. D. (West)	1 14 40.5	0 5 15.8	9 3 34.5	7 4 12.4	5 47 23.9	4 57 17.2	7 33 31.1
True Z. D. at Sector	1 14 38.45	0 5 13.35	9 3 30.95	7 4 10.6	5 47 20.55	4 57 13.05	7 33 32.8
Point South of Sector	+ 1.1	+ 1.1	+ 1.1	+ 1.1	+ 1.1	+ 1.1	- 1.1
True Z.D. 1 Jan. 1764	1 14 39.55	0 5 14.45	9 3 32.05	7 4 11.7	5 47 21.65	4 57 14.15	7 33 31.7

Date 1763	Alpha Lyrae		
	o	'	"

Plane EAST

The mean day of the observations in all the stars is 23rd of December except Alpha Persei which is the 27th, and Alpha Lyrae which is the 26th, etc.

Plane WEST

The mean day for Alpha Lyrae is the second of January, all the others is the first.

	1	22	5.5
	1	22	6.0
	1	22	4.2
	1	22	5.2

The small numbers in the line * are the precessions from December 23 to January 1; they are not used in bringing out the Latitude, etc., that being accounted for in the Stars' Declinations.

			+ 0.1
			- 9.4
			+ 1.5
	1	21	57.4
	1	21	57.4
	38	34	34.0
	39	56	31.4

1 21 57.4 = Mean Zenith Distance the first of January

From the foregoing the mean of the Latitudes given by the five different Stars is at the Observatory equal to 39° 56' 30".2
The Southernmost point of the City of Philadelphia is south of this point   0 1.1

Dec. 31	1	22	1.0
1764 Jan. 4	1	22	1.5

True Latitude of the Southernmost point
of the City of Philadelphia equals   39° 56' 29".1 North

Or the Latitude thus determined and given in to the Proprietors

Mean 2 Jan.	1	22	1.2
			- 2.0
			- 9.4
			+ 1.5
	1	21	51.3
	38	34	34.0
		56	25.3
		56	31.4
	39	56	28.4
	1	21	57.4
	1	21	51.3
	1	21	54.35
			- 1.1
	1	21	53.25

	Delta Persei	Capella	Beta Aurigae	Castor	Alpha Lyrae
True Zenith Distance of the Star the 1st Jan. 1764	7° 4' 11".6	5° 47' 21".6	4° 57' 14".2	7° 33' 31".6	1° 21' 53".2
Their Declinations according to Dr. Bradley, 1st Jan. 1764	47° 0' 40".0	45 43 53 .0	44 53 44 .2	32 22 56 .8	38 34 34.0
Latitude of the South point of Philadelphia by the different stars	39 56 28 .4	39 56 31 .4	39 56 30 .0	39 56 28 .4	39 56 27 .2

	28.4
	31.4
	30.0
	28.4
	27.2
39° 56' 29".1	as above

33

Gentlemen:

I hope you have pleased yourselves with good horses
and an agreeable companion.
The Temporary Line went through the Township of Darby
and the plantation of Thomas Lyeth - through Springfield at Samuel
Lewis' - through Providence Township at John Worral's - through Edgmont
Township at the widow Yarrels - through Thornburg at Isaac Vernon's -
through West Town at Joseph Hunts and through West Bradford at
Abraham Marshalls and John Newtons.
At the last place we began to set off the fifteen statute
miles and we found it to be about one mile from Philadelphia.
It is believed that either here or at some place about five or
six miles more west there will be found the most level ground.
You can go near one Mr. Thomas Woodward's plantation in
Marlboro Township. He is a surveyor and well acquainted with this
country and can be of great use to you in showing you the
best ground in any part of Chester County contiguous to the County
of Newcastle.   34
I am sure everybody will be glad to oblige you and
do you all the service in their power as soon as they are made
acquainted with your fullest characters and the business you
are employed in. I heartily wish you a good Journey and am

      Gentlemen

        Your most humble servant

        Richard Peters

To: Messrs: Mason and Dixon   35

(Editorial note:
On this page is shown the envelope in which the preceding letter was dispatched, viz:)

    To

      Messrs. Mason and Dixon

        Mathematicians
           at
         Wuaco   36

1764
January
4   Finished our observations at Philadelphia
5   Computing the result of the stars true zenith distances from our observations
6   Computing the result of the stars true zenith distances from our observations
7   Set out from Philadelphia with a Quadrant to find (nearby) a
        place in the Forks of Brandywine having the same Parallel
        as the Southernmost point of the City of Philadelphia.
8 Sun. Fixed on the House of Mr. John Harland's (about 31
        miles West of Philadelphia) to bring our Instruments to.
9   Returned to Philadelphia
10   Prepared for moving our Instruments
11   The Observatory taken down and put with the rest of our Instruments
        into the wagons, except the Telescope, etc., of the Sector
        which was carried on the Springs (with Feather bed under it)
        of a single Horse chair.

1764
January
12   Left Philadelphia and reached Chester
13   Lodged at Esquire Worths
14   Arrived at Mr. Harlands and set up the sector in his
      Garden (inclosed in a tent), and in the Evening brought the
      Instrument into the Meridian, and took the following observations

Plane WEST

Star Magnitudes	Star Names	Right Ascension h m		Nearest point on the Sector o '		Revolutions and Seconds on the Micrometer R "		Difference R "		Apparent Zenith Distance o ' "		
	Capella	4	59	5	50-	6	46.5	2	38.2	5	47	37.8
						4	8+					
	Beta Aurigae			4	55+	1	12.5	2	46.0	4	57	30.0
						4	6.5					
	Castor			7	35-	2	15.5	2	11.0	7	33	5.0
						4	26.5					37

15 Sun. Cloudy   Turned the Instrument facing the EAST
16   Brought the Instrument into the Meridian and took the following Observations

	Capella	4	59	5	50-	5	44	2	39.5	5	47	36.5
						8	31.5					
	Beta Aurigae			4	55+	9	4	2	47.7	4	57	31.7
						6	8+					

From these Observations finding we were very near the Parallel
of the Southernmost point of the City of Philadelphia we ordered
Carpenters to Erect the Observatory.

Plane EAST Sector in the Tent

17	Gamma Andromedae	1	15-	3	14.0		0.0	1	15	0.0N
				3	14.0					
	Beta Persei	0	5+	4	0	0	40.0	0	5	40.0
				3	12					
	Delta Persei	7	5-	9	14.5	0	30.5	7	4	29.5
				9	45					
18	Cloudy									
19	Gamma Andromedae	1	15-	9	11.5	0	5.5	1	14	54.5
				9	17					
	Beta Persei	0	5+	10	10+	0	39.6	0	5	39.6
				9	23-					
	Delta Persei	7	5-	7	34.5	0	29	7	4	31.0
				8	11.5					38
20	Gamma Andromedae	1	15+	5	13-	0	2.2	1	15	2.2
				5	10.5					
	Beta Persei	0	5+	5	45.5	0	39	0	5	39.0
				5	6.5					
	Alpha Persei	9	5-	2	10	1	21	9	3	47.0
				3	31					
	Delta Persei	7	5-	4	1-	0	29.8	7	4	30.2
				4	30.5					
21	Gamma Andromedae	1	15+	7	3+	0	1.3	1	15	1.3
				7	2					
	Beta Persei	0	5+	6	11.5	0	37.5	0	5	37.5
				5	26					
	Alpha Persei	9	5-	5	33	1	18.3	9	3	49.7
				6	51+					
	Delta Persei	7	5-	7	32+	0	29.2	7	4	30.8
				8	9.5					
22 Sun.	Gamma Andromedae	1	15+	3	46.7	0	1.2	1	15	1.2
				3	45.5					
	Beta Persei	0	5+	3	51	0	38	0	5	38.0
				3	13					
	Delta Persei	7	5-	4	28+	0	29	7	4	31.0
				5	5+					

Removed the Sector into the Observatory and in the Evening brought it into the Meridian

Plane WEST

N. B. The Sector stands 9 1/2 yards more South in the Observatory than it did in the Tent,
therefore 0."3 must be added to all Northern Stars observed in the Tent.   39

	Star Magnitudes	Star Names	Right Ascension		Nearest point on the Sector		Revolutions and Seconds on the Micrometer		Difference		Apparent Zenith Distance		
			h	m	o	'	R	"	R	"	o	'	"
24	Snow												
25	Snow												
26		Gamma Andromedae	1	15+			6	3+	0	4.7	1	15	4.7N
							6	8					
		Beta Persei	0	5+			5	26	0	41.7	0	5	41.7
							6	15.7					
		Delta Persei	7	5-			6	26	0	27.2	7	4	32.8
							5	50.5					
27		Gamma Andromedae	1	15+			11	37+	0	5.7	Hazy		
							11	43					
		Beta Persei	0	5+			10	16.5	0	41.0	0	5	41.0
							11	5.5					
		Alpha Persei	9	5-			9	50.5	1	11.0	9	3	57.0
							8	39.5					
		Capella	5	50-			6	42-	2	29.2	5	47	46.8
							4	12.5					
		Alpha Lyrae	1	20+			6	31	2	13.5	1	21	57.5S
							4	17.5					
28		Gamma Andromedae	1	15+			6	48	0	4.5	1	15	4.5
							7	0.5					
		Beta Persei	0	5+			6	45	0	44	0	5	44
							7	37					
		Alpha Persei	9	5-			7	17.5	1	10.5	9	3	57.5
							6	7					
		Delta Persei	7	5-			6	12	0	27	7	4	33.0
							5	37					
		Capella	5	50-			6	16	2	29	5	47	47.0
							3	39					
		Beta Aurigae	4	55+			4	8+	3	2.4	4	57	38.4
							7	11-					
		Alpha Lyrae	1	20+			5	20.5	2	13.0	1	21	57.0S
							3	7.5					40
29 Sun.		Gamma Andromedae	1	15+			2	42.5	0	5.5	1	15	5.5N
							2	48					
		Beta Persei	0	5+			3	00	0	44.0	0	5	44.0
							3	44					
		Alpha Persei	9	5-			6	28	1	12.7	9	3	55.3
							5	15+					
		Delta Persei	7	5-			4	50+	0	27.3	7	4	32.7
							4	23					
		Capella	5	50-			4	30+	2	29.3	5	47	46.7
							2	1					
		Beta Aurigae	4	55+			4	9+	3	0.4	4	57	36.4
							7	10-					
30	Cloudy												
31	Cloudy												
February													
1	Cloudy												
2		Capella	5	50-			8	23.5	2	28.2	5	47	47.8
							5	47.3					
		Beta Aurigae	4	55+			8	2	3	2	4	57	38.0
							11	4					

Feb.	Star Magnitudes	Star Names	Right Ascension		Nearest point on the Sector		Revolutions and Seconds on the Micrometer		Difference		Apparent Zenith Distance		
			h	m	o	'	R	"	R	"	o	'	"
3		Delta Persei	7	5-			4	51	0	27.5	7	4	32.5
							4	23.5					
		Capella	5	50-			6	43.8	2	31.3	5	47	44.7
							4	12.5					
		Castor	7	35-			10	3+	2	9.4	7	33	6.6
							12	13-					
4	Cloudy												
5 Sun.		Alpha Cygni	4	30+			14	10-	0	13.0			
							14	23					41
		Beta Aurigae	4	55+			15	5.5	3	0.8	4	57	36.8
							18	6+					
		Castor	7	35-			11	46+	2	11.2	7	33	4.8
							14	5.5					
6		Beta Aurigae	4	55+			15	46.5	3	0.2	4	57	36.2
							18	47-					
		Castor	7	35-			0	45.5	2	10.5	7	33	5.5
							3	4					
7	Cloudy												
8		Beta Aurigae	4	55+			14	1.7	3	3.8	4	57	39.8
							17	5.5					
		Castor	7	35-			14	39.5	2	9.2	7	33	6.8
							16	49-					
9	Cloudy												
10		Alpha Lyrae	1	20+			6	1.5	2	19.8	1	22	3.8
							3	34-					
11		Equal Altitudes of Capella											

Time by Watch

h	m	s	h	m	s	
4	12	55	5	29	12	)
4	14	15	5	30	42	} Hence Capella passed the Meridian of the Transit Instrument
4	15	43	5	32	8	) at 4h 52m 29s and it was observed to pass the Vertical wire in the Sector at 4h 52m 11s

12	Cloudy												42
13		Alpha Lyrae	1	20+			15	34.3	2	17.3	1	22	1.3 S
							13	17					

Turned the Instrument   Plane EAST

14	Cloudy												
15	Cloudy												
16	Cloudy till	Alpha Lyrae	1	20+			3	20+	2	24.2	1	22	8.2
	Alpha Lyrae came						5	44.5					
17	Cloudy												
18		Beta Aurigae	4	55+			6	40.7	2	51.7	4	57	35.7
							3	41.0					
19 Sun.	Cloudy												
20		Capella	5	50-			15	23	2	37	5	47	39.0
							18	8					
		Beta Aurigae	4	55+			18	47	2	50.7	4	57	34.7
							15	48+					
		Castor	7	35-			14	47	2	8.7	7	33	7.3
							12	38+					
		Equal Altitudes of Capella											

Time by Watch

h	m	s	h	m	s	
4	10	16	5	36	3	)
4	11	37	5	37	20	} Hence Capella crossed the Meridian of the Transit Instrument
4	12	57	5	38	39	) at 4h 54m 29s and it was observed to cross the vertical wire in the Sector at 4h 54m 34s

43

17

1764

Feb.	Star Magnitudes	Star Names	Right Ascension		Nearest point on the Sector		Revolutions and Seconds on the Micrometer		Difference		Apparent Zenith Distance		
			h	m	o	'	R	"	R	"	o	'	"
20		Alpha Lyrae			1	20+	7	40.5	2	26.5	1	22	10.5
							10	15					
21		Capella			5	50-	5	22	2	37.3	5	47	38.7
							8	7+					
		Beta Aurigae			4	55+	9	48+	2	51.0	4	57	35.0
							6	49+					
		Castor			7	35-	6	43-	2	9.7	7	33	6.3
							4	33					
		Alpha Lyrae			1	20+	8	20-	2	24.8	1	22	8.8
							10	44.5					
22		Capella			5	50-	6	51-	2	38.0	5	47	38.0
							9	37-					
		Beta Aurigae			4	55+	10	27-	2	51.2	4	57	35.2
							7	27.5					
		Castor			7	35-	7	7	2	10.3	7	33	5.7
							4	49-					
		Alpha Lyrae			1	20+	9	14-	2	25.8	1	22	9.8
							11	39.5					
23	Cloudy												
24	Cloudy	Mr. Loxley (carpenter) brought levels, etc., for measuring the 15 Statute miles Horizontal.											
25	Cloudy												
26 Sun.	Cloudy till	Alpha Lyrae came			1	20+	9	35-	2	26.8	1	22	10.8
							12	9.5					
27	Cloudy												
28		Castor			7	35-	15	48-	2	9.4	7	33	6.6
							13	38+					
		Alpha Lyrae			1	20+	9	14	2	25.5	1	22	9.5
							11	39.5					

44

Star Zenith Distances at the point N
Sector in the Tent.   Plane EAST

1764 January	Star Name Gamma Andromedae			Star Name Beta Persei			Star Name Alpha Persei			Star Name Delta Persei		
	o	'	"	o	'	"	o	'	"	o	'	"
17	1	15	00.0	0	5	40.0				7	4	29.5
19				0	5	39.6				7	4	31.0
20	1	15	02.2	0	5	39.0	9	3	47.0	7	4	30.2
21	1	15	01.3	0	5	37.5	9	3	49.7	7	4	30.8
22	1	15	01.2	0	5	38.0				7	4	31.0
Mean, January 20	1	15	1.2	0	5	38.8	9	3	48.3	7	4	30.5
Aberration in Declination			- 10.0			- 9.1			-11.4			-10.4
Deviation in Declination			- 3.3			- 5.7			- 6.2			- 6.7
Precession from 1 January 1764			- 1.0			- 0.8			- 0.7			- 0.7
Refraction			+ 1.4			+ 0.1			+10.5			+ 8.3
Observatory South of the Tent			+ 0.3			+ 0.3			+ 0.3			+ 0.3
Mean Zenith Distances, 1 Jan. 1764	1	14	48.6	0	5	23.6	9	3	40.8	7	4	21.3

Sector in the Observatory   Plane WEST

January	Gamma Andromedae			Beta Persei			Alpha Persei			Delta Persei			
	o	'	"	o	'	"	o	'	"	o	'	"	
26	1	15	4.7	0	5	41.7				7	4	32.8	
27	1	15	5.7	0	5	41.0	9	3	57.0				
28	1	15	4.5	0	5	44.0	9	3	57.5	7	4	33.0	
29	1	15	5.5	0	5	44.0	9	3	55.3	7	4	32.7	
Mean January 27.5	1	15	5.1	0	5	42.7	9	3	56.6	7	4	32.8	
Aberration in Declination			-9.0			- 8.6			-11.1			-10.3	
Deviation in Declination			-3.3			- 5.7			- 6.2			- 6.7	
Precession from 1 January 1764			-1.3			- 1.1			- 1.0			- 0.9	
Refraction			+1.4			+ 0.1			+10.5			+ 8.3	
Mean Zenith Distance, 1 Jan. 1764	1	14	52.9	0	5	27.4	9	3	48.8	7	4	23.2	
Mean Z. D., 1 Jan. 1764, Plane EAST	1	14	48.6	0	5	23.6	9	3	40.8	7	4	21.3	
True Z. D. at Mr. Harlands, 1 Jan. 1764	1	14	50.8	0	5	25.5	9	3	44.8	.7	4	22.2	
True Z. D. at Philadelphia	1	14	39.5	0	5	14.45	9	3	32.1	7	4	11.7	
Hence we are South of the Parallel required	0	0	11.3	0	0	11.0	0	0	12.7	0	0	10.5	45

Star Zenith Distances at the point N
Zenith Distances, Plane WEST

1764		Capella				Beta Aurigae				Castor				Alpha Lyrae		
		o	'	"		o	'	"		o	'	"		o	'	"
January	27	5	47	46.8									27	1	21	57.5
	28	5	47	47.0	28	4	57	38.4					28	1	21	57.0
	29	5	47	46.7	29	4	57	36.4						1	21	57.3
February	2	5	47	47.8	2	4	57	38.0					Aber.			-9.5
	3	5	47	44.7					3	7	33	6.6	Devi.			-9.4
					5	4	57	36.8	5	7	33	4.8	Prec.			+0.2
					6	4	57	36.2	6	7	33	5.5	Refr.			+1.5
									8	7	33	6.8		1	21	40.1
													11	1	22	3.8
													13	1	22	1.3
Mean	30	5	47	46.6	1	4	57	37.2	5.5	7	33	5.9	12	1	22	2.5
Aberration in Declination				-7.4				-5.7				-0.6				-13.0
Deviation				-8.8				-9.2				+9.1				-9.4
Precession from 1 Jan. 1764				-0.4				-0.1				-0.7				+0.3
Refraction				+6.7				+5.8				+8.8				+1.5
Mean Z. D. 1 January 1764		5	47	36.7		4	57	28.0		7	33	22.5		1	21	41.9
														1	21	40.1
														1	21	41.0

Plane EAST

1764	Capella			Beta Aurigae			Castor			Alpha Lyrae		
	o	'	''	o	'	''	o	'	''	o	'	''
February										16	1	22	8.2
				18	4	57	35.7						
	20	5	47	39.0	20	4	57	34.7	20	7	33	7.3	20	1	22	10.5
	21	5	47	38.7	21	4	57	35.0	21	7	33	6.3	21	1	22	8.8
	22	5	47	38.0	22	4	57	35.2	22	7	33	5.7	22	1	22	9.8
												26	1	22	10.8
Mean	21	5	47	38.6	21	4	57	35.2	21	7	33	6.4	21	1	22	9.6
Aberration				-8.0				-6.9				+0.5				-14.8
Deviation				-8.8				-9.2				+9.1				-9.4
Precession from 1 Jan. 1764				-0.7				-0.2				-0.95				+0.35
Refraction				+6.7				+5.8				+8.8				+1.5
Mean Z. D. 1 Jan. 1764		5	47	27.8		4	57	24.7		7	33	23.8		1	21	47.3
The Same, Plane WEST		5	47	36.7		4	57	28.0		7	33	22.5		1	21	41.0
True Z.D. at Mr. Harlands, 1 Jan.		5	47	32.3		4	57	26.3		7	33	23.1		1	21	44.2
The Same at Phila.		5	47	21.6		4	57	14.15		7	33	31.75		1	21	53.2
Hence we are South of the required Parallel			0	10.7			0	12.1				8.6			0	9.0 46

From the foregoing the mean of the results from the different stars as follows.

		'	''
Gamma Andromedae	0	⎧11.3
		⎪11.3
		⎨11.3
		⎩11.3
Beta Persei		⎧11.0
		⎪11.0
		⎨11.0
		⎩11.0
Alpha Persei		12.7
Delta Persei		⎧10.5
		⎨10.5
		⎩10.5
Capella		⎧10.7
		⎨10.7
		⎪10.7
		⎩10.7
Beta Aurigae		⎧12.1
		⎨12.1
		⎩12.1
Castor		⎧8.6
		⎪8.6
		⎨8.6
		⎩8.6
Alpha Lyrae		⎧9.0
		⎨9.0
		⎩9.0
Mean	0	10.5

Mean   0   10.5 = 356.8 yards (69.5 miles to a degree) that the Sector is South of the Parallel of the Southernmost point of the City of Philadelphia

N. B.   After measuring the 15 Statute miles Horizontal and finding the arch in the Heavens corresponding, if it does not agree to 69.5 miles to a degree we should account for the 10.''5 accordingly.

44

For the Latitude of the Observatory at Mr. Harlands

	Delta Persei			Capella			Beta Aurigae			Castor			Alpha Lyrae		
	o	'	"	o	'	"	o	'	"	o	'	"	o	'	"
True Z. D., 1st Jan. 1764	7	4	22.2	5	47	32.3	4	57	26.3	7	33	23.1	1	21	44.2
Stars Declinations by Dr. Bradley	47	0	40.0	45	43	53.0	44	53	44.2	32	22	56.8	38	34	34.0
Latitude by the different stars	39	56	17.8	39	56	20.7	39	56	17.9	39	56	19.9	39	56	18.2
			20.7												
			17.9												
			19.9												
			18.2												

Mean   39   56   18.9 = The Latitude of the Observatory in Brandywine

              39   56   29.1 = Latitude of the South point of the City of Philadelphia

Difference   10.2   That we are to the Southward at Mr. Harlands, but
The mean of the results from the Zenith distances of 8 stars
must be preferred to that of five.   47

1764

February	28	Finished our observations of the star's Zenith Distances at Mr. Harlands in the Forks of Brandywine.
	29	Computing the true Zenith Distances of the stars from our observations.
March	1	Computing as on February 29
	2	Cloudy
	3	Cloudy
	4	Cloudy (Sunday)
	5	By the Pole Star's transiting the Meridian we placed a mark in the Meridian northward, but it was rendered a little dubious on account of flying clouds.
	6	Cloudy
	7	Cloudy
	8	Cloudy
	9	Cloudy and Snow
	10	Cloudy
	11	Cloudy (Sunday)
	12	Cloudy and Snow
	13	Cloudy and Rain
	14	Cloudy
	15	Cloudy
	16	Proved the mark in the Meridian Northward
	17	Employed one man, cutting a visto in the Meridian Southward. This Evening at 8h 21m 59s apparent time the Eclipse of the Moon Ended.
	18	(Sunday) N. B. The edge of the Sun's Shadow on the Moons disk was the best defined I ever saw, the air was so clear it was remarkably distinct from the penumbral shade.
	19	Employed four men cutting a visto in the Meridian Southward
	20	Employed four men as on March 19. 48
	21	Employed four men cutting a visto in the Meridian Southward
	22	Employed four men cutting the Meridian Southward as before
	23	Employed four men as on March 22
	24	Employed four men as on March 22
	25	(Sunday)
	26	Employed five men as on March 22
	27	Employed five men as on March 22
	28	Employed five men as on March 22
	29	Employed five men as on March 22
	30	Employed five men as on March 22
	31	Employed five men as on March 22
April	1	(Sunday)

April   2   Began to measure from our observatory (at Mr. Harland's). Employed the five men.

Chains	Links	Levels	
9	61		
		4	These 4 levels 22 feet each (The Levels were found not so proper for use as the 16.5 feet)
2	91		Entered the Brandywine
28	00		Entered the Brandywine again
9	00		
		17	of the 16.5 feet Levels, which we shall use through the whole
9	00		
		20	
7	00		To a stob on the N. side of the Brandywine the third time.
2	04		To a mark on the S. side of the Brandywine
		40	
		60	
59	89	141	To a mark in Mr. Wilson's field
35	25		
95	14 = Sum		49

April   1
        3   Rain
        4

Chains	Links	Levels	
30	00		Measured the chain
4	00		
		31	
		9	
1	00		
		10	
		30	
46	00		
		10	
40	00		This reached to the Road leading from Peckway to Wilmington wanting half a chain.
54	00		
		8	
49	80		
70	00		
		20	
6	00		
		8	
26	00		
		10	
5	00		
		5	
4	00		
		11	
16	00		
		3	
5	00		
		30	
26	00		
		6	This reaches to the North Edge of the high road leading from Philadelphia to Nottingham. Mr. Charles Hall's, East about seventy yards.
382	80	191	
47	75		
430	55 = Sum		50

1764			Chains	Links	Levels	
April	5		46	00		Found the chain a little too long. Corrected it.
					10	
			10	00		
					30	
			3	00		
					7	
			7	50		
					18	
			44	50		
					10	
			7	00		
					10	
			5	00		
					20	
			28	38		
			9	55		To a tree marked with 5 notches (in a wood) about 150 or 200 yards South East of Mr. Milhouses, Proved the Meridian and found it very exact.
			160	93	105	187. 18 = Sum
	6	Employed five men in continuing the Meridian				
	7	Employed five men as on April 6th				
	8	(Sunday)				
	9		80	00		This reached to Mr. Joseph Freads. Chain correct.
			31	00		
					20	
			21	00		
					10	
			19	00		
					29	
			10	03		
			161	03	59	175. 78 = Sum
	10	Employed five men continuing the Meridian				
	11	Employed five men as on April 10th.				51
	12				9	This morning examined the chain and found it just.
			80	00		Employed five men measuring, etc.
			24	00		
					8	
			7	00		
					7	
			5	50		
					6	
			2	50		
					30	
			35	00		
					10	
			47	00		This just crosses Pikes creek
					30	
			11	14		
			60	92		To a tree in the fence of the South end of a ground belonging to Mr. Bryan.
			273	06	100	298. 06 = Sum

		Miles	Chains	Links	
Sum		14	66	70	
			16	23 = 10'.5 = 357 yards. The Observatory South of the Parallel of the Southernmost point of the City of Philadelphia
		15	2	93	Set the Observatory back 2 1/2 chains

52

	13	Returned to Brandywine with the Labourers.
	14	Prepared for removing, employed the five men as before.
	15	(Sunday)
	16	Ditto.
	17	Ditto.

1764
April

18   Set out from Brandywine with our Observatory and Instruments in four waggons. Employed the five
      Labourers in carrying one of the Instruments.
19   Employed five men setting up the Observatory. (Rain the greatest part of the day.)
20   Ditto.
21   Four Labourers returned home and were discharged, one kept to provide provisions, etc. Set up the Sector.
22   (Sunday) Set out to Philadelphia to acquaint the Commissioners we were arrived at the south end
      of the 15 miles.
23   At Philadelphia.
24   At Philadelphia. (Sent an Express to Horatio Sharp, Esquire, Governour of Maryland, to acquaint him of
      our being at the South end of the 15 miles.)
25   Returned from Philadelphia.
26   Cloudy
27   Cloudy and rain.
28   Ditto. Heavy Rain.
29   (Sunday) Ditto.
30   Cloudy

May

1   Cloudy
2   Cloudy
3   Brought the Instrument into the Meridian.   53

	Star Magnitudes	Star Names	Right Ascension		Nearest Point on the Sector		Revolutions and Seconds on the Micrometer		Difference		Apparent Zenith Distance		
			h	m	o	'	R	"	R	"	o	'	"
4	Cloudy												
5		Castor			7	20+	6	29			7	20	15.3
							6	44+			very faint		
		Alpha Lyrae			1	10-	6	46+	0	47.3	1	9	12.7
							5	51					
		Alpha Cygni			4	45-	6	47	2	19.0	4	42	57.0
							9	14			faint		
6	(Sunday)	Castor (I now opened the aperture)			7	20+	7	48.5	0	13.2	7	20	13.2
							8	10-			still faint		
		Alpha Lyrae			1	10-	7	22	0	49.5	1	9	10.5
							6	24.5					
7		Capella			6	0+	6	16+	0	29.8	6	0	29.8
							5	38.5					
		Alpha Lyrae			1	10-	8	42.5	0	50.0	1	9	10.0
							7	44.5					
8		Capella			6	0+	5	43	0	28+	6	0	28.3
							5	15-					
9		Capella			6	0+	3	50	0	29.0	6	0	29.0
							3	21					
		Alpha Lyrae			1	10-	8	24.5	0	49.5	1	9	10.5
							7	27					
10		Alpha Lyrae			1	10-	8	16+	0	48.8	1	9	11.2
							7	19.5					
		Alpha Cygni			4	45-	9	45.5	2	15.2	4	43	0.8
							12	9-					
11		Alpha Lyrae			1	10-	6	34	0	51.0	1	9	9.0
							5	35					
		Alpha Cygni			4	45-	8	6-	2	17.8	4	42	58.2
							10	23.5					
12		Alpha Lyrae			1	10-	6	28	0	50	1	9	10.0
							5	30					
		Alpha Cygni			4	45-	7	9	2	13.3	4	43	2.7
							9	22+					

54

1764 May	Star Magnitudes	Star Names	Right Ascension		Nearest Point on the Sector		Revolutions and Seconds on the Micrometer		Difference		Apparent Zenith Distance		
			h	m	o	'	R	"	R	"	o	'	"
13	(Sunday)	Capella	6	0+			10	32	0	30.0	6	0	30.0
							10	02					
		Castor	7	20+			10	51					
							11	11					
		Alpha Lyrae	1	10-			11	46+	0	52.3	1	9	7.7
							10	46					
		Delta Cygni	4	50+			14	41+	0	6.3	4	50	6.3
							14	35					
		Gamma Cygni	0	15-			11	6.5	2	16.5	0	12	59.5
							8	42					
		Alpha Cygni	4	45-			8	26.5	2	16.0	4	43	0.0
							10	42.5					

14   Began to measure back again to Mr. Harlands where the Observatory last stood in the Forks of Brandywine. Employed five men.

Chains	Links	Levels	
72	00		
		31	
47	00		
		10	
36	00		
		24	
18	50		
		10	
80	00		
25	70		
279	20	75	To a mark in a wood.
18	75		
297	95	= Sum	
10	00		
		29	
19	00		
		20	
20	00		
		10	
30	00		
		13	
78	80		
157	80		From the last Mark to a Mark near Mr. Milhouse's.
18	00		
175	80	= Sum	
15	40	00	
		13	
4	50		
		15	
6	00		
		10	
47	00		
		8	
7	00		
		10	
7	00		
		10	
10	00		
		8	
47	72		
169	22	74	From the last mark to a mark to the North Side of the Road leading from Philadelphia to Nottingham.
18	50		
187	72	= Sum	

55

1764 May	Chains	Links	Levels	
15	30	00		
			20	
	10	00		
	12	00		
			10	
	38	00		
	80	00		
	80	00		
	71	50		
			5	
	47	00		
			6	
	1	00		
			15	
	39	80		
	409	30	56	From the last mark to one in Mr. Wilson's field.
	14	00		
	423	30 = Sum		

56

16			21	
	5	03		
			59	
	2	04		
	8	00		
			15	
	10	00		
			14	
	7	00		
	2	00		
	26	50		
	7	38		
	67	95	109	From the mark in Mr. Wilson's field to where the Sector stood.
	27	25		
	95	20 = Sum		

Upon casting up these measurements I found there was a disagreement between the mark in Mr. Wilson's field and that by the Road leading from Philadelphia to Nottingham; and also between that in the Road and Mr. Milhouse's, we therefore began again at the Mark in Mr. Wilson's field and measured in our return as follows.

17	34	00		
			39	
	1	00		
			40	
	38	58		
			10	
	40	00		
	80	00		
	30	00		
	80	00		
	33	00		
			3	
	4	00		
			11	
	10	00		
	13	00		
			25	
	27	61		
	391	19	128	From the mark in Mr. Wilson's field to the Road from Philadelphia to Nottingham.
	32	00		
	423	19		

57

	Chains	Links	Levels
May	60	00	
18			24
	3	00	
			7
	7	50	
			18
	44	50	
			10
	7	00	
			10
	5	00	
			20
	37	94	
	164	94	89
	22	25	
	187	19	= Sum

From the Road to the mark near Mr. Milhouse's.

From the foregoing the results are as follows

	Chains	Links			Chains	Links
From the Observatory to the mark	95	14	= First Measure			
in Mr. Wilson's field	95	20	= Second Measure	Mean =	95	17
From Mr. Wilson's field to the Road	430	55	= First Measure			
from Philadelphia to Nottingham	423	30	= Second Measure	Mean =	423	25
	423	19	= Third Measure			
From the above Road to the	187	18	= First Measure	The mean of		
Mark near Mr. Milhouse's	187	72	= Second Measure	the first	187	18
	187	19	= Third Measure	and third		
From Mr. Milhouse's to	175	78	= First Measure			
the mark in ---------	175	80	= Second Measure	Mean =	175	79
From the last mark to the	298	06	= First Measure			
mark in Mr. Bryans field	297	95	= Second Measure	Mean =	298	01
				Sum =	1179	40

For small inclinations of Hills, etc., not accounted for (not measured with the levels) we Judge

	Chains	Links
71 Links ought to be subtracted from the Sum and it leaves	1178	69
The Parallel of the South Point of Philadelphia North of the	16	23
Sector in the Forks of the Brandywine	1194	92
Sum = 14 miles 74 chains 92 links		

58

	Miles	Chains	Links	
	15	00	00	
	14	74	92	
Hence the Mark in Mr. Bryan's field is	0	5	08	North of true point and as
the Sector was set North from the above mark	0	2	52	
The Sector now stands	0	7	60	North of the point (and)

15 Statute miles South of the Parallel required.

	Chains	Links	
The Distance from the Observatory in Brandywine to the mark in Mr. Bryan's field =	1178	69	
Distance of the Observatory in Mr. Bryan's field North of the mark =	2	52	Subtract
rest the Horizontal distance between the Points where the Sector stood	1176	17	

1764
May

19 Attended the Commissioners of both Provinces at Newcastle.

	Star Magnitudes	Star Names	Right Ascension		Nearest Point on the Sector		Revolutions and Seconds on the Micrometer		Difference		Apparent Zenith Distance		
			h	m	o	'	R	''	R	''	o	'	''
		Alpha Lyrae	1	10-			17	25	0	54.5	1	9	5.5
							16	22.5					
		Delta Cygni	4	50+			16	30.5	0	8.0	4	50	8.0
							16	22.5					
		Gamma Cygni	0	15-			18	30	2	16.0	0	13	0.0
							16	14					
		Alpha Cygni	4	45-			13	22	2	15.0	4	43	1.0
							15	37					
20	(Sunday)	Delta Cygni	4	50+			4	50	0	9.0	4	50	9.0
							4	41					
		Gamma Cygni	0	15-			9	0.5	2	18.0	0	12	58.0
							6	34.5					
		Alpha Cygni	4	45-			5	34	2	14.5	0	43	1.5
							7	48.5					

21 Attended the Commissioners.
22 Attended the Commissioners.

	Star Magnitudes	Star Names	Right Ascension		Nearest Point on the Sector		Revolutions and Seconds on the Micrometer		Difference		Apparent Zenith Distance		
23		Alpha Lyrae	1	10-			8	7-	1	4.2	1	9	3.8 N
							7	2.5					
		Delta Cygni	4	50+			8	5+	0	11.3	4	50	11.3
							7	46					
		Gamma Cygni	0	15-			7	38	2	19.0	0	12	57.0
							5	19					
		Alpha Cygni	4	45-			5	38.5			4	43	0.5
							8	2					
24	Cloudy												
25		Alpha Lyrae	1	10-			9	29+	1	4.3	1	9	3.7
							8	25					
		Delta Cygni	4	50+			8	32+	0	9.6	4	50	9.6
							8	23-					
		Gamma Cygni	0	15-			8	41.5	2	20.0	0	12	56.0
							6	21.5					
		Alpha Cygni	4	45-			6	1+			4	43	2.3
							8	15					

26 Turned the Instrument and made the following observations

Plane WEST

	Star Names	Right Ascension		Nearest Point on the Sector		Revolutions and Seconds on the Micrometer		Difference		Apparent Zenith Distance		
	Gamma Cygni	0	15-			2	15+	2	23.4	0	12	52.6
						4	39-					
	Alpha Cygni	4	45-			3	49-			4	43	4.3
						1	37					
27 (Sunday)	Alpha Lyrae	1	10-			4	5	1	9.0	1	8	59.0
						5	14					
	Delta Cygni	4	50+			5	35.5	0	14.2	4	50	14.8
						5	50+					
	Gamma Cygni	0	15-			7	28	2	25.0	0	12	51.0
						10	01					
	Alpha Cygni	4	45-			6	44.5	2	11.8	4	43	4.2
						4	33-					

1764 May	Star Magnitudes	Star Names	Right Ascension		Nearest Point on the Sector		Revolutions and Seconds on the Micrometer		Difference		Apparent Zenith Distance		
			h	m	o	'	R	"	R	"	o	'	"
28		Capella			6	0+	5	43+	0	32.7	6	0	32.7
							6	24					
		Alpha Lyrae			1	10-	5	1.5	1	8.5	1	8	59.5
							6	10					
		Delta Cygni			4	50+	6	2	0	15.0	4	50	15.0
							6	17					
		Gamma Cygni			0	15-	6	7.5	2	25.0	0	12	51.0
							8	32.5					
		Alpha Cygni			4	15-	8	14	2	12.0	4	43	4.0
							6	2			hazy		
29	Cloudy												
30	Cloudy												
31	Cloudy												
June													
1		Capella			6	0+	5	40-	0	32.3	6	0	32.3
							6	20					
2	Cloudy												
3	(Sunday)	Alpha Lyrae			1	10-	5	11.5	1	10.0	1	8	58.0
							6	21.5					
		Delta Cygni			4	50+	6	38	0	15.0	4	50	15.0
							7	01					
		Gamma Cygni			0	15-	7	30.5			0	12	51.0
							10	3.5					
		Alpha Cygni			4	45-	9	32.5	2	8.5	4	43	7.5
							7	24					61
4		Alpha Lyrae			1	10-	7	28+	1	8.2	1	8	59.8
							8	36.5					
		Delta Cygni			4	50+	10	9	0	15.3	4	50	15.3
							10	24+					
		Gamma Cygni			0	15-	9	39+	2	25.7	0	12	50.3
							12	13					
		Alpha Cygni			4	45-	12	12+	2	10.6	4	43	5.4
							10	2-					
5		Capella			6	0+	9	10.8	0	31.7	6	0	31.7
							9	42.5					
		Delta Cygni			4	50+	9	29-	0	16.8	4	50	16.8
							9	45.5					
		Gamma Cygni			0	15-	10	32.5	2	26.3	0	12	49.7
							12	50-					
		Alpha Cygni			4	45-	12	35.5	2	9.5	4	43	6.5
							10	26					
6		Alpha Lyrae			1	10-	7	50.5	1	9.8	1	8	58.2
							9	8+					
		Delta Cygni			4	50+	10	42-	0	16.3	4	50	16.3
							11	6					
		Gamma Cygni			0	15-	10	32.5	2	26.0	0	12	50.0
							13	6.5					
		Alpha Cygni			4	45-	15	13-	2	8.2	4	43	7.8
							19	4.5					
7		Alpha Lyrae			1	10-	4	47+	1	10.7	1	8	57.3
							6	6					
		Gamma Cygni			0	15-	6	17-	2	27.0	0	12	49.0
							8	44-					
		Alpha Cygni			4	45-	7	38	2	8.0	4	43	8.0
							5	30					62

1764 June	Star Magnitudes	Star Names	Right Ascension		Nearest Point on the Sector		Revolutions and Seconds on the Micrometer		Difference		Apparent Zenith Distance		
			h	m	o	'	R	"	R	"	o	'	"
8		Alpha Lyrae			1	10-	5	11	1	10.7	1	8	57.3
							6	22-					
		Delta Cygni			4	50	5	25	0	18.0	4	50	18.0
							5	43					
		Gamma Cygni			0	15-	5	17.5			0	12	48.0
							7	45.5					
		Alpha Cygni			4	45-	7	45-			4	43	8.3
							5	37					
9		Alpha Lyrae			1	10-	5	3			very hazy		
							6	19.5					

10   (Sunday)
11   Computing the true Zenith Distances of the Stars.
12   Ditto. The results whereof follow.

63

		Capella		
1764		o	'	"
May	7	6	0	29.8
	8	6	0	28.3
	9	6	0	29.0
	13	6	0	30.0
Mean of first set	10	6	0	29.3
Aberration				-1.5
Nutation				-9.0
Precession from 1 Jan. 1764				-1.9
Refraction				+7.0
True Zenith Distance 1 Jan. 1764		6	0	23.9

64

Zenith Distance of Stars near the end of the 15 miles South of Philadelphia

Plane EAST

Alpha Lyrae

May	o	'	''
6	1	9	10.5
7		9	10.0
9			10.5
11			9.0
12			10.0
13			7.7
Mean of the 1st Set 10	1	9	9.6
Aberration			-12.3
Nutation			-9.4
Precession from 1 Jan. 1764			+1.1
Refraction			+1.2
True Z. D. 1 Jan. 1764	1	8	50.2

True Z. D. the 1st of Jan. 1764 from the mean of all the five Observations

May	o	'	''
19	1	9	5.5
23		9	3.8
25		9	3.7
Mean of the 2nd Set 22	1	9	4.3
Aberration			-9.5
Nutation			-9.4
Precession			+1.1
Refraction			+1.2
Mean	1	8	47.7
Mean above		8	50.2
Mean of all the observations the 1st Jan. 1764	1	8	49.0

Delta Cygni

May	o	'	''
13	4	50	6.3
Abb.			+14.9
Devi.			+ 8.74
Prec.			-3.05
Ref.			+5.6
	4	50	32.5
19	4	50	8.0
20	4	50	9.0
23	4	50	11.3
25	4	50	9.6
22	4	50	9.5
Abb.			+13.2
Nutation			+8.74
Prec.			-3.25
Ref.			+5.6
Mean	4	50	33.8
Mean	4	50	32.5
	4	50	33.15

Gamma Cygni

May	o	'	''
13	0	12	59.5
			-15.0
			-8.1
			+4.0
			+0.2
	0	12	40.6
19	0	13	0.0
20		12	58.0
23		12	57.0
25		12	56.0
22	0	12	57.75
			-13.5
			-8.1
			+4.3
			+0.2
	0	12	40.6
	0	12	40.6
	0	12	40.6

Alpha Cygni

May	o	'	''
10	4	43	0.8
11	4	42	58.2
12	4	43	2.7
13	4	43	0.0
11.5 (Mean date)	4	43	0.4
Abb.			+16.5
Devi.			+7.6
Prec.			-4.5
Ref.			+5.5
Mean	4	43	25.5
19	4	43	1.0
20		43	1.5
23		43	0.5
25		43	2.3
22	4	43	1.3
Abb.			+14.9
Nutation			+7.6
Prec.			-4.8
Ref.			+5.5
Mean	4	43	24.5
Mean	4	43	25.4

True Zenith Distance 1st of Jan. 1764 from the mean of all the Observations.   4 43 25.0

65

Zenith Distance of Stars at the end of 15 miles South of Philadelphia

Plane WEST

1764		Capella o ' "	Alpha Lyrae o ' "
May	27		1 8 59.0
	28	6 0 32.7	8 59.5
June	1	0 32.3	
	3		8 58.0
	4		8 59.8
	5	0 31.7	
	6		8 58.2
	7		8 57.3
	8		8 57.3
Mean	1 & 3	6 0 32.2 June 1	1 8 58.4 June 3
Aberration		+1.4	−6.3
Nutation		−9.0	−9.4
Precession from 1st Jan. 1764		−2.2	+1.1
Refraction		+7.0	+1.2
Mean Zenith Distance 1st Jan. 1764, Plane WEST		6 0 29.4	1 8 45.0
Ditto., Plane EAST		6 0 23.9	1 8 49.0
True Zenith Distance, the 1st of January 1764 at the Sector.		6 0 26.6	1 8 47.0
The Sector stands North of the true point 7 Chains, 91 Links (5".20)		+5.20	−5.20
True Zenith Distances 15 Miles South of the Southernmost point of the City of Philadelphia on the 1st of January 1764		6 0 31.80	1 8 41.80

And these (and those on the following page) are our Radical Points for running the Western Line.

Zenith Distances of Stars at the End of 15 miles South of Philadelphia

Plane WEST

1764	Delta Cygni o ' "	Gamma Cygni o ' "	Alpha Cygni o ' "
May 26		0 12 52.6	4 43 4.3
27	4 50 14.8	12 51.0	43 4.2
28	4 50 15.0	12 51.0	43 4.0
June 3	50 15.0	12 51.0	43 7.5
4	50 15.3	12 50.3	43 5.4
5	50 16.8	12 49.8	43 6.5
6	50 16.3	12 50.0	43 7.8
7		12 49.0	43 8.0
8	50 18.0	12 48.0	43 8.3
Mean 3	4 50 15.9	0 12 50.3	4 43 6.2
Aberration	+10.4	−11.3	+12.8
Nutation	+8.74	−8.1	+7.6
Precession from 1st Jan. 1764	−3.40	+4.6	−5.2
Refraction	+5.6	+0.2	+5.5
Mean Zenith Distance, 1st Jan. 1764 Plane of the Sector (WEST)	4 50 37.24	0 12 35.7	4 43 26.9
Ditto, Plane EAST	4 50 33.15	0 12 40.60	4 43 25.0
True Zenith Distance, the 1st of Jan. 1764 at the Sector	4 50 35.19	0 12 38.20	4 43 25.95
The Sector stands North of the true point 7 Chains 91 Links = 5".20	+5.20	−5.20	+5.20
True Zenith Distances 15 miles South of the Southernmost point of the City of Philadelphia on the 1st of January 1764	4 50 40.40	0 12 33.00	4 43 31.20

And these (and those of the preceding page) are Radical Points for running the Western Line.

From the foregoing observations the Zenith Distance of Capella at the Observatory   6° 0' 26."6 N, and of Alpha Lyrae   1° 08' 47."0 S

In the Forks of Brandywine their Zenith Distances were   5° 47' 32."3 N, and Alpha Lyrae   1° 21' 44."2 N

Difference   0° 12' 54.3   0° 12' 57.2

                                          57.2

Mean   0° 12' 55."8 This corresponds to 1176 chains 17 links =

The distance on a Horizontal measure between the points where the Sector stood. Hence then the Real quantity corresponding to the 10."5 that the Sector stood South in the Forks of Brandywine, we have thus

As (12' 55."8) : (1176 chains 17 links) : : 10."5 : (15 chains 92 links)

But in our measurement we allowed 16 chains 23 links for 10."5. Hence the true point is 0 chains 31 links South of the point 7 chains 60 links that is 7 chains 91 links South of the Sector in the Observatory. And the angle corresponding to this will be as

(1176.17 chains) : (12' 55."8) : : (7 chains 91 links) : 5."2 to be applied to the Star Zenith Distances, all ready done in the page before.

As (12' 55."8) : (1176 chains 17 links) : : 60' : (5457 chains 86.5 links) = 68.223 miles

Hence 33.35 yards = one second, therefore 100.05 feet = 1". This determination by two stars observed at Brandywine and at the end 15 miles South: The following by three stars at the said end and at Philadelphia.

NOTE: The Point 15 miles South of the Southernmost Point of the City of Philadelphia is situated in Mill Creek Hundred in the County of Newcastle, in a Plantation belonging to Mr. Alexander Bryan. The Middle of the Front of Mr. Bryan's House, bears from the point 37° 52' Northwesterly distant 23.38 chains (each chain 22 yards). It is close by the East side of a small Run, the Head of which is due North distant 5.00 chains. From the Point to the Middle of a small rivulet called Muddy Run, on a due South course is 7.15 chains.   68

For the Latitude at the End of 15 Miles South of Philadelphia

	Capella			Alpha Lyrae			Alpha Cygni		
	o	'	"	o	'	"	o	'	"
True Zenith Distance 1st January 1764	6	0	31.8	1	08	41.8	4	43	31.2
Declination, 1st Jan. 1764	45	43	53.0	38	36	34.0	44	26	48.9
Latitude	39	43	21.2	39	43	15.8	39	43	17.7
			15.8						
			17.7						
Mean	39	43	18.2	= Latitude North					
The Latitude of South Point of Phila.	39	56	29.1						
Difference	0	13	10.9	Corresponding to 15 Horizontal Statute Miles. Then					

as (13' 10."9) : 15 : : 60' : 68.277

B. Mr. Bryan's
P. The point 15 miles South of Philadelphia
S. A Station North of the point P, and B due West from S.

As P S 1846   3.2662317
Rad   10.
S B 1435   3.1568519
Tang Angle P (37° 52')   9.8906202
That is, Mr. Bryan's House bears 37° 52' Northwesterly

As sin B (52° 08')   9.8973199
P S 1846   3.2662317
Rad   10.
P B 23.38   3.3689118
Hence the distance of Mr. Bryan's House from the Point is 23.38 chains.

Figure 69

Our Parallel = that of the South point of Philadelphia
in the Forks of Brandywine; fell about
16 chains North of what the Surveyor made it (about
28 years since) when they ran the Temporary Line:
But it agreed very near to what one Mr. Taylor
made it some years before.

Our Point 15 miles South of Philadelphia came out 46
chains North of what it was settled when the Temporary
Line was run: But at this time it was agreed between
the Proprietors that it should be 15.25 miles and some
odd chains South of the Southernmost point of the City
of Philadelphia.

The Parallel from Philadelphia (South Point) was run by
former Surveyors three times by Compass; by which it appears
the point from whence we began to run our 15 miles South
is 31 miles _____ chains West from Philadelphia.   70

1764
June
13 Packing up the Instruments and preparing to set out for the Middle Point (of the Peninsula
    formed by the Sea and Chesapeake Bay) in order to run the Tangent Line.
14 Waggons etc. arrived at Newcastle with Tents, etc.
15 Sent our Instruments from the Observatory to Capt. Rice's.
16 Engaged our old hands at Brandywine (Except Mr. Baily) to go with us.
17 (Sunday)
18 The Waggons set out from Newcastle.
19 Joined the waggons and arrived at Dover at night.
20 At Esquire White's.
21 At Mr. Brown's.
22 At the River Nanticoke; pitched our Tents on its Banks.
23 Engaged ax men, etc. The whole company including Steward, Tent keepers, Cooks, Chain
    carriers, etc. amounting to 39. Two Waggons, Eight Horses, etc.
24 (Sunday)
25 Crossed the River Nanticoke in canoes and went to the Middle Point, fixed up the
    Transit Instrument and began to produce an arch of a Great Circle in the direction last run.
26 Produced the Line and set up the 1st, 2nd and 3rd Mile Posts.   71
27 Rain
28 Produced the Line and set up the 4th and 5th Mile Posts
29 Fixed the 6th Mile Post
30 Produced the Line across the River Nanticoke. Measured the breadth of the River by angles
    taken by a Hadley's Quadrant and a Base Line upon the North Side of the River as by the Figure.

Entrance of the River from the Middle Point is 6 Miles 70 Chains 25 Links
July
1   (Sunday)
2   Put down the 7 Mile Post
3   Put down the 8th and 9th Mile Posts
4   Put down the 10th and 11th Mile Posts
5   Put down the 12th, 13th and 14th Mile Posts
6   Put down the 15th Mile Post
7   Put down the 16th Mile Post   Figure
8   (Sunday)   72

For the breadth of the River Nanticoke

(Editor's transcription

log 8	=	0.9030899
log sin 46° 02'	=	9.8571799
		10.7602678
log sin 39° 35'	=	9.8042757
log N S	=	0.9559921

N S = 9 chains 4 links)

(Original Documentation)

as sine 39° 35'	9.8042757
to 8 ch.	0.9030899
:: Sine 46° 2'	9.8571779
to N S 9 chs 4 links	0.9559921

Figure
73

July

9	Produced the line and set the 17th, 18th and 19th Mile Posts
10	Produced the Line and set the 20th Mile Post
11	Put down the 21st Mile Post on the South Side of Marshy Hope
12	Set the 22nd
13	Set the 23 and 24th
14	Gave the overseer of the Ax Men a proper direction, and set out for Coll. Loyds in Talbot County, Maryland, about 40 miles distant.
15	(Sunday)
16	Produced the Line and Set the 25th and 26th Mile Posts
17	Ditto 27th and 28th
18	Ditto 29 and 30th
19	Ditto 31 and 32
20	Ditto 33rd
21	Ditto 34, 35, and 36th
22	(Sunday)
23	Ditto 37
24	Ditto 38 and 39th
25	Ditto 40 and 41st. Crossed the River Choptank
26	Ditto 42 and 43rd.
27	Produced the Line
28	Ditto and fixed the 44th Mile Post
29	(Sunday)
30	Ditto and fixed the 45th and 46th
31	Ditto. 47th and 48th

74

August

1	Ditto. 49th and 50th
2	Ditto. 51st
3	Ditto. 52 and 53
4	Ditto. 54 and 55
5	(Sunday)
6	Ditto. 56th Mile Post
7	Ditto. 57 and 58th
8	Ditto. 59th and 60th
9	Ditto. 61
10	Ditto. 62
11	Ditto. 63 and 64th
12	(Sunday)
13	Ditto. 65 and 66th
14	Ditto. 67th
15	Produced the Line and fixed the 68th and 69th Mile Posts. The 69th Mile Post Stands on the South Side of Bohemia River near low water mark.
16	Produced the Line and put down the 70th Mile Post.
17	Ditto. 71
18	Ditto. 72 and 73rd. Sent two Expresses viz., one to his Excellency Horatio Sharp, Esquire, Governor of Maryland, and the other to the Honourable James Hamilton, Esquire, at Philadelphia to acquaint them that we expected to be up with the Line in 8 or 10 days.
19	(Sunday)
20	Set the 74th Mile Post
21	Ditto. 75th and 76th. Crossed Broad Creek

75

1764
August

22	Ditto. 77th
23	Ditto. 78 and 79th
24	Ditto. 80th
25	Ditto. 81st and produced the Line till we judged we were past the Point settled before to be the Tangent Point in the circle round Newcastle of 12 Miles Radius.
26	(Sunday) In the Evening sent the Waggon to Philadelphia to be repaired, and to bring four small Tents, etc.
27	Opened a Visto and produced the Line run (by the former surveyors) from Newcastle Court House 'till it intercepted the Line we Run.

The Distance from the Point of Intersection above mentioned, and the Point esteemed to be the Tangent Point in the Circle round Newcastle of 12 Miles Radius is = 22.51 Chains. *

The Distance from the Point marked Middle to the Said Point of intersection is = 81 Miles 78 Chains 31 Links. (The distance will be 81.78.25 when at Right angles: and the Perpendicular to the 12 mile Post, 22.50 chains.)

The angle made by our Line and the Radius Produced from Newcastle is 89° 50' - Measured by a Hadley's Quadrant.

  * To prove that the Chain Carriers had made no error in the measurement of this 22.51 Chains; I took a man with me, a few days after, and measured it myself; and made it within a Link of the same.

NB We set out from the Middle Point (as observed in the minutes of the 25th of June) in the direction that the surveyors before run their 3rd Line; what our Line varies from theirs to the Westward may be seen by the following Table.

Mile Post	Chains and Links to the West of Theirs	
0	0	00
1	0	01 nearly
5	0	16.5
10	0	58
15	1	24
20	2	13
25	3	14
30	4	40
35	5	55
40	6	46
45	7	30
50	8	17
55	8	98
60	9	80
65	10	86
70	12	14
75	14	00
80	16	25

This we measured at every 5 Mile Post at Right angles to our Line as we came up.

and at 81 miles 78 chains 31 links it was 17 chains 25 links. This was in the direction of the Radius from Newcastle.

1764 Observations made in Running the Tangent Line
June
26   Attempted to take the passage of some stars (near the North Pole) over the
direction of the Line, but nothing was done with certainty.

29   Time of Watch

h	m	s		h	m	s	
15	1	56		16	7	16	⎫
	3	50			9	12	⎬ Equal altitudes of Alpha Coronae Borealis
	5	48			11	5	⎭

Then cloudy

July
1   (Sunday)

2	17	17	3		18	15	37	⎫
		20	33			19	45	⎬ Equal altitudes of Alpha Ophiuchi
		24	48			23	26	⎭
	19	9	48		20	57	40	
		12	00		21	00	12	
		14	40		00	2	32	

For the Surveyors Offsets from their third or last Line
They were 5 chains 26 links to the West when at Right Angles nearly to the Point
12 Miles from Newcastle and then 81 miles about 7 chains from the Middle Point

Miles	80	75	70	65	60
	1.9030899	1.9030899	1.9030899	1.9030899	1.9030899
	2.7209857	2.7209857	2.7209857	2.7209857	2.7209857
	4.6240756	4.6240756	4.6240756	4.6240756	4.6240756
	1.9133051	1.9133051	1.9133051	1.9133051	1.9133051
	2.7107705	1.0750613	1.8450980	2.7107705	2.7107705
		2.7209857	2.7209857	1.8129134	1.7781513
514	4.5960470	4.5660837	2.7209857	2.7209857	
links	1.9133051	1.9133051	4.5338991	4.4991370	
	2.6827419	2.6527786	1.9133051	1.9133051	
			2.6205940	2.5858319	
	4.82	4.49	4.17	3.85	
30	1.379	35	5		

30		35	5
1.4771212		1.5440680	0.6985700
2.7209857		2.7209857	2.7209857
4.1981069		4.2650537	3.4195557
1.9133051		1.9133051	1.9133051
2.2848018		2.3517486	1.5062506
1.93		32.1 links	

78

as 81 miles 78 chains 25 links: 22 chains 50 links: ; 80 miles : (x miles)
∴ 81.978 (miles) : 2250 Links : : 80 : (x)

	80 miles	75	70	65	60	55	50	45	
	1.9030899	1.8750613	1.8450980	1.8129134	1.7781513	1.7403627	1.6989700	1.6532125	
	3.3521825	3.3521825	3.3521825	3.3521825	3.3521825	3.3521825	3.3521825	3.3521825	
	5.2552724	5.2272438	5.1972705	5.1650969	5.1303338	5.0925452	5.0511525	5.0053950	
81.978 log	1.9136973	1.9136973	1.9136973	1.9136973	1.9136973	1.9136973	1.9136973	1.9136973	
	3.3415751	3.3135465	3.2835732	3.2513996	3.2166365	3.1788479	3.1374552	3.0916977	
Offset chs.	21.96	20.58	19.21	17.84	16.47	15.10	13.72	12.35	

	40 miles	35	30	25	20	15	10	5	0
	1.6020600	1.5440680	1.4771212	1.3979400	1.3010300	1.1760913	1.0000000	0.6989700	
	3.3521825	3.3521825	3.3521825	3.3521825	3.3521825	3.3521825	3.3521825	3.3521825	
	4.9542425	4.8962505	4.8293037	4.7501225	4.6532125	4.5282738	4.3521825	4.0511525	
	1.9136973	1.9136973	1.9136973	1.9136973	1.9136973	1.9136973	1.9136973	1.9136973	
	3.0405452	2.9825532	2.9156064	2.8364252	2.7395152	2.6145765	2.4384852	2.1374552	
	10.98	9.61	8.23	6.86	5.49	4.12	2.74	1.37	0

These are our offsets to the East of our 1st Line   79

From the foregoing taking the distance of the Post (fixed 12 miles from Newcastle)
from our line 22.50 chains when at Right Angles (98° 50' making no sensible error)
at the distance from the Middle Point 81 miles 78 chains 25 links our offsets to the
Eastward will be as follows.

Miles from the Middle Post			Offsets Eastward	
Miles	Chains	Links	Chains	Links
81	78	25	22	50
80			21	96
75			20	58
70			19	21
65			17	84
60			16	47
55			15	10
50			13	72
45			12	35
40			10	98
35			9	61
30			8	23
25			6	86
20			5	49
15			4	12
10			2	74
5			1	37
0			0	00

From the Post (12 miles from Newcastle) to the
Mark the Surveyors left in their line, at nearly
right angles with the Post is 5.26 chains.
Hence their offsets to the East will be

At miles

Miles from the Middle Point			Offsets EAST		Hence from the NB in the last page, their offsets from our Line will be at		
Miles	Chains	Links	Chains	Links	Miles	Chains	Links
81	75	00	5	26			
80			5	14	80	21	39
75			4	82	75	18	82
70			4	49	70	16	63
65			4	17	65	15	03
60			3	85	60	13	65
55			3	53	55	12	51
50			3	20	50	11	37
45			2	88	45	10	18
40			2	56	40	9	02
35			2	25	35	7	80
30			1	92	30	6	33
25			1	60	25	4	74
20			1	28	20	3	41
15			0	96	15	2	20
10			0	64	10	1	22
5			0	32	5	0	48.5
0			0	0	0	0	0

From the above our offsets will be to
the EAST of the offsets made by the third
or last Line at *

Miles	Chains	Links
80	0	57
75	1	76
70	2	58
65	2	81
60	2	82
55	2	59
50	2	35
45	2	17
40	1	96
35	1	81
30	1	90
25	2	12
20	2	08
15	1	92
10	1	52
5	0	89
0	0	00

1764
August
28
29
30
31
September
1
2 (Sunday)
3

Set off the 80 miles offset.
Waited for the Waggon, etc.

1764

September

4   The Waggons not returning, we set out on our return toward the Middle Point to make
    our offsets at every 5th Mile Post as per Table marked *. This day set off the 75th Mile offset.

5   Set off the 70 and 65 Mile offsets.

6   Ditto: the 60, 55 and 50 Mile (offsets)

7   Ditto: 45 and 40 Mile (offsets)

8   Ditto: 35, 30 and 25 Mile (offsets)

9   (Sunday) Ditto: 20, 15 and 10 Mile (offsets)

10 At Mr. Twiford's on the banks of the River Nanticoke

11 Ditto

12 Ditto

13 The Waggons with Tents, etc. came to Mr. Twiford's
    Thursday the 13th of September; went to see Pocomoke Swamp; It's about 30 Miles in Length
    and 14 in breadth: (The West Line from the Sea to the Middle Point passes through it): There
    is the greatest quantity of Timber I ever saw: Above the Tallest Oak, Beech, Poplar, Hickory,
    Holly and Fir; Towers the lofty Cedar: (without a Branch), till its ever green conical top; seems   81
    to reach the clouds: The pleasing sight of which; renewed my wishes to see Mount Lebanon.

14 Engaging ax men, providing Boards for marks, etc.

15 Ditto

16 (Sunday)

17 Went to the 10th Mile Post, and began to find a direction for the
    Visto that should pass through our offsets.

18 Ditto. Set up three marks, one near the 10 Mile Post, one half a mile
    North of it, and the other one mile South.

19 Found the Three Marks were not in a right line, but on moving the Middle one
    half an Inch (East) the three marks made a right Line.

20 Run the Line down towards the Middle Point, about two miles.

21 Continued Ditto: and crossed the River Nanticoke at 6 miles, one chain and 92 Links from
    the Middle Point, found we were to the West, of what we should be (according to the 1st
    Line) five inches.

22 Continued Ditto: to the 5th Mile Post, etc., and found we were
    ten inches to the West of the 5 Mile offset.

23 (Sunday)

24 Continued the Line to the 3 Mile Post.

25 Continued Ditto to the Middle Point and found we were two feet two inches to the West of the
    said Point, This difference being so very small in the Radius of 10.5 miles its correction
    would bear no proportion to the loss of time on the part of the Honorable Proprietories, we
    therefore resolved to return to the 10 Mile Post and continue the direction towards the
    12 Mile Post from Newcastle.

26 Returned to Mr. Twifords.   82

27 Began in our former direction and continued the Line to the 13 Mile Post.

28 Continued the Line to 15 1/2 and found we were at the 15 Mile offset 4 Inches to the Eastward.

29 Continued the Line to about 17 Mile Post.

30 (Sunday)

October

1   Continued the Line to the 20 Mile Post, and measured the distance of our Line
    from the Offset and found we were four feet Eight Inches to the Eastward.

2   Continued the Line to the 22 Mile Post

3   Continued Ditto: to the 24 Mile Post

4   Continued Ditto: to the 26 Mile Post nearly, and Measured the Distance of our Line from
    the 25 Mile offset, and found we were Seven feet four Inches to the Eastward.

5   Continued the Line to the 28 Mile Post

6   Continued Ditto: to the 30 Mile and Measured the distance of our Line from
    the offset, and found we were Eight feet three Inches to the Eastward.

7   (Sunday) Set out for Col. Lloyd's

8   Returned from Ditto.   83

9   Continued the Line to the 32 Mile Post

10 Continued Ditto: to the 34 Ditto:

11 Continued Ditto: to the 36 Mile Post and Measured the distance of our Line from
    the 35 Mile offset, and found we were Seven feet and six Inches to the Eastward of the offset.

12 Continued the Line to the 38 Mile Post.

13 Continued the Line to the 40 Mile Post and found we were Eight feet five Inches
    to the Eastward of the offset.

1764

October

14   (Sunday)

15   Continued the Line opposite the 42 Mile Post

16   Continued the Line to the 44 Mile Post

17   Continued the Line and measured the distance of our Line from the 45 Mile offset
and found we were Nine feet six Inches to the Eastward of said offset.

18   Continued the Line to the 46 Mile

19   Continued Ditto to the 48 Mile Post

20   Continued Ditto to the 50 Mile offset nearly.

21   (Sunday)

22   Continued the Line to about the 52 Mile Post. Measured the Distance of our Line from
the 50 Mile offset, and found we were Ten feet Eleven Inches to the East of the said offset.   84

23   Continued the Line to opposite the 54 Mile Post nearly

24   Continued Ditto to the 55 Mile Post nearly

25   Continued Ditto to about the 57 Mile Post and Measured the Distance of our Line from
the 55 Mile offset and found we were Eleven feet one Inch to the Eastward.

26   Continued Ditto opposite the 59 Mile Post

27   Continued Ditto to the 61 Mile Post and Measured the distance of our Line
from the 60 Mile offset and found we were distant therefrom, Ten feet six Inches Eastward

28   (Sunday)

29   Continued the Line to the 62 Mile Post

30   Continued Ditto to about the 63rd Mile Post

31   Continued Ditto to the 66 Mile Post and measured the Distance of our Line
from the 65 Mile offset and found we were Eleven feet seven Inches to the Eastward

November

1   The fogs and mist so thick that we could not proceed.

2   Weather Ditto. Attended the Commissioners at George Town.

3   Weather still so thick that we could not proceed.

4   (Sunday)   85

5   Continued the Line

6   Continued the Line and measured the distance of the 70 Mile offset and
found we were Twelve feet Eleven Inches to the Eastward of the offset.

7   Continued the Line

8   Continued the Line and measured the distance of the 75th Mile offset and found we
were fifteen feet seven Inches to the Eastward of the said offset.

9   Continued the Line to the 80 Mile offset and Measured the distance of Line
from the said offset and found we were Sixteen feet seven Inches to the Eastward.

10   Continued the line to the Point shown us to be the Tangent Point (in the Direction of the
Radius of 12 Miles from Newcastle mentioned in the Minutes of the 25th and 27th of
August) and measured the distance of our line from the said Post or Point, and found
we were Sixteen feet and Nine inches to the Eastward of the said Point. We also
continued our line 52.5 yards when it was opposite the Post marked X_{II}^{T} and found we
were Sixteen feet from the said Post Eastward. We continued our Line 41.5 yards
farther and then we were opposite the Post marked T P. We measured the distance
of our Line from the said Post and found we were fifteen feet two inches and a half
to the Eastward.   86

10   These three Posts were settled by the former surveyors and supposed to be in
the Periphery of the circle round Newcastle. Discharged the ax men.

11   (Sunday)

12   Sent two Expresses, viz, one to his Excellency, Horatio Sharpe, Esq., Governor of
Maryland, and the other to the Honorable James Hamilton, Esquire, to acquaint them we
finished our second Line on Saturday last.

From the foregoing our second or last Line falling two feet two inches to the West
of the Middle Point, and Sixteen feet nine Inches to the East of the Point esteemed or
shown us to be the Tangent Point we have the Point of intersection where our second
Line crossed the true Line thus as 16 ft. 9 in. + 2 ft. 2 in. : 82 miles : : 2 ft. 2 in. : 9.39 miles.
Hence the true offsets of our second Line at every 5 Mile Post as follows.

Miles from the Middle Point	Offsets in Feet	Inches	
0	2	2	To the Eastward of our second Line
5	1	0	
10	0	2.2	
15	1	4	
20	2	6	
25	3	8	
30	4	10	
35	5	11	
40	7	1	To the Westward of our second Line for to give the Tangent Line from the Post shown us to be the Tangent Point.
45	8	3	
50	9	5	
55	10	6	
60	11	8	
65	12	10	
70	14	0	
75	15	2	
80	16	4	
82	16	9	

Our measurements from the offsets of our first Line being
collected are as of the following Table

Miles from the Middle Point	Our second Line from the Offsets Feet	Inches	
0	2	2	Westward
5	0	10	
10	0	0	
15	0	4	
20	4	8	
25	7	4	
30	8	3	
35	7	6	
40	8	5	
45	9	6	
50	10	11	Our second Line to the Eastward of the offsets of our first Line.
55	11	1	
60	10	6	
65	11	7	
70	12	11	
75	15	7	
80	16	7	
82	16	9	

1764
November

12   From the two last Tables we have the difference of the Results
of our two Tangent Lines as follows at every five mile Post.

Miles from the Middle Point	Feet	Inches
0	0	0
5	0	2
10	0	2.2
15	1	0
20	2	2
25	3	8
30	3	5
35	1	7
40	1	4
45	1	3
50	1	6
55	0	7
60	1	2
65	1	3
70	1	1
75	0	5
80	0	3
82	0	0

From the whole we consider that the offset Posts
made from our first Line standing in our
second Visto are (as near as practicable)
in the true Tangent Line.

88

13   From the Data in minutes of the 27th of August we computed how far the true Tangent Point
would be distant from the Post (Shown us to be the Tangent Point) and found it would not
pass one inch to the Eastward or Westward.
On measuring the angle of our last Line with the direction from Newcastle it was so near
a right angle, that, on a mean from our Lines, the above mentioned Post is the true Tangent Point.
From the whole we conclude that the offset Posts in our last Visto marked MD are
(or near as is practicable) in the true Tangent Line.

14

15

16

17   Waiting for the Commissioners

18   (Sunday)

19

20

21   The Commissioners of both Provinces met at Christana Bridge in the county of Newcastle.

22   Attended the Commissioners at Ditto.

23   At this meeting the Gentlemen Commissioners came to a resolution that what

24   we had done relating to the Lines should stand as finished.

25   (Sunday)

26   Discharged all hands and left off for the winter season. Returned to Mr. Harlands in the
Forks of Brandywine.

December

4   Wrote to the Honorable Proprietors to acquaint them we have finished the Tangent Line.   89

1765
January

10   Left Brandywine and proceeded to Lancaster (distance about 35 miles) a Town in Pennsylvania,
distant from Philadelphia 75 Miles, bearing nearly due West. What brought me here was my
curiosity to see the place where was perpetrated last Winter the Horrid and inhuman murder
of 26 Indians, Men, Women and Children, leaving none alive to tell. These poor unhappy
creatures had always lived under the protection of the Pennsylvania Government and had Lands
alloted for them a few Miles from Lancaster by the late celebrated William Penn, Esquire, Proprietor.
They had received notice of the intention of some of the back inhabitants and fled to the Gaol
(jail) to save themselves. The keeper made the door fast, but it was broken open; and two
men went in and executed the bloody scene; while about 50 of their party sat on Horse Back without;
armed with Guns, etc.   Strange it was that the Town though as large as most Market
Towns in England, never offered to oppose them, though its more than probable they on request
might have been assisted by a Company of his Majesties Troops who were then in the Town......
no honor to them! What was laid to the Indians charge was that they held a private correspondence
with the Enemy Indians; but this could never be proved against the men and the women and children
(some in their Mothers wombs that never saw light) could not be guilty.
Wrote a letter from hence to Mr. Kingston.

1765
January

17   Returning at Pechway, I fell in company with Mr. Samuel Smith who in the year 1736 was Sheriff of Lancaster County, now three counties, Lancaster, York and Cumberland, who informed me that the People near the supposed Boundary Line were then at open war. About ten miles from Lancaster on the River Susquehanna one Mr. Crisep defended his house as being in Maryland, with 14 Men, which he surrounded with about 55. They would not surrender (but kept firing out) till the House was set on fire, and one man in the House lost his life coming out.

19   At Brandywine

90

February

11   Left Brandywine and proceeded for New York.

13   Crossed the River Schuylkill near the Swedes-ford and lodged at Mr. McLanes Commissary for the Lines.

14   Passed the Delaware (about 1/4 mile wide) on Ice: my Horse near being lost.

15   Passed through Prince Town in the Jerseys; here is the most Elegant built Colledge I have seen in America. Lodged at Brunswick.

16   Passed through Elizabeth Town, crossed the River in to Staten Island, and over the Bay (about 10 miles wide) to New York.

17   (Sunday) At New York. (Actually recorded as York).

18   At Ditto.

19   Ditto. Wrote to Mr. Williams.

20   In Long Island

21   Returned to Staten Island and took the Eastern Road; down for Perth Amboy in the Jerseys.

22   Passed through the Freeholds, Mount Pleasant and Mount

23   Holly in the Jerseys.

24   (Sunday) Met some boys just come out of a Quaker Meeting House as if the De(vi)l had been with them. I could by no means get my Horse by them. I gave the Horse a light blow on the Head with my whip which brought him to the ground as if shot dead. I over his Head, my hat one way wig another and whip another, fine sport for the boys. However I got up as did my Horse after some time and I led him by the Meeting House, (the Friends pouring out) very serene, as if all had been well. But

25   Lay too - my Hip being hurt very much by the fall.

26   Crossed Racoon Creek.

27   Crossed the River Delaware to Newcastle and went to Newark (Delaware).

91

(Undated)

16 ft. 9 in. + 2 ft. 2 in. : 82 miles : : 2 ft. 2 in. : 9.39 miles (The point of intersection of second line with the true line.)

Hence the offsets of our second Line

Miles from the Middle Point	Feet	Inches	
0	2	2	To the East of the Second Line
5	1	0	
10	0	2.2	
15	1	4	
20	2	6	
25	3	8	
30	4	10	
35	5	11	
40	7	1	To the Westward
45	8	3	
50	9	5	
55	10	6	
60	11	8	
65	12	10	
70	14	0	
75	15	2	
80	16	4	
82	16	9	

92

(Undated)

Given LP = 6558.31 (chains)
LN = 982.51 (chains) To find PN
Angle PLN = 89° 50'

LP = 6558.31
LN = 982.51
Sum = 7540.82 (log 7540.82) = 3.8774186
Difference = 5575.80 (log 5575.80) , = 3.7663072

Log Tang 45° 05 = 10.0012633

13.7475705

(log tan) 36° 33' 35" = 9.8701519

45 5 0
81° 38 35" = Angle LNP

As (log) sin LNP.... 81° 38' 35" = 9.9953639
: (log) LP 6558.31 3.8167920
: : (log) Sine 89° 50' PLN 9.9999982

13.8167902
: PN 6628.67 3.8214263

As (log) PNHypot 6628.67 = 3.8214263
Rad = 10.
(log) NQ 960 chains = 2.9822712
∴ (log) Sine of angle QPN 8° 19' 38" = 9.1608449
Complement angle QNP 81° 40' 22"

Angle LNP 81° 38' 35"
Angle LNQ 1' 47" = angle **PNQ** Complement 89° 58' 13" = (Angle) NRQ
(Angle) QRN = Complement 89° 58' 13"

As Sine QRN 89° 58' 13" 9.9999999
: QN 960.00 2.9822712
Rad 10.
to Hypotenuse RN 960, 1/46 of a link 2.9822713

180° 00' 00"
1 47 = (Angle) RNQ = (Angle) BNQ
179° 58' 13"

89 59 06 = One half = Angle NBQ = Angle BQN
as (log) Sine 89° 59' 6" (Angle) NBQ 10.0000000
to (log) QN 960.00 12.9822712
: : (log) Sine PNQ 1' 47" 6.7149586
: BQ 0.498 chains 9.6972298

Figure 93

Therefore 0 chains 50 Links to be set off with an angle of 89° 59' 06" = Angle QBN
(Paper frayed). Point B from the direction BN from Newcastle.

68

(Undated)

	(logarithms)
As Sum	3.8774186
to Difference	3.7163072
Tangent 45° 2.'5	10.0006317
	13.7469389
36° 31' 11"	9.8695203
45 2 30	

LNP = 81° 33' 41" (log) Sine   =   9.9952864
LP = 6558.31   3.8167920
PLN 89° 55' (log) Sine   9.9999995
                                13.8167915
PN 6629.87   3.8215051

(log) PN   3.8215051
(log) R   10.
(log) NQ   2.9822712
(log) Sine 8° 19' 32" = QPN =   9.1607661
          90°
QNP =   81° 40' 28"
LNP =   81° 33' 41"
QNR =   6' 47"
QRN =   89° 53' 13" = (log) Sine 9.9999991
(log) 960.00   2.9822712
                            10.
(log) 960   2.9822721

From the Angles and Radius NQ and QN = SQ
is had, then to find dl, op, etc.
Set Sl = any measured distance : then
QS - Sl = lQ = Ng and also
lg = QN. hence in the Triangle
dNg given dN = 12 = Rad. and gN
find the perpendicular dg. Then dg - lg = dl = what
is to be laid off at Right Angles to the Meridian

Figure
95

1764
June
26   Observations for determining the time of stars passing the Azimuth corresponding to
our first Line from the Middle Point to the twelve Mile Post from Newcastle.

Time of Watch

	h	m	s	h	m	s	
							Attempted to take the passage of some stars near the North Pole, but nothing was done with certainty.
29	15	1	56	16	17	16	
		3	50		9	12	Equal altitudes of Alpha Coronae Borealis
		5	48		11	5	

Then Cloudy

July
1 (Sunday)

	h	m	s	h	m	s		
	16	9	50	- - - - - - -			Equal altitudes of Antares	Right Ascension = 16h 15m 1s (on) August 1, 1764
		22	25	- - - - - - -				
	- - - - - - -			17	0	47		
	19	44	22	- - - - - - -			Ditto of Alpha Aquilae	Right Ascension = 19h 39m 18s (on) August 1, 1764
		57	10	20	4	15		
				20	16	50		
	22	23	46	1st wire of Telescope				
	22	46	50	Middle Ditto			The star next the Pole Star in the Tail of the	
	23	14	46	Third Ditto			Lesser Bear, passed in the direction of the Line.	

69

1764						
July		Time by the Watch				
	h	m	s	h	m	s
2	17	17	3	18	15	37
		20	33		19	45	Equal altitudes of Alpha Ophiuchi
		24	48		23	26

Equal altitudes of Alpha Ophiuchi

	19	9	48	20	57	40
		12	00	21	00	12
		14	40		2	32

Equal altitudes of Alpha Aquilae

Cloudy when the star next the Pole Star in the Tail of the Lesser
Bear passed the direction of the Line.

4	15	52	36	17	18	32
		57	55		24	45
	16	4	4		30	30

Equal altitudes of Antares

	19	27	58	20	36	55
		31	28		40	55
		35	30		44	28

Equal altitudes of Alpha Aquilae

Cloudy

5	19	32	40	20	36	57
		36	24		41	12
		40	34		46	50

Equal altitudes of Alpha Aquilae

	22	32	10	1st wire	
		55	10	Middle	The star next the Pole Star in the Tail of the Lesser Bear passed the direction of the Line.

	23	28	10	Alpha Ursae Majoris under the Pole Star.

6	7	14	15	7	45	30
		18	12		50	56

Equal altitudes of Sun's upper Limb

		23	34		Sun's center passed the Meridian by the Watch	7h 34m 33s

Sun's Right Ascension at this time (the difference of the Meridian from Paris by the Lunar
Eclipse of March 17th) = 5h 14m 41s   7   4   55

Watch too fast for Sidereal Time   0h 29m 38s

	19	26	30	20	48	5
		29	32		51	15
		32	48		54	18

Equal altitudes of Alpha Aquilae

Cloudy 1st wire and middle   Ditto

	23	26	00	The star next to the Pole Star passed by third or last wire

Alpha Aquilae passed the Meridian by the Watch   20h 10m 25s

This star's Right Ascension   19   39   18

Watch too fast for Sidereal Time   31m 37s

The star in the Tail of the Lesser Bear passed the last wire at	23h 26m 00s
Time in passing from the Middle wire to the last by observation 1st July	27 56
Star at the Middle Wire, that is, in the direction of the Line	22h 58m 04s
Watch too fast at this time	31 30
Right Ascension of the Mid Heaven	22h 26m 34s at the

time of the star next the Pole Star in the tail of the Lesser Bear passed
an Azimuth in the direction of the Line.

10	15	49	00	17	5	10	Equal altitudes of Antares, hence passed at	16h 33m 36s
		55	00		12	17		16 15 01
	16	2	8		18	3	Watch fast	18m 35s

	19	29	26	20	15	36	Alpha Aquilae, hence this star passed at	19h 57m 58s
		34	18		21	40		19 39 18
		40	21		26	30	Watch fast	18m 40s

	22	21	30	1st wire	The star next the Pole Star in the Tail of Ursae Minoris
		44	45	Middle	passed the Azimuth of the Line.
	23	12	35	Third	

		12	35	Star passed the Azimuth at	22h 44m 45s

Watch faster than by the above star   18   44

Right Ascension Mid Heaven when the star passed 22h 26m 01s
the Azimuth

1764   Time by the Watch

July		h	m	s	h	m	s	
11		7	17	55	7	49	42	⎫
			21	38		53	45	⎬ Equal altitudes of Sun's upper Limb
			26	37		58	48	⎭
			30	35	8	2	30	Ditto. Sun's Lower Limb

Hence the Sun passed by the Watch at   7h 40m 11s

Right Ascension of Sun   7   25   20

                       Watch fast   14m 51s   very dubious

24		16	37	35	- - - - - -	⎫
		- - - - - -	- - - - - -	⎬ Antares. Hence Antares passed at 16h 47m 48s
		- - - - - -	16 58 00	⎭ Right Ascension Antares 16 15 1

                       Watch fast   32m 47s

             The motion was very slow

		19	33	7	20	42	52	⎫
			36	48		46	47	⎬ Alpha Aquilae. Hence star passed at 20h 11m 49s
			40	50		50	14	⎭ Right Ascension 19 39 18

                       Watch fast   32m 31s

		22	35	40	1st wire	⎫
			58	15	Middle	⎬ The star next the Pole Star in the Tail of Ursae Minoris
		23	26	10	Third	⎭

From the last wire   23h 26m 10s

Subtract time from middle   27   56   by observation on the

                                     1st of February

                    22h 58m 14s   Star next the Pole Star

                                     passed the direction of the

                                     Line

Watch fast   32m 18s

Right Ascension Mid-Heaven   22h 25m 56s

when the Star next the Pole

Star passed the Line   98

25		19	19	00	clouds	⎫
			21	35	21 2 40	⎬ Equal altitudes of Alpha Aquilae. Hence star passed at 20h 12m 8s
			24	25	5 18	⎭ Right Ascension 19h 39m 18s

                             Watch fast   32m 50s

		22	36	3	1st wire	⎫
			58	50	Middle, cloudy till a little past.	⎬ The Star next the Pole Star in the Tail of
		23	27	00	3rd wire	⎭ Ursae Minoris passed the Direction of the Line.

By observation on 1st

of July from the first

wire to Middle   23   4   and from middle wire to third   27m 56s

On the 5th of July   23   0

On the 10th   23   15   and 10th Ditto   27   50

Mean   23   6   Mean   27   53

Passed the 1st wire above

             at 22   36   3   Passed above   23   27   00

Middle wire at   22   59   9   Middle at   22   59   7

                            By the first wire   59   9

                            Mean   22h 59m 8s =

The time by the Watch when the star passed the Direction of the Line.

26		8	33	40	9	8	38	⎫
			37	56		14	39	⎬ Equal altitudes of Sun's upper Limb
			44	7		19	2	⎭

Hence Sun passed the Meridian at   8h 56m 21s

Right Ascension of Sun   8   25   26

Watch fast   30m 55s

Watch fast when Alpha Aquilae passed 32   50

                                   1m 55s

Then as $12^h.2 : 1^m 55^s :: 2^h.75 : 26^s$ which subtract from   32m 50s

                                                    0   26

Watch fast when star passed the Line   32   24

Passed the Middle wire at time above   22   59   08

Right Ascension Mid-Heaven when star passed the   22h 26m 44s

direction of the Line on the 25th, that is this morning

Time by the Watch

	h	m	s	h	m	s			h	m	s
July											
27	18	10	45	19	45	4 ⎫	Equal altitudes Alpha Lyrae	Hence this star passed at	18	59	00
		11	54		46	10 ⎬	Zenith Distance about 11°.	Right Ascension	18	28	58
		12	56		47	11 ⎭		Watch fast		30	2
	20	33	58	21	30	50 ⎫	Equal altitudes, Alpha Cygni	Hence this star passed at	21	3	58
		35	33		32	23 ⎬	Zenith Distance, 8°	Right Ascension of Star	20	33	25
		37	3		33	58 ⎭		Watch fast		30	33
	22	34	7	1st wire		⎫	The star next the Pole star in the Tail of Ursae Minoris passed				
		57	36	Middle		⎬	Azimuth in the direction of the Line				
		24	19	3rd wire		⎭	Watch fast when star passed the Direction		31m	01s	

Star passed at 22h 57m 36s
Right Ascension mid-heaven 22h 26m 35s

	h	m	s	h	m	s			h	m	s
30	18	03	40	20	2	50 ⎫					
		33	42	- - - - - - ⎬			Equal altitudes, Alpha Lyrae.	Hence this star passed at	19	18	51
		34	55		4	59 ⎭		Right Ascension	18	28	58
								Watch fast		49	53
	20	56	12	21	49	13 ⎫					
		57	56		50	52 ⎬	Equal altitudes, Alpha Cygni.	Hence this star passed at	21	24	23
		59	36		52	26 ⎭		Right Ascension	20	33	25
								Watch fast		50	58
	23	18	25	Middle wire.			Star passed the direction of the Line.				

Star in the Tail next the Pole star passed the direction of the Line 23 18 25
Watch fast 51 57
Right ascension mid-heaven when the star crossed the line 22 26 28

	h	m	s	h	m	s			h	m	s
August											
17	18	47	25	19	-	- - - ⎫					
		48	24		37	00 ⎬	Equal altitudes, Alpha Lyrae.	Hence this star passed at	19	12	42
		49	33		38	00 ⎭		Right Ascension	18	28	58
								Watch fast		43	44
	20	42	45	21	50	48 ⎫					
		44	8		52	12 ⎬	Equal altitudes, Alpha Cygni	Hence this star passed at	21	18	9
		45	30		53	30 ⎭		Right Ascension	20	33	25
								Watch fast		44	44
	23	12	48	Middle			Star in the Tail of Ursae Minoris next the Pole star passed the direction of the Line				

Star in the Tail passed at 23 12 48
Watch fast at this time 45 39
Right ascension, mid-heaven when the star passed the Line 22 27 9

	h	m	s	h	m	s			h	m	s
27	18	54	38	19	58	50 ⎫					
		55	40		59	54 ⎬	Equal altitudes of Alpha Lyrae.	Hence the star passed at	19	27	47
		56	44	20	0	57 ⎭		Right ascension	18	28	58
								Watch fast		58	49
	21	6	32	21	54	46 ⎫					
		8	4		56	25 ⎬	Equal altitudes of Alpha Cygni.	Hence the star passed at	21	32	31
		9	44		58	2 ⎭		Right ascension	20	33	25
								Watch fast		59	6
	23	25	55				The star in the Tail of Ursae Minoris passed the direction of the Line				

Star in the Tail passed at 23 25 55
Watch fast at this time 59 21
Right ascension mid-Heaven when star passed the Line 22 26 34

(Undated)

For the angle the 1st and middle wires make in the Transit Instrument

(logarithm)

as AC	335.94	12.5262617
: R		10.
: : 1.1666		10.0669220
: Tang. Angle BAC	12' 00"	7.5406603

= Angle of the two wires, and the time of the star in the Tail
of Ursae Minoris, passing this angle as follows by
different observations.

on July	1st	23'	4"
	5th	23	00
	10th	23	15
	27th	23	29
Mean of 12 minutes		23'	12"

and this time the star is passing an angle of 12' 00"

(Then follow two sets of logarithmic calculations which were deleted)

N. B. The method of finding above the angle subtended between the first and middle wires
was thus - A mark BC was placed at such distance that the wires bisected the
points B and C: Then BC being measured it was = 1.1666 feet and the
distance from the Instrument at A, to C = 335.94 feet; hence the Angle
BAC = 12' 00" as above.

Figure
101

(Undated)

The foregoing Observations were made with the Transit Instrument
in the following manner.

Before we left off in the Evening a mark was placed at the distance
of 1/2 or 3/4 of a mile in the Line Northwards : Then after the equal altitudes
were observed, the Instrument was adjusted as when we gave off. Then a
candle being placed in the center of the Mark; the middle wire in the
Telescope was brought to bisect the light of the candle. (The line of collimation
being just, and the Level proving the Horizontal position of the axis.) Then the Telescope
being elevated to the Star, the time (by the watch) of the stars passing the
middle wire (with which the Line was run) was taken.

The Watch with which these observations were made, had only the Hour
and minute Hands; therefore the seconds must not be expected as from
a good time Piece, nor does the nature of the Problem require it, as the
star made use of, (Delta Ursae Minoris) was at the time of observation nearly
passing the Tangent of its circle around the Pole. Consequently its apparent
motion (was) very slow.

102

1765
March

1   Began to prepare for running the Western Line: the method of proceeding as follows.

Let P be the Pole, ABCD the Parallel of Latitude to be drawn.
AC the arch of a great circle. At pleasure suppose = 10 minutes
(which we shall set out with on the first station, and in order to
find the direction AC, there is given in the Right Angled Spherical Triangle EPA
AP = Complement of Latitude = 50° 16' 42".6 ⎫ Hence Angle PAE = 89° 55' 51" =
AE = One-half AC = 5'   ⎭
the angle from the North Westward : and to lay off this angle with the
Transit Instrument by the Stars; Let P be the Pole
Z the Zenith and S the place of the star. Then in the oblique angled
Spherical Triangle SPZ, there is given
SP = the star's distance from the Pole
ZP = the Complement of the Latitude
Angle SZP = 89° 55' 51" = the star's azimuth from the North when it will
be on the direction AEC above. To find the angle SPZ or angle at the
Pole when the star is on the said azimuth.

1 The angle SPZ being added to the star's Right Ascension: if to the Westward of the meridian or subtracted if the Star is to the Eastward; gives the Right Ascension of the Mid-Heaven, when the star is upon the azimuth Required. In this manner the Right Ascension of the Mid-Heaven for different stars is as follows. -----Next to find by the clock when the star will be on the said azimuth, two equal altitudes of the same star before the time are observed, whence the time is gained. At this instant of time the Middle Wire is brought to bisect the star, and in that position

(The axis of the Telescope, etc., being Horizontal) the vertical axis is made fast: Then the Telescope is brought parallel to the Horizon, and a Mark set

by the help of a candle (at the distance of 1/2 or 3/4 of a mile) so that the middle wire bisects it.

In this manner we proceed with 3 or 4 different stars and find that

at the distance of 1/2 a mile the extremes of the distances of the marks made by the different stars will not in general exceed 5 or 6 inches. Figures a and b
  103

The line AC being run with the Transit Instrument, at C we set up the Sector to prove or correct the work, by observing the Zenith Distances of the same stars that were observed at the point A.

At C, we find a new direction as before, etc., etc.

The greatest distance EB to be laid off from the right Line AEC when AE = 5' is 17.14 feet. 104

2 Computing the star Azimuths, etc., for the direction Westward

3 (Sunday)

4

19 Cloudy, Heavy rains, etc.

20 Made some observations to find the Direction and placed one mark at the distance of one-half mile, etc.

21 Snow

22 Snow

23 Snow

24 (Sunday) At 9 in the Morning the Snow was two feet nine or ten inches deep in general, where the wind had not the least effect to heap it.

25⎫
26⎬ Snow still so deep we could not proceed.
27⎭

28 Made a few observations, but dubious.

29 Cloudy

30 Ditto. Messrs. Darby and Cope, chain carriers, came from the Lower Counties.

31 (Sunday) Ditto

April

1 Cloudy

2 Ditto

3 Ditto

4 Made more observations for finding the direction West: See them in the 6th page following. 105

Aldebaran

h m s
4 22 29 1/2   Right Ascension in time, Aldebaran
4 22 28 1/2   or 29s and Distance to Pole = 73° 48' 56".4

   o   '   "
   Sirius
98 38 37
     3 32   (Precession)
98 42 9   = 6h 34m 49s = Right Ascension Sirius
Note: These Right Ascensions, etc., are for the end of March 1765.

   Castor
109 48 46
    +5 5
109 53 51   = 7h 19m 35.5s = Right Ascension Castor
          Distance to Pole = 57° 37' 12"

   Procyon
111 40 57
    4 12
111 45 9   = 7h 27m 1s = Right Ascension Procyon. Distance to Pole = 84° 11' 15"

   Pollux
112 39 4
    4 55
112 43 59   = 7h 30m 56s = Right Ascension Pollux
          Distance to Pole = 61° 25' 37"

   Spica
198 8 44
    4 8
198 12 52   = 13h 12m 51.5s = Right Ascension Spica. To Pole 99° 55' 44"

   Arcturus
211 10 43
   +3 42
211 14 35   = 14h 4m 58s = Right Ascension Arcturus. Distance to Pole = 69° 34' 58"

Eta (Tauri) Pleiades - (Alcyone)

	Right Ascension	Declination
1760 =	53° 18' 51"	23° 20' 40"
	+4 52	+1' 06"
	53° 23' 43" = 3h 33m 35s = Right Ascension	23° 21' 46"

Distance to Pole = 66° 38' 14"   106

Computations, etc. for finding the Direction

Latitude   39° 43' 18" of the point 15 Miles South of Philadelphia
Complement   50   16   42   (log) comp. Sine =   0.1139879
                       10   00   (log) ditto Sine   =   0.1139879
Sum   100° 43' 24"
1/2   50   21   42   (log) Sine   =   9.8865061
Difference   0   5   0   (log) Sine   =   7.1626960
                                                                    17.2772079 -20
                                                                     8.6386039 -10

0.1139879   0.1139879
2.5362745   2.8373039
9.8865361   9.8865361
7.1626960   7.1626960
19.6994945   20.0005239
9.8497472 -10 = (log cos)
(Angle) = 44° 57' 55" x 2 = 89° 55' 50"
= Angle LBP

Aldebaran   (log)
as Sine SP 73° 58' 56" = 9.9828030
:   Sine Z 89   55   50   = 9.9999997
: : Sine PZ 50   16   42   = 9.8860155
                                          19.8860152
:   Sine ZSP 53° 9' 6"   9.9032122 -10

(Pole to Star)   73° 58' 56"
(Pole to Zenith)   50   16   42
Difference   23° 42' 14"
One-half =   11° 51' 7"   (log)
Angles   89° 55' 50"   As Sine 1/2 diff. sides   11° 51' 7" = 9.3125
                          53   9   6   : Tang 1/2 difference angles 18° 23' 22" = 9.5217278
Difference   36° 46' 44"   : Sine 1/2 Sum of sides   62° 7' 49" = 9.9464586
One-half =   18° 23' 22"   19.4681864
                                                To CoTang 1/2 Angle P   34° 56' 51" = 10.1556210
Sum of the Sides = 124° 15' 38"   Double   69° 53' 42" = SPZ
One-half   = 62° 7' 49"   in time   4h 39m 35s
                                                Right Ascension Aldebaran   4h 22m 28.5s
Right Ascension Mid-Heaven when Aldebaran passes the Azimuth   9h 2m 3.5s

                 Alpha Orionis

Right Ascension = 85° 37' 3" = 5h 42m 28s   Distance to Pole = 82° 39' 41"
                          (log)   (log)
Sine   82° 39' 41" = 9.9964279   Sine   16° 11' 30" = 9.4453729
Sine   89° 55' 51" = 9.9999997   Sine   66° 28' 12" = 9.9622988
Sine   50° 16' 42" = 9.8860155   Tang   19° 32' 23" = 9.5500047
                                   19.8860152   19.5124035
Sine S   50° 51' 5"   9.8895873   CoTang   40° 35' 45" 10.0670306

Sides   82° 39' 41"   Difference = 32° 22' 59"   2(40° 35' 45") = 81° 11' 30" = 5h 24m 46s
             50° 16' 42"   One-half =   16° 11' 30"   Right Ascension =   5h 42m 28s
Sum   132° 56' 23"   Right Ascension Mid-Heaven =   11h 7m 14s
One-half   66° 28' 12"   Angles   89° 55' 51"   when Alpha Orionis passes
                                             50° 51' 5"
                                             39° 4' 46"   Figures a, b, and c
                           One-half =   19° 32' 23"   107

		(log)
Rad		10.0000000
Sine	50° 16' 42'' (PB) =	9.8860155
Sine	89° 55' 51'' =	9.9999997
Sine PZ	50° 16' 41.''83 =	9.8860152 here the difference

between PB and PL (=RL) being but 3 in the last place

as 175 : 10'' : : 3 : .171 of a second = 17.1 feet = RL   108

(Miscellaneous multiplication and long division, not transcribed)   109

148° 57' 47'' = 9h 55m 51s = Right Ascension, Regulus. Distance to Pole = 76° 53' 40''

		(log)
As Sine	76° 53' 40'' =	9.9885384
Sine	89 55 54 =	9.9999997
Sine	50 16 42 =	9.8860155
		19.8860152
Sine Angle at Star	=	9.8974768 -10 Angle at Star = 52° 09' 36''

Sides	76° 53' 40''	Difference	26° 36' 58''
	50 16 42	One-half	13 18 29
Sum	127° 10' 22''		
One-half	63° 35' 11''		

Angles   89° 55' 51''
          52 9 36
Difference 37° 46' 15''
One-half   18° 53' 7''

As Sine one-half difference Sides	13° 18' 29'' =	9.3620889
: Tangent one-half difference Angles	18° 53' 7'' =	9.5341397
: Sine one-half Sum of Sides	63° 35' 11'' =	9.9521170
		19.4862567
to CoTang 1/2 Angle P	36° 55' 8'' =	10.1241678

73° 50' 16'' = 4h 55m 21s

Right Ascension, Regulus   = 9h 55m 51s
Right Ascension, Mid-Heaven   = 14h 51m 12s, when Regulus passes the Azimuth

		(log)
Sine	69° 34' 58'' =	9.9718217 Arcturus
Sine	89 55 51 =	9.9999997
Sine	50 16 42 =	9.8860155
		19.8860152
Sine of (55° 9' 24'' = S) =		9.9141935

Sides	69° 34' 58''	Difference	19° 18' 16''	Angles	89° 55' 51''
	50° 16' 42''	One-half	9 39 8		55 9 24
Sum	119° 51' 40''				34° 46' 27''
One-half	59° 55' 50''			One-half	17° 23' 14''

		(log)
As Sine	9° 39' 8'' =	9.2244486
Tang	17 23 14 =	9.4957331
Sine	59 55 50 =	9.9372263
		19.4329594
To CoTang	31 44 44 =	10.2085108

63 29 28 = 4h 13m 58s

Right Ascension Arcturus = 14h 4m 58s
Right Ascension Mid-Heaven 9h 51m 00s when Arcturus is in the Azimuth East

Figures a and b
110

(Undated)

Right Ascension 7h 27m 1s Procyon to Pole 84° 11' 15"

(log)

Sine	84°	11'	15"	=	9.9977613
Sine	89	55	51	=	9.9999997
Sine	50	16	42	=	9.8860155
					19.8860152
Sine S	50°	38'	10"	=	9.8882539

Sides	84°	11'	15"	Difference	=	33°	54'	33"	Angles	89°	55'	51"
	50	16	42	One-half	=	16	57	17		50	38	10
Sum	134°	27'	57"						Difference	39°	17'	41"
One-half	67°	13'	58"						One-half	19°	38'	50"

(log)

Sine	16°	57'	17"	=	9.4648112
Tang	19	38	50	=	9.5526840
Sine	67	13	58	=	9.9647708
					19.5174548
CoTang 1/2 (41	32		9)	=	10.0526436
83°	4'	18"	=	5h 32m 17s	
Right Ascension			=	7h 27m 1s	
Right Ascension Mid-Heaven			12h 59m 18s	when Procyon passes	

Right Ascension 11h 37m 5s Beta Leonis to Pole 74° 7' 1"

(log)

Sine	74°	7'	1"	=	9.9830948	
Sine	89	55	51	=	9.9999997	(Editorial Note: S is the angle at the star between
Sine	50	16	42	=	9.8860155	the pole and the zenith.)
					19.8860152	
Sine Angle S 53° 6' 1"				=	9.9029204	

Sides	74°	7'	1"	Difference	23°	50'	19"	Angles	89°	55'	51"
	50	16	42	One-half	11	55	10		53	6	1
Sum	124°	23'	43"					Difference	36°	49'	50"
One-half	62°	11'	52"					One-half	18°	24'	55"

(log)

Sine	11°	55'	10"	=	9.3149963
Tang	18	24	55	=	9.5223815
Sine	62	11	52	=	9.9467287
					19.4691102
CoTang 1/2 angle					10.1541139

One-half angle = 35° 2' 27"

Angle =	70°	4'	54"	=	4h 40m 20s
Right Ascension			=	11h 37m 5s	
Right Ascension Mid-Heaven			16h 17m 25s	when Beta Leonis in on the Azimuth	

Figure
111

78

(Undated)

For the Direction to intersect the Parallel 10' West by using stars to the Eastward

Right Ascension of Eta Pleiades = 3h 33m 35s, Polar Distance = 66° 38' 14"
Here the Angle SZP = Comp. of AZP to 180° = 90° 4' 9", then as before
                          (log)

As Sine   66° 38' 14" = 9.9628485   (Editorial Note: The star which Mason lists as
: Sine   90 4 9 = 9.9999997   Eta Pleiades appears to be Eta
: : Sine   50 16 42 = 9.8860155   Tauri, i. e., Alcyone.)
: Sine Angle ZSP 56° 54' 50" 9.9231667

Sides   66° 38' 14"   Angles   90° 4' 9"
             50 16 42   56 54 50
Sum   116° 54' 56" Difference 16° 21' 32"   Difference 33° 9' 19"
One-half 58° 27' 28" One-half   8° 10' 46"   One-half 16° 34' 40"

As Sine   8° 10' 46" = 9.1531250
: Tang 1/2 Diff 16° 34' 40" = 9.4737652
Sine   58° 27' 28" = 9.9305695
                      19.4043347
To CoTang 1/2 58° 33' 56" = 10.2512097
Right Ascension   =   3h 33m 35s
Right Ascension of the Mid-Heaven = 23° 39' 19" when Eta (Tauri) Pleiades is on the Azimuth East at
                                    90° 4' 9" from North

Right Ascension Aldebaran   4h 22m 29s   Polar Distance = 73° 58' 55"
                      (log)
As Sine   73° 58' 55" = 9.9828030
: Sine   90 04 09
: : Sine   50° 16' 42"
: Sine of 53 09 06
              90 4 9
Difference   36° 55' 3"
One-half   18° 27' 32" Diff. Angles
                              (log)
As Sine one-half Diff. Sides 11° 51' 7" = 9.3125654
: Tangent   18 27 32 = 9.5234833
: : Sine one-half Sum Sides 62 07 49 = 9.9464586
                                19.4699419
CoTangent   34° 50' 20" = 10.1573765
(Double Angle) =   69° 40' 40" = 4h 38m 43s
Right Ascension Aldebaran =   4h 22m 29s
Right Ascension Mid-Heaven   =   23h 43m 46s when Aldebaran will be on the   Figure
Azimuth 90° 4' 9" which Line produced west will cut the parallel at 10' West.   112

(Undated)

Right Ascension   28° 25' 28"
                          +4' 43"
                        28° 30' 11" = 1h 54m 1s. Alpha Arietis Polar Distance = 67° 39' 23"

As Sine	67°	39'	23"	=	9.9661045	
: (Sine)	90	4	09	=	9.9999997	
: : (Sine)	50	16	42	=	9.8860155	
					19.8860152	
(Sine) angle ZSP	56°	15'	46"	=	9.9199107	

Sides	67° 39' 23"	Difference	17° 22' 41"	Angles	90° 04' 09"
	50 16 42	One-half	8 41 20		56 15 46
Sum	117° 56' 05"			Difference	33° 48' 23"
One-half	58° 58' 02"			One-half	16° 54' 12"

                                (log)

As Sine	8°	41'	20"	=	9.1791757
: Tangent	16	54	12	=	9.4827118
: : Sine	58	58	02	=	9.9329162
					19.4156280
CoTangent	30°	07'	14"	=	10.2364523

Double = 60° 14' 28" =   4h 00m 58s   Figure

Right Ascension of Alpha Arietis   1h 54m 01s

Right Ascension Mid-Heaven   21h 53m 03s   when Alpha Arietis will be on the Azimuth
                                       of 90° 04' 09" in the East   113

1765
April
4

h m s	h m s	h m s	h m s	
9 34 27	10 54 56	20 35 18	10 17 38	Regulus
37 16	57 58	20 34 14		
40 21.5				

Right Ascension of Regulus   9 55 52
Clock too fast   21 46

h m s	h m s	h m s	h m s	
11 39 10.5				
45 18	12 12 43	23 58 01	11 58 58	Beta Leonis
	12 18 40	3 57 50.5		

Right Ascension Beta Leonis   11 37 5
Clock too fast   21 53

Hence	12 59 18
	+ 21 46
Clock gains	+12
	13 21 16 = time by the clock when Procyon will be on the Azimuth

	14 51 12
	+ 21 46
Clock gains	+ 00 18
	15 13 16 = time by the clock when Regulus will be Ditto.

	16 17 24
	+ 21 46
Clock gains	+ 0 23
	16 39 33 = (Time) when Beta Leonis will be Ditto.

At these three different times we placed three marks at the distance
of about one-half mile. One mark was placed on the 20th of March. The extreme of the
distances of these four marks; that is
from the Northernmost of them to the Southernmost was 18 inches.   114

		Right Ascension			R. A. in time			Polar Distance			Time when West or East			
		o	'	"	h	m	s	o	'	"	h	m	s	
1	Aldebaran	63	37	22	4	22	29	73	58	55	9	2	3	West
	Arcturus	211	14	47	14	4	59	69	35	02	9	51	1	East
	Alpha Orionis	85	37	13	5	42	29	82	39	27	11	7	13	West
	Procyon	111	45	25	7	27	1	84	11	16	12	59	18	West
	Regulus	148	57	59	9	55	52	76	53	46	14	51	12	West
	Beta Leonis	174	16	14	11	37	5	74	7	1	16	17	24	West
	Sirius	98	42	31	6	34	50							
	Castor	109	54	06	7	19	36							
	Pollux	112	44	15	7	30	57							
	Spica	198	13	04	13	12	52							

1765
March

	Time by Clock									Passed the Meridian				
	h	m	s	h	m	s	h	m	s	h	m	s		
20	7	00	02	7	59	32	15	3	41				}	Equal altitudes
	7	02	00	8	01	44+	15	3	44+	7	31	52-	}	Pollux
	7	04	09+	8	03	42	15	3	44					
	9	34	54	10	01	55	19	53	50					
		40	47+		12	45-	19	53	32	9	56	46	}	Regulus
		51	55		18	37.5	19	53	31.5					
	11	08	08				Alpha Orionis						)	
	13	00	13				Procyon						}	Passed the Azimuth by the Clock
	14	52	07				Regulus						)	
	15	28	59.5	16	52	07+	32	33	10				)	
		34	35		58	39	32	33	14	16	16	36	}	Antares
		41	03	17	04	10	32	33	9.5				)	
28	9	21	13	10	49	56	20	16	35				)	
		23	49		52	47	20	16	36	10	08	18	}	Regulus
		26	39		55	24+	20	16	37				)	
										Hence clock too fast 12m 26s				
	11	12	01	12	21	20	23	39	31				)	
		14	59		24	38	23	39	37	11	49	47	}	
		18	11		27	34.5	23	39	35.5				)	Hence clock too fast 12m 42s from

these stars. The clock will gain of siderial time 29 seconds from Regulus
passing the meridian to the time when Procyon will be in
the meridian, then 12m 26s + 29s = +12m 55s clock fast
or 12h 59m 18s + 12m 55s = 13h 12m 13s Procyon West by the clock
and Regulus will be West by the clock at 15h 04m 25s   115

April
5   Began to run the western Line in the direction of the mean of the four marks
6   Continued Ditto
7   (Sunday)
8   Continued Ditto. Crossed White Clay creek at the distance from the
Post marked West (15 Miles South of Philadelphia) one mile 58 chains
9   Continued Ditto
10 Continued Ditto. Crossed Little Christianna Creek at the distance from Ditto (Post
marked West) 3 Miles 25 chains. At 3 Miles 49 Chains went through Mr. Price's House.
11 Continued Ditto. Four Miles 9 chains to great Christianna Creek
12 Continued Ditto. Crossed the Greater Elk River at the distance of 5 Miles 65 Chains.
Crossed the Lesser Elk at 8 Miles 59 Chains.
13 Continued Ditto. Crossed the Road from Acterara to Christianna Bridge at
12 miles nine chains from the said Post
14 (Sunday)
15 Returned to the end of the Line for the Sector
16 Set up the Sector in our direction at the distance of 12 Statute Miles 25 Chains
from the Point where we began and made the following observations.   116

Plane of the Sector East

	Star Name	Nearest Point on the Sector			Revolutions and Seconds on the Micrometer		Difference		Apparent Zenith Distance		
		o	'	"	R	"	'	"	o	'	"
16	Alpha Lyrae	1	10	-	14	36.5	0	56.0	1	9	4.0 S
					13	32.5					
17	Capella	6	0	+	9	22.5	0	42.0	6	0	42.0
					8	32.5					
	Alpha Lyrae	1	10	-	5	3.5	0	55.0	1	9	5.0
					4	05					
	Gamma Cygni	0	15	-	4	11.0	2	14.5			
					1	32.5					
	Alpha Cygni	4	45	-	1	10-	1	42.3	4	43	17.7
					3	8					
18	Alpha Lyrae	1	10	-	10	25	0	54.7	1	9	5.3
					9	22+					
19	Alpha Lyrae	1	10	-	9	1+	0	53.3	1	9	6.7
					8	0					
20	Capella	6	0	+	7	37	0	37.7	6	0	37.7 faint
					6	51+					
	Alpha Lyrae	1	10	-	7	27	0	54.5	1	9	5.5
					6	24.5					
	Alpha Cygni	4	45	-	9	51.5	1	46.5	4	43	13.5
					12	2					
21 (Sunday)	Capella	6	0	+	12	46.5	0	41.5	6	0	41.5
					12	5					

Then turned the Instrument   Plane of the Sector West

	Star Name										
21 (Sunday)	Alpha Lyrae	1	10	-	11	2.5	0	58.0	1	9	2.0
					12	8.5					
22	Cloudy										
23	Capella	6	0	+	7	31.5	0	48.2	6	0	48.2
					8	28-					
	Alpha Lyrae	1	10	-	8	42	1	1	1	8	59.0
					9	51					
	Alpha Cygni	4	45	-	6	33-	1	40.7	4	43	19.3
					4	36					
24	Capella	6	0		3	32.5	0	44.5	6	0	44.5
					4	25					
	Alpha Lyrae	1	10	-	8	31+	0	59.7	1	9	0.3
					9	39					
	Alpha Cygni	4	45	-	9	39.5	1	45.0	4	43	15.0
					7	38.5					

117

25   For the direction of the Line

```
        9h 41m 46s
            49   47.5                    19h 59m 27.5s    9h 59m 44s   Beta Leonis Equal Altitudes
                    10h 17m 41.5s                         9  55  52    Right Ascension (Beta Leonis)
                                                          3m 52s       Clock too fast
        10h 49m 45s    12h 27m 50.5s    23h 22m 11+s )   11h 41m 6s    Beta Leonis
            51   57         30   14         22   11  }   11  37   5    Right Ascension Ditto
            54   21-        32   27         22   12  )    4m  1s       Clock fast
```

Now as 101' : 9'' : : 82' : 7''   Then   12h 59m 18s Procyon
                                           +   4   1
                                           +   0   7
Procyon on the Azimuth by the clock   13h 03m 36s   (Addition error)

```
A little     13h 46m 31s    14h 21m 46s    28h 18m 19s )
dubious on       50   57        27   25        18   22  }   14h 09m 10s   Arcturus
account of       56   33        31   49        18   20  )   14   4   59   Right Ascension
a screw not                                                 4m  11s      Clock fast
quite fast.
```

1765
April
.25

$$14h\ 51m\ 12s$$
$$+\ 4\quad\ \ 1$$
$$+\ 0\quad 17$$
$$\overline{14h\ 55m\ 30s}\ =\ \text{Regulus on the Azimuth by the Clock}$$

$$16h\ 17m\ 24s$$
$$+\ 4\quad\ \ 1$$
$$+\ 25$$
$$\overline{16h\ 21m\ 50s}\quad \text{Beta Leonis on the Azimuth by the Clock}$$

$$18h\ 33m\ 12s\quad \text{Alpha Lyrae passed the Meridian by the sector}$$
$$18h\ 29m\ 00s\quad \text{Right Ascension}$$
$$\overline{\quad\ 4m\ 12s}\quad \text{Clock fast}$$

25		Alpha Lyrae	1° 10'	12 R 38"	0' 57.5"	1° 09' 2.5"	
				13 43.5			118
26	Cloudy						
27		11h 11m 8s-	12h 08m 3.5s	23h 27m 08s+			
		14 31	12 37	27 08	11h 43m 34s	Beta Leonis	
		18 30	16 42	27 12.5	11 37 5	= Right Ascension	
					6 29	= Clock fast	

For the offsets from our line to the first Station, where the greatest error was by the Sector = 43 yards
First for the offsets corresponding to the circle BCW
W, the point set out from 15 miles South of Philadelphia
WS, the Arch run = WB (infinitely near) = WS = 12.312 Miles = 10' 50" Hence in the Right
Angled Spherical Triangle PDW = DBP, we have PW = Complement of latitude = 50° 16' 40".00 and
DW = 5' 25", hence DP = 50° 16' 39".784
Then PW - DP = DC = 0".216 = 21.6 feet = the greatest offset. And for the intermediate offsets,
Given DP and Da, Db, Dc, etc. = the Sides in minutes and seconds corresponding to the Miles,
to find the Hypothenuses Pa, Pb, Pc, etc. Each of which being subtracted from PW leaves the offsets,
aw, bo, cq, etc., as by table one.   And BS = 43 yards
The offsets in the Triangle WBS are at the Miles as according to Table second.

Table 1					Table 2	Table 1 + Table 2 =			
Miles from the Point W	Sides Da, Db from the Middle in Miles	Sides Da, Db in Minutes and Seconds	Hence the Hypotenuse Pa, Pb, etc.	PW-Pa, Pb, etc Equal the offsets an, bo, cq, etc.	Miles Feet from W	the true offset from the line we ran, viz. WS			
						Miles	Feet	Chains	Links
1	5.844	5' 9"	50°16'39".980	0' 0".020 = 2.0ft.	1 = 10.5	1	12.5	0	19
2	4.844	4 17	16 39.902	0 0.098 = 9.8	2 = 21.0	2	30.8	0	46.5
3	3.844	3 23	39.859	0 0.141 = 14.1	3 = 31.5	3	45.6	0	69+
4	2.844	2 30	39.824	0 0.176 = 17.6	4 = 42	4	59.6	0	90
5	1.844	0 57	39.824	0 0.176 = 19	5 = 52.5	5	72.1	1	09
6	0.844	0 44	39.784	0 0.216 = 21.6	6 = 63	6	84.6	1	28
6.156	Middle	0 00	50 16 39.784	0 0.216 = 21.6	7 = 73.5	7	95.1	1	44
7	1.156	1 01	16 39.784	0 0.216 = 21.6	8 = 84	8	103.6	1	57
8	2.156	1 54	16 39.824	0 0.176 = 19.6	9 = 94.5	9	112.1	1	70
9	3.156	2 47	16 39.824	0 0.176 = 17.6	10 = 105	10	119.1	1	80.5
10	4.156	3 40	16 39.859	0 0.141 = 14.1	11 = 115	11	124.5	1	90
11	5.156	4 32	16 39.941	0 0.059+= 9.5	12 = 126	12	128.0	1	94
12	6.156	5 24	16 39.980	0 0.020 = 2.0	12.312=129	12.312	129.0	1	95.5
12.312	6.468	5	50 16 40.000	0 0.000 = 0.0		To be laid off to the			Fig.
∴ 12 miles 25 chains						Southward			119

Zenith Distances of Stars at the First Point from the 15 Mile Post South of Philadelphia

Plane of the Sector East

1765 April	Capella	Alpha Lyrae	Alpha Cygni	
16		1° 9' 4".0		Mean Day
17	6° 0' 42".0	9 5.0	4° 43' 17".7	Capella 19.5
18		9 5.3		Alpha Lyrae 19.10h in morning
19		9 6.7		Alpha Cygni 19.5
20		9 5.5	4 43 13.5	At Paris
21	6 0 41.5			
Mean	6° 0' 41.8"	1° 9' 5.3"	4° 43' 15.6"	Mean Day of
Aberration	-4.2	-16.0	+18.0	(Alpha) Cygni is
Deviation	-9.3	-8.8	+6.0	19.5 at Paris
Precession	-6.9	+3.3	-16.2	
Refraction	+7.0	+1.2	+5.5	
Mean Z. D. 1 Jan. 1764 Plane East	6° 0' 28.4"	1° 8' 45.0"	4° 43' 28.9"	

Plane of the Sector West

April	Alpha Lyrae	Capella	Alpha Cygni	
21	1° 9' 2.0"			Mean Day
23	1 8 59.0			(Alpha) Lyrae 24th – 5' 00"
24	1 9 0.3	6° 0' 48.2"	4° 43' 15.0"	Capella 23d 17h
		6 0 44.5	4 43 19.3	Alpha Cygni 24.5d
25	1 9 2.5			
Mean	1° 9' 0.95"	6° 0' 46.35"	4° 43' 17.2"	
	-15.34	-3.7	+17.9	
	-8.8	-9.3	+6.0	
	+3.3	-6.9	-16.3	
	+1.2	+7.0	+5.5	
Mean Z. D. 1 Jan. 1764 Plane West	1° 8' 41.3"	6° 0' 33.5"	4° 43' 30.3"	
Ditto, Plane East	1 8 45.0	6 0 28.4	4 43 28.9	
True Zenith Distance	1° 8' 43.15"	6° 0' 30.95"	4° 43' 29.6"	
At the Post marked West it was	1 8 41.8	6 0 31.8	4 43 31.2	
Difference = what	0' 1.35"	0' 0.85"	0' 1.6"	
we are too much	North	North	North	

120

Now for the mean of these as follows

Alpha Lyrae { 1.35 1.35 1.35 1.35 1.35

Alpha Cygni { 1.60 1.60

Capella { 0.85 0.85

Mean 1.29" = 43 yards that we are to the Northward.
Hence the offsets to the Southward as in the leaf before.

1765
April
28 (Sunday)
29 Began to run the Line in the Direction we found last viz. on the 25th Instant
30 Continued Ditto and crossed the main Branch of North East River at 14 Miles 2 Chains.
Sent Expresses to the Commissioners to acquaint them we would be at the River Susquehanna in 12 days.

1765
May
1 Continued the Line
2 Rain
3 Continued the Line
4 Continued ditto
5 (Sunday)
6 Continued Ditto
7 Continued Ditto
8 Continued Ditto and crossed the River Actarara at 20 Miles 61 Chains. 121
9 Continued the Line and crossed Acterara at 20 Miles 71 Chains
Crossed Ditto a third time at 21 Miles and 25 Chains
Note at each of these times the River ran nearly at Right Angles with the Line;
its breadth was about 50 yards.
10 Continued Ditto
11 Continued Ditto and crossed Coniwingo Creek at 23 Miles 67 Chains
At 26 Miles 3 Chains 93 Links Reached the East Side of the River Susquehannah.
Crossed the River nearly at Right Angles
12 (Sunday) Set up the Sector in our direction at the distance of 25 Miles and 75 Chains
from the point where we began; and made the following observations:

Plane East

Star Name	Nearest Point on the Sector		Revolutions and Seconds on the Micrometer		Difference		Apparent Zenith Distance		
	o	'	R	"	'	"	o	'	"
Alpha Lyrae	1	10-	15	13.2	0	57.0	1	09	03.0
			14	8.2					
Delta Cygni	4	50+	13	0.5	0	20.5	4	50	20.5
			12	32.0					
Gamma Cygni	0	15-	7	33.0	2	16.7	0	12	43.3
			5	0.3					
13 Delta Cygni	4	50+	1	47.0	0	18.5	4	50	18.5
			1	28.5					
Gamma Cygni	0	15-	7	23.5	2	14.2	0	12	45.8
			4	45.3					
Alpha Cygni	4	45-	1	47.5	1	42.8	4	43	17.2
			3	46.3					

14 Cloudy

Star Name									
15 Capella	6	00+	9	14.3	0	39.0	6	00	39.0
			8	27.3					
Alpha Lyrae	1	10-	10	6.0	0	56.0	1	09	04.0
			9	2.0					
Delta Cygni	4	50+	8	6.3	0	17.8	4	50	17.8
			7	40.5					
Gamma Cygni	0	15-	10	4.0	2	15.5	0	12	44.5
			7	24.5					

16 Cloudy
17 Cloudy. Continued our direction over the River Susquehanna

Star Name									
18 Capella	6	00+	6	35	0	38.0	6	00	38.0
			5	49					
Alpha Lyrae	1	10-	7	17	0	58.0	1	09	2.0
			6	11					
Delta Cygni	4	50+	6	43-	0	20.4	4	50	20.4
			6	22+					
Alpha Cygni	4	45-	6	20+	1	42.7	4	43	17.3
			8	19					
19 (Sunday) Capella	6	00+	6	37.5	0	35.8	6	00	35.8
			6	2-					
Alpha Lyrae	1	10-	3	39.5	0	59.2	1	09	00.8
			2	32+					
Delta Cygni	4	50+	8	42+	0	20.3	4	50	20.3
			8	22					

122

123

1765
May

	Star Name	Nearest Point on the Sector		Revolutions and Seconds on the Micrometer		Difference		Apparent Zenith Distance		
		o	'	R	"	'	"	o	'	"
19	(Sunday) Gamma Cygni	0	15-	9	10	2	16.0	0	12	44.0
				6	30					
	Alpha Cygni	4	45-	6	41	1	43.7	4	43	16.3
				8	41-					

For a Direction Westward when AB = 20' of an arch of a Great Circle

(log)

As Tang. PB 50° 16' 40" =   10.0804662
: Rad   10.
: : Tang. AL = LB 10' 00" =   7.4637273
Cosine Angle LBP 89° 51' 41" =   7.3832611

And
As Rad   10.
:   Sine   50° 16' 42"   PB   9.8860155
: : Sine   89   51   41   LBP   9.9999987
:   Sine   50   16   41.26= PL   9.8860142
     50   16   42.00= PR
       00'   0.74" = LR = 24.68 yards = the greatest offset, this being
so great, will throw it out of the Visto too much; therefore shall proceed to
find a new direction on the former arch AB = 10', thus

Right Ascension of Star   On the West Azimuth
  9h   55m   52s   14h   51m   12s   Regulus
11   37   5   16   17   24   Beta Leonis
12   43   38   Epsilon Ursae Majoris: Alioth
14   4   59   18   18   56   Arcturus

Time by the clock
12h   28m   19s
       35   27   13h   05m   53s   25h   41m   20s   12h   50m   42s   Equal altitudes of Epsilon
                                                                  Ursae Majoris: Alioth
                       13m   08s   25h   41m   27s   12h   43m   38s = Right Ascension of Alioth
                                                          7m   04s   Clock too fast

13h   51m   54s-   14h   19m   42s   28h   24m   04s
       56m   44s   14h   27m   26.5s   28h   24m   10.5s   14h   12m   05s   Arcturus
14h   4m   22s   14h   32m   22s   28h   24m   16s   14h   04m   59s = Right Ascension
                                                           07m   06s   Clock too fast

                     14h   58m   19s   Regulus
Hence at   16h   24m   34s   Beta Leonis   Will be on the Western Azimuth of 89° 55' 51"
                     18h   26m   11s   Arcturus

At these times we placed three marks at the distance (across the River) of 76 chains 60 links   Figure
They differ (that is from the Northernmost to the Southernmost) Seventeen inches.   124

Turned the Sector, Plane West

		Nearest Point on the Sector		Revolutions and Seconds on the Micrometer		Difference		Apparent Zenith Distance		
20	Cloudy									
21	Alpha Lyrae	1°	10'-	7	14+	1'	1.7"	1°	8'	58.3"
				8	24					
	Delta Cygni	4	50+	8	36	0	22.0	4	50	22.0
				9	6					
	Gamma Cygni	0	15-	8	49.5	2	19.2	0	12	40.8
				11	33-					
	Alpha Cygni	4	45-	10	8	1	43.3	4	43	16.7
				8	9-					

May	Star Name	Nearest Point on the Sector		Revolutions and Seconds on the Micrometer		Difference		Apparent Zenith Distance			
		o	'	R	"	'	"	o	'	"	
22	Capella	6	0+	8	33	0	40.0	6	00	40.0	very hazy
				9	21						
	Alpha Lyrae	1	10-	7	45+	1	2.7	1	08	57.3	
				9	4						
	Delta Cygni	4	50+	10	30	0	22.5	4	50	22.5	
				11	0.5						
	Gamma Cygni	0	15-	9	25	2	19.7	0	12	40.3	
				12	9-						
	Alpha Cygni	4	45-	13	32	1	42.5	4	43	17.5	
				11	33.5						
23	Capella	6	00+	6	41+	0	34.0	6	00	34.0	very dubious
				7	23+						
	Alpha Lyrae	1	10-	6	32	1	3.5	1	08	56.5	
				7	43.5						
	Delta Cygni	4	50	6	38+	0	22.0	4	50	22.0	
				7	8+						
	Gamma Cygni	0	15-	6	8	2	21.0	0	12	39.0	
				8	45						
	Alpha Cygni	4	45-	9	22-	1	41.2	4	43	18.8	
				7	24.5						
24	Capella	6	00+	5	48.5	0	39.2	6	00	39.2	
				6	36-						
	Alpha Lyrae	1	10-	7	10	1	4.0	1	08	56.0	
				8	22						
	Delta Cygni	4	50+	9	42	0	23.0	4	50	23.0	
				10	13						
	Gamma Cygni	0	15-	10	25.5	2	21.0	0	12	39.0	
				13	10.5						
	Alpha Cygni	4	45-	17	3	1	41.0	4	43	19.0	
				15	6						
25	Capella	6	00+	9	14.5	0	39.0	6	00	39.0	
				10	1.5						
26	(Sunday) Capella	6	00+	13	19.5	0	35.8	6	00	35.8	
				14	3+						

Computing our observations

27   Computing our observations. The Result whereof as follows

May the 25th in the Evening a storm of Thunder and Lightning: about sun set I was returning from the other Side of the River, and at the distance of about 1.5 Mile the Lightning fell in perpendicular streaks, (about a foot in breadth to appearance) from the cloud to the ground. This was the first Lightning I ever saw in streaks continued without the least break through the whole, all the way from the Cloud to the Horizon.

Plane of the Sector East

1765 May	Capella			May	Alpha Lyrae			May	Delta Cygni			May	Gamma Cygni			May	Alpha Cygni		
	o	'	"		o	'	"		o	'	"		o	'	"		o	'	"
(Sun.) 12				12	1	09	3.0	12	4	50	20.5	12	0	12	43.3				
13								13		50	18.5	13		12	45.8	13	4	43	17.2
15	6	00	39.0	15	1	09	4.0	15		50	17.8	15		12	44.5				
18		00	38.0	18		09	2.0	18		50	20.4					18		43	17.3
19		00	35.0	19		09	0.8	19		50	20.3	19		12	44.0	19		43	16.3
Mean 17 1/3	6	00	37.6	16	1	09	2.45	15.4	4	50	19.5	14.75	0	12	44.4	16.67	4	43	16.9
Aberration			-0.7				-10.96				+14.6				-14.8				+15.85
Deviation			-9.29				-8.7				+7.39				-6.46				+5.86
Precession			-7.26				+3.45				-11.33				+15.24				-17.05
Refraction			+7.0				+1.2				+5.6				+0.2				+5.5
Mean Z. D. Plane East	6	00	27.35		1	08	47.44		4	50	35.76		0	12	38.58		4	43	27.06

125

126

Plane of the Sector West

1765 May	Capella °	'	"	May	Alpha Lyrae °	'	"	May	Delta Cygni °	'	"	May	Gamma Cygni °	'	"	May	Alpha Cygni °	'	"
21				21	1	08	58.3	21	4	50	22.0	21	0	12	40.8	21	4	43	16.7
22				22	1	08	57.3	22	4	50	22.5	22		12	40.3	22		43	17.5
23				23		08	56.5	23		50	22.0	23		12	39.0	23		43	18.8
24	6	00	39.2	24		08	56.0	24		50	23.0	24		12	39.0	24		43	19.0
25	6	00	39.0																
(Mean) 24.5	6	00	39.1	22.5	1	08	57.0	22.5	4	50	22.4	22.5	0	12	39.8	22.5	4	43	18.0
Aberration			+0.27				-9.4				+13.14				-13.52				+14.9
Deviation			-9.29				-8.7				+7.39				-6.46				+5.86
Precession			-7.37				+3.5				-11.5				+15.45				-17.3
Refraction			+7.0				+1.2				+5.6				+0.2				+5.5
Mean Z. D.	6	00	29.71		1	08	43.6		4	50	37.03		0	12	35.47		4	43	26.96
Plane West																			
Plane East	6	00	27.35		1	08	47.44		4	50	35.76		0	12	38.58		4	43	27.06
True Z. D. 1st Jan. 1764	6	00	28.53		1	08	45.5		4	50	36.4		0	12	37.02		4	43	27.01
Ditto at the Post Marked West	6	00	31.8		1	08	41.8		4	50	40.4		0	12	33.0		4	43	31.2
Difference what we are too much North	0		3.27		0		3.7		0		4.0		0		4.02		0		4.19

	3.27
	3.7
	4.0
	4.02
	4.19
Mean	3.836 = 5 chains 80 links from hence the offsets to our last station from 127

(Undated)

From the Line we have run ST = 13 miles 50 chains will be
found to consist of three parts, viz. 1st the circular part
COB = Table 1 CD = SB = a constant quantity
= 43 yards = Table 2, and the Triangle DTS when DT =
(5.80 chains - DC = BS = 43 yards) 3.85 chains.
= Table 3. The Sum of these three Tables are the
offsets to the Southward.

Miles from the post W where we began	Table 1 Offsets for the Circle + Feet	Table 2 Constant + Feet	Table 3 Triangle + Feet	Sum = True offsets to the Southward Feet	=	Chains	Links
At S 12.312	0.0	129	00.0	129	=	1	95
13	7.0	129	13.0	149	=	2	26
14	16.1	129	31.5	176.5	=	2	67.5
15	20.0	129	50.0	199	=	3	01.5
16	23.6	129	69.0	221.5	=	3	36
17	25.0	129	87.5	241.5	=	3	66
18	25.0	129	106	260	=	3	94
19	27.5	129	125	281.5	=	4	26.5
20	27.5	129	144	300.5	=	4	55
21	25.6	129	163	317.5	=	4	81
22	23.6	129	182	335		5	08
23	19.7	129	201	350	=	5	30
24	16.1	129	219	364	=	5	51
25	7.9	129	237	374	=	5	66
25 miles 75.5 chains	0.0	129	254	383	=	5	80

Figure
128

(Undated)

      For the Breadth of the River Susquehannah

      A, a Mark on the East Side of
         the River 2.50 chains.
      B, a Mark on the West Side 1.10 chains
      BC a Base on the West Side = 13.82 chains
      Angles measured as by Figure

		(log)
As Sine	9° 53' =	9.2346249
: CB	13.82 =	1,1405080
:: Sine	62° 17' =	9.9470700
: AB	71.28 chains =	1.8529531

Subtract   3.60 = the distance of the Mark from the River
Rest   67.68 = Breadth of the River

Miles	Chains	Links	
26	1	43	from the Point where we began to the
	71	28	Mark on the West Side
26	72	71	= Distance of the Mark on the West Side, where the chain
			Carriers are to begin again.

N. B. Angles measured with a Hadley's Quadrant of 18 inches Radius

Figure
129

1765
May
26   (Sunday)
     Time by the Clock
     At 15h 41m 11.5s by the Clock Alpha Leonis Emerged from the Moon

18	43	53	Alpha Lyrae passed the Meridian by the Sector. R. A.	18h 29m 1s
				18 43 53
				14m 52s

20	48	15	Alpha Cygni Ditto. Right Ascension	20h 33m 27s
				48 15
				14m 48s

3h 47m 6s	5h 10m 53s	Equal Altitudes Sun's Limbs
49 6	13 20	Hence the Sun's center crossed the Meridian by
51 19	15 30	the clock at 4h 34m 4.3s
52 34	16 51	Sun's Right Ascension 4h 18m 39 s
54 51	Mid.	15m 25.3s Clock fast
3 57 17	5 21 2	

27   5h 14m 31s   Capella passed Meridian by the Sector   R. A. =   4h 59m 22s
                                                    5   14   31
                                                     15m   9s

N. B. Clouds prevented observing the Immersion of the Star but the
      Emergence from the Moon was observed with Certainty, with
      a Reflector that magnified about 70 Times.

      The Observations were made in the Line on the East Side of the River
      Susquehannah 1.5 miles to the South of Peach Bottom Ferry, about
      20 miles North of the Head of Chesapeake Bay and 57 miles
      West from Philadelphia.

130

28   Packing up the Instruments, etc.
29   Set out on our return to lay off the offsets; and reached the 20 Mile Post
30   Set off the offsets to the 15 Mile Post.
31   Continued Ditto to the 4 Mile Post
June
1   At the Tangent Point and found a direction for Running a North Line by the
      Pole Star and Alioth. Proved the First Meridian by four other stars and found it very good.
2   (Sunday)

3   Proceeded to run the North Line

Sent Expresses to Annapolis and Philadelphia to acquaint the Commissioners
we should finish the Line between the Tangent Point and the Parallel this week.
Continued Ditto and Measured the Angle formed by the Radius from Newcastle
and the North Line, and found it = 86° 32'

Hence the offsets at Right angles to the Westward from the Meridian for
the Boundaries of Newcastle County as follows:

Distances from the Tangent Point		Offsets		
Chains	Links	Chains	Links	
0	00	0	00	
8	05	0	46	
18	05	0	92	
28	05	1	28.5	
38	05	1	54.5	
48	05	1	70.5	
58	05	1	75.5	Middle or greatest offset
68	05	1	70.5	
78	05	1	54.5	
88	05	1	28.5	
98	05	0	92	
108	05	0	46	
116	10	0	00	

That is, 1 mile 36 chains 10 links = the distance
in the Circle on a due North Course from the
Tangent Point.   131

1   To find the Meridian at the Tangent Point

Pole Star	0	11°	15'	21" aberration accounted for
Alioth	6	10°	54'	29"
			20'	52" = 1m 23.5s that Epsilon Ursae Majoris will

be on the Meridian (earlier), than the Pole Star, therefore this time must elapse, or nearly,
before the Pole Star is on the Meridian.

R. A. in Motion			R. A. Star in Time				
			13h	12m	52s	Spica	
			14	04	59	Arcturus	
7	12°	57'	18"	14	51	49	Beta Ursae Minoris
	231	11	27	15	24	46	Alpha Coronae Borealis
	243	46	2	16	15	4	Antares
8	21	18	51	17	25	15	Beta Draconis
8	27	47	24	17	51	10	Gamma Draconis
	277	14	56	18	29	00	Alpha Lyrae
	294	50	1	19	39	20	Alpha Aquilae
	308	21	40	20	33	27	Alpha Cygni
				19	37	39	Delta Cygni the 1st of September
				4	59	24	Capella June 1st

June 1st

A mark being placed North by the Pole Star and Alioth, the
Instrument was turned to the South; and the Passage of Spica over
the Meridian by the Clock at

						15h	33m	14.5s	
						13h	12m	52 s	= Right Ascension Spica
						2h	20m	22 s	Clock fast by Spica
15h	41m	1.5s	17h	05m	17s	32h	50m	50 s	16h 25m 25s Equal alt. Arct.
	43	13		7	37		50	50	14h 4m 59s Right Ascension
	45	33		9	47		50	48.5	2h 20m 26s Clock fast, Arct.
17h	17m	4.5s	18h	08m	31s	35h	30m	31 s	17h 45m 15.5s Equal alt. of
	19	22		11	8.5		30	31	Alpha Coronae Borealis
	22	00		13	26		30	30.5	15 24 46 Right Ascension
									2h 20m 29.5s Clock fast by
									Alpha Coronae Borealis

From hence at	18h	35m	36s	Antares will pass the Meridian
by the Clock	19	45	50	Beta Draconis Ditto. (A Dubious Observation was made on this star).
	20	11	47	Gamma Draconis Ditto
	22	0	1	Alpha Aquilae Ditto

At these times the stars were set to the Middle Wire of the
Transit Instrument and then run down to the Horizon and at the distance
of about 180 Yards the extremes differed only two Inches from the
Mark placed by the Pole Star and Alioth.

(Undated)

The Work as follows for finding the Offsets for the Boundaries of Newcastle County

(A Column of logarithmic calculations not transcribed.)

Here let NA (be) the Radius from Newcastle

A PB the Meridian Northing
Angle NAB = 86° 32' Measured: Then
Angle ANP = 3° 28' and by Trigonometry

As Rad.		10.0000000
:Hyp AN 12 miles = 96,000 links =		4.9822712
::Sine ANP = 3° 28'	=	8.7815244
:AP = PB 5804.9	=	3.7637956
11609.8 = AB		
As Sine 3° 28'	=	8.7815244
:AP 5804.9 Links	=	3.7637956
::Sine 86° 32'	=	9.9992046
		13.7630002
:PN 95824.5	=	4.9814758
DN 96000		

175.5 = DP = the greatest offsets

Distance		Offsets	
Chains	Links	Chains	Links
8	05	0	46
18	05	0	92
28	05	1	28.5
38	05	1	54.5
48	05	1	70.5
58	05	1	75.5
68	05	1	70.5
78	05	1	54.5
88	05	1	28.5
98	05	0	92
108	05	0	46
116	10	0	00

75.5 - Middle or greatest (offset) DP and according to the property
of the Circle this point is due West from Newcastle.

Miles	Chains	Links
1	36	10

the Distance in the Circle on a due North Course.

Figure
133

1765
June

4   Set off the offsets, etc. Mr. Enoch Morgan's
House at 71 chains from the Tangent Point, is 5 chains East of the
Circular Line.

5   Continued the Line to about the 4 Mile Post

6 Continued Ditto to the Parallel of Latitude 15 Miles South
of the Southernmost point of the city of Philadelphia.
*From the Tangent Point to the said Parallel on a due
North course is 5 miles one chain and 50 links horizontal
measure.
*On December 10th and 11th, 1766 Messrs. Darby and Cope remeasured
this line and found it 5 Miles two chains and 43 Links.
At 2 Miles 78 Chains from the Tangent Point Mr. Golespier
Meeting - House 10 Chains to the Eastward of the North Line.
At 3 Miles two Chains from Ditto crossed the Road leading
from Newark to Nottingham.
At 3 Miles 3 Chains, Mr. John Rankin's House to
the West of the Line 50 Links.
At 3 Miles 45 Chains crossed Christianna Creek.
At 4 Miles 68 Chains crossed the road leading from
Newark to the Cross Roads.
The Meridian from the Tangent Point crossed the Parallel
at 2 Miles 79 Chains 27 Links, from the Point
where we began to run the Parallel.

7 Note : At the point of intersection of the Parallel of Latitude
and the Meridian from the Tangent Point, we placed a Post
marked W on the West Side and N on the North Side.
It stands in a meadow belonging to Captain John Singleton, 13 chains
50 Links to the North of the Road leading from Newark to the
Cross Roads and 25 chains 73 Links to the East of Little
Christianna Creek, also it is 49 chains 73 links to the East
of Mr. Rice Price's House.   134

7
8
9 Sunday
10
11 Waiting for the Commissioners
12
13
14
15

16 Sunday

17 The Commissioners of both Provinces met at
Christianna Bridge in Newcastle County.

18 Seven Stones were set as Marks for Boundaries,
viz. one at the Tangent Point, four in the Periphery
of the circle around Newcastle, one between the
Intersection of the Periphery with the North Line and the
Intersection of the North Line and Parallel; and one at
the Intersection of the North Line with the Parallel
of Latitude 15 Miles South of the Southernmost Point of
the City of Philadelphia.
The Gentlemen Commissioners present.
Received our Instructions to continue the Parallel
of Latitude (in the same manner we have run it to the
River Susquehannah) as far as the country is
inhabited, etc.

19 Prepared to return to the River Susquehannah.

20 Wrote to the Honorable Proprietors of Maryland
and Pennsylvania.

21 Set out for the River.

22 Reached Ditto at Peach Bottom Ferry.   135

23 Sunday

24   In order to fall into the true Latitude, at the
distance of 11.37 Miles from a point on the East Side
of the River Susquehannah, we changed the direction
found by the stars on the 19th of May, thus,
as 11.37 miles : 580 links, the whole error :: 1 mile 14 chains 92 links = Radius we measured:
68.5 links. This 68.5 Links we laid off at Right Angles to
the Southward of the direction found by the stars and there placed
a mark, and in the direction of this, and the Mark
on the East Side of the River (where the Radius 1 mile 14 chains 92 links
began) we proceeded to Run the Line.
Continued the Line.

25   Rain

26   Continued the Line. At 28 Miles from
the Post Marked West Mr. Daniel Camel's House
4 Chains to the South of the Line.
At 28 Miles 69 Chains crossed the Road leading from
Rock Run to York; at this Road a School House one
chain to the Southward.

27   Continued the Line. At 30 Miles 42 Chains Mr. James
McKenley's House 3 Chains to the North.

28   Continued the Line.

29   Continued the Line. At 31 Miles 13 Chains Mr. James
Reed's House, one chain to the North.

30 Sunday

July

1   Continued the Line.

2   Continued the Line. At 34 Miles 77 Chains Mr. Thomas Matson's House five Links to the North.

3   Continued the Line. At 37 Miles 17 Chains 98 Links we supposed to be in the true Parallel and
changed our direction to the Northward as follows.
Here PD, PA and PB = complement of Latitude of the true parallel.
SP = Complement of Latitude at the Sector on the East Side of Susquehannah = 50° 16' 36''17
SC the direction from thence by the stars
SN = 1 mile 14 chains 92 Links = a Radius measured which gives NM = 60.5 Links. See page before.
Hence the angle NSM thus

$$\text{(log)}$$

as 9492 Links = NS = 3.9773577
: Rad   = 10.
:: 60.5 NM   = 1.7817554
: Tang NSM 0°21'55'' = 7.8043977
Angle PSC 89°55'51''   See minutes following April 4th.
Angle PSA 90°17'46''   Now in this oblique angled Spherical Triangle.
PSA there is given this angle and SP = 50° 16' 36''17, also AP = 50° 16' 40''

Hence the angle SAP	=	89°	33'	58''
and the angle BAC	=	89°	55'	51''
Sum	=	179°	29'	49''
Subtract from		180°	00'	00''
Rest	=	0°	30'	11''

= angle dAo which we must lay
off to the North at Right Angles to the Course SA to give the course
AB to be again in the true Parallel at B, when we have run
AB = (10' on the arch of a great circle) = 11.37 Miles. In order to lay off this angle let Ad
be measured 40 chains. Then

$$\text{(log)}$$

as Rad   10.
: 40 Chains   1.6020600
:: Sine 30' 11'' dAo 7.9432479
: do, 35.1 Links 9.5453079 At A the ground not admitting Links   Links
to measure Ad = 40 Chains, but only 24 Chains 71 Links. Then as 40:35.1.::24.71:21.7
= what we laid off at Right Angles from SAd, which gave the line AoB
which we measured as follows.

Figure
137

1765
July
4 Continued the Line.
5 Continued the Line. At 43 Miles Mr. Andrew Boyd's House 13 Chains North.
6 Continued the Line.
7 Sunday
8 Continued the Line. At 44 Miles 00 Chains Mr. Henry Wood's House 3 Chains North.
9 Continued the Line. At 46 Miles 40 Chains crossed the main Branch of Deer Creek.
10 Continued the Line.
11 Waggons brought the Instruments.
12 Set up the Sector in our Direction at the Distance of 48 Miles 64 Chains 5 Links from the Post marked
West, in Mr. Bryan's field, and made the following observations. 138

Plane of the Sector East

	Star Name	Nearest Point on the Sector		Revolutions and Seconds on the Micrometer		Difference		Apparent Zenith Distance		
		o	'	R	"	'	"	o	'	"
12	Alpha Lyrae	1	10-	4	11-	1	20.2	1	08	39.8
				2	34.5					
	Gamma Cygni	0	15-	4	19	2	37.0	0	12	23.0
				1	18					
	Alpha Cygni	4	45-	6	37	1	22.7	4	43	37.3
				8	16-					
	Capella	6	00+	11	10					
				10	21.5					
13	Alpha Lyrae	1	10-	9	42+	1	19.6	1	8	40.4
				8	15-					
	Capella	6	00+	7	45.5	0	33.0	6	0	33.0
				7	12.5					
14 Sun.	Alpha Lyrae	1	10-	5	51	1	20.3	1	8	39.7
				4	23-					
	Gamma Cygni	0	15-	6	6-					
				3	2.5					
	Capella	6	00+	4	43	0	33.5	6	0	33.5
				4	9.5					
15	Alpha Lyrae	1	10-	9	10	1	20.0	1	8	40.0
				7	34					
	Delta Cygni	4	50+	9	1	0	42.3	4	50	42.3
				8	11-					
	Gamma Cygni	0	15-	7	50+	2	38.3	0	12	21.7
				4	48					
	Alpha Cygni	4	45-	5	23.5	1	20.2	4	43	39.8
				7	00-					
16	Alpha Lyrae	1	10-	9	28.5	1	21.0	1	08	39.0
				7	51.5					
	Delta Cygni	4	50+	9	6.5	0	43.0	4	50	43.0
				8	15.5					
	Gamma Cygni	0	15-	9	29.5	2	37.5	0	12	22.5
				6	28					
	Alpha Cygni	4	45-	7	23.5	1	21.5	4	43	38.5
				9	1					

139

1765
July
17

Turned the Instrument

Plane of the Sector West

Star Name	Nearest Point on the Sector		Revolutions and Seconds on the Micrometer		Difference		Apparent Zenith Distance		
	o	'	R	"	'	"	o	'	"
Alpha Lyrae	1	10-	8	11.5	1	23.5	1	08	36.5
			9	43					
Delta Cygni	4	50+	10	00	0	46.3	4	50	46.3
			10	46+					
Gamma Cygni	0	15-	10	14	2	38.3	0	12	21.7
			13	16+					
Alpha Cygni	4	45-	12	30	1	21.5	4	43	38.5
			11	0.5					
Capella	6	00+	9	18.5	0	37.0	6	0	37.0
			10	3.5					
Alpha Lyrae	1	10-	10	5-	1	21.8	1	08	38.2
			11	34.5					
Delta Cygni	4	50+	11	50	0	45.7	4	50	45.7
			12	44-					
Gamma Cygni	0	15-	11	46+	2	39.7	0	12	20.3
			14	50					
Alpha Cygni	4	45-	14	21+	1	19.3	4	43	40.7
			12	46					
Capella	6	0+	5	48+	0	38.4	6	00	38.4
			6	35-					
Alpha Lyrae	1	10-	6	2	1	23.5	1	08	36.5
			7	33.5					
Delta Cygni	4	50+	6	36	0	46.3	4	50	46.3
			7	30+					
Gamma Cygni	0	15-	7	6	2	39.7	0	12	20.3
			10	10-					
Alpha Cygni	4	45-	10	9	1	19.0	4	43	41.0
			8	34					
Capella	6	0+	7	41	0	35.0	6	00	35.0
			8	24					
Alpha Lyrae	1	10-	10	34	1	22.0	1	08	38.0
			12	12					
Delt a Cygni	4	50+	14	30	0	45.5	4	50	45.5
			15	23.5					
Gamma Cygni	0	15-	15	21-	2	42.0	0	12	18.0
			18	27-					
Alpha Cygni	4	45-	17	7+	1	18.8	4	43	41.2
			15	32.5					
Capella	6	0+	12	7.5	0	36.0	6	00	36.0
			12	43.5					

Date markers: 17 (Alpha Lyrae–Capella), 18 (Alpha Lyrae–Capella), 19 (Alpha Lyrae–Capella), 20 (Alpha Lyrae–Capella)

140

18   For the Direction at the Third Point from **Mr.** Bryan's near the
Road Leading from York Town to Baltimore

Right Ascension

	Arc			Time			
	277°	44'	57"	18h	29m	00s	Alpha Lyrae
	308°	21'	40"	20h	33m	27s	Alpha Cygni

Right ascension Mid-Heaven   23h   39m   19s   Eta Pleiades (Tauri) on the Azimuth in the East
Right ascension Ditto   23h   43m   46s   Aldebaran in Ditto

18h	20m	16s	⎫	
	21m	22s	⎬ (Indistinct)	Equal Altitudes: Alpha Lyrae
	22m	31s	⎭	
19h	14m	11.5s	⎫	
	17m	04s	⎬	Ditto. Delta Cygni

At	18h	39m	22s	Alpha Lyrae passed the Meridian by the Sector		
	5h	10m	09s	Capella Ditto		

19   At   ⎧ 18h   40m   42s   Alpha Lyrae ⎫
               ⎨ 20h   45m   06s   Alpha Cygni ⎬ Passed the Meridian by the Sector
               (Indistinct)   Capella   ⎭

20   18h   03m   58s   19h   15m   30s+   27h   21m   38s

		5m	01s+		16m	37s-		18h 40m 49s	Equal Altitudes of Alpha Lyrae
		6m	07s		17m	40s	R. A. =	18h 29m 00s	
								11m 49s	Clock fast

20h	04m	59s	21h	23m	08s				
	06m	17s		24m	29s	41h 30m 16s	20h 45m 23s	Ditto Alpha Cygni	
	07m	38s		25m	47s	R. A.	20h 33m 27s		
							11m 56s	Clock fast	

Hence by the Clock at   22h   05m   4s   Alpha Arietis   Will be on the Azimuth
                                   23h   51m   26s   Eta Pleiades (Tauri)   of 90°   04'   09"   in
                                   23h   55m   53s   Aldebaran   the East

When Alpha Arietis passed the (Calculated) Azimuth we placed a Mark.
Cloudy when the other stars passed.   141

21 Sun.   Time by the Watch   For the Direction

18h	(13m)	22	19h	08m	45.5s	37h 24m 17.5s			
	14m	25s		09m	53s	24m 18s	18h 42m 09s	Equal altitudes, Alpha Lyrae	
	15m	32s		10m	56s	24m 18s	18h 29m 00s		
							13m 09s	Clock fast	

Alpha Lyrae	18h	42m	00s	Passed the Meridian by the Sector
Alpha Cygni	20h	46m	25.5s	

20h	07m	41s	21h	23m	0.5s	41h 33m 22.5s		
	8m	59s		24m	23s	33m 22s	20h 46m 41.5s	Equal altitudes of Alpha
	10m	22s		25m	42s	33m 23s		Cygni
							20h 33m 27s	= Right Ascension of Star
							13m 14.5s	Clock fast

as 124' : 5".5 : : 80' : 3"

21h	53m	03s	
+	13m	14.5s	
+	00m	03s	
22h	06m	20.5s	Alpha Arietis will be on the Azimuth

23h	39m	19s	
+	13m	14s	
+	0	08s	
23h	52m	41.5s	Eta Pleiades (Tauri) Ditto

23h	43m	46s	
+	13m	16.5s	
+	0m	08s	
23h	57m	8.5s	Aldebaran will be on Ditto
At		58m	28s	Aldebaran passed the vertical wire

1765
July

21   When Alpha Arietis and Aldebaran passed the said Azimuth we placed two
marks. The extremes of the differences between these and that placed last
night was Six Inches at the distance from the Transit Instrument
19.31 Chains.
We compared the Line we ran in last; with this new direction found by the stars
and at the above distance 19 chains 31 links it agreed within two inches.

22   Computing our observations as follows.

Plane East

	Alpha Lyrae			Delta Cygni				Gamma Cygni				Alpha Cygni				Capella			
	o	'	"		o	'	"		o	'	"		o	'	"		o	'	"
12	1	08	39.8					12	0	12	23.0	12	4	43	37.3				
13		08	40.4													13	6	00	33.3
14			39.7													14		00	33.5
15			40.0		15	4	50	42.3	15	0	12	21.7	15	4	43	39.8				
16			39.0		16	4	50	43.0	16	0	12	22.5	16	4	43	38.5				
Mean 14.5	1	08	39.78	16	4	50	42.65	14.2	0	12	22.40	14.2 4	43		38.53	14.9 6		00	33.25
Aberration			+5.36				- 1.87				- 0.21				+ 1.79				+ 6.23
Deviation			-8.25				+ 7.11				- 6.08				+ 5.48				- 9.20
Precession			+3.87				-12.72				+17.08				- 19.12				- 8.10
Refraction			+1.20				+ 5.60				+ 0.20				+ 5.50				+ 7.00
Mean Zenith Distance	1	08	41.66		4	50	40.77		0	12	33.39		4	43	32.18		6	00	29.18

Plane West

	Alpha Lyrae			Delta Cygni				Gamma Cygni				Alpha Cygni				Capella			
17	1	08	36.5	17	4	50	46.3	17	0	12	21.7	17	4	43	38.5	17	6	00	37.0
18		08	38.2	18			45.7	18			20.3	18			40.7	18			38.4
19			36.5	19			46.3	19			20.3	19			41.0	19			35.0
20			38.0	20			45.5	20			18.0	20			41.2	20			36.0
Mean 19.0	1	08	37.30	19.0	4	50	45.95	19.0	0	12	20.07	19.0	4	43	40.35	19.0	6	00	36.60
Aberration			+ 6.60				- 2.78				+ 0.99				+ 0.54				+ 6.63
Deviation			- 8.55				+ 7.11				- 6.08				+ 5.48				- 9.20
Precession			+ 3.89				-12.79				+17.21				-19.26				- 8.17
Refraction			+ 1.20				+ 5.60				+ 0.20				+ 5.50				+ 7.00
	1	08	40.44	19.0	4	50	43.09		0	12	32.39		4	43	32.61		6	00	32.86
Plane East	1	08	41.66		4	50	40.77		0	12	33.39		4	43	32.18		6	00	29.18
True Zen. Dist. 1st Jan 1764	1	08	41.05		4	50	41.93		0	12	32.89		4	43	32.39		6	00	31.02
Ditto at the Post Marked West	1	08	41.80		4	50	40.40		0	12	33.00		4	43	31.20		6	00	31.80
Difference what we are too much			0.75 South				1.53 South				00.11 South				1.19 South				0.78 North

+0.75
+1.53
+0.11
+1.19
————
 3.58
-0.78
————
5)2.80
————
0.56 second = 56 feet = 85 links, that we are to the
South of the true parallel from the mean of all the stars.

(Undated)   Hence the offsets at every mile from the River Susquehannah as follows

Here C d D the true parallel
D' the Sector at the River
D Ditto at the first station from the River
D'C = 5.88 Chains North of **P**arallel
DF = 0.85 South of Ditto, then
dE = 0.38 = Error South (at the **M**iddle nearly) where we changed
the direction; found by proportion, etc.
Then the offsets from the direction DE and EF at every mile **P**ost, will consist
of two parts, thus,

Miles from the **P**ost Marked West	Offsets for the arch dc +		Offsets for the Triangle dDC +		True offsets to the **P**arallel		
	Chains	Links	Chains	Links	Chains	Links	
26	0	1	5	76	5	77	South
27		10	5	20	5	30	
28		17	4	65	4	82	
29		22	4	10	4	32	
30		25	3	56	3	81	
31		27	3	02	3	29	
32		27	2	47	2	74	
33		26	1	92	2	18	
34		23	1	37	1	60	
35		18	0	82	1	00	
36		12	0	27	0	39	S. At 37.225 miles, Angular Point
37		4	0	28	0	24	N. (Offset) = 40-2=38 Links North
38		6-	0	42	0	36	
39		14	0	46	0	32	
40		20	0	50	0	30	
41		24	0	54	0	30	
42		27	0	58	0	31	
43		27	0	62	0	35	
44		27	0	66	0	39	
45		24	0	70	0	46	
46		20	0	74	0	54	
47		14	0	78	0	64	
48		6	0	82	0	76	
48 mi. 64 ch. 05 li.		0	0	85	0	85	North

Figure
144

1765
July
23   Packing up Instruments; Laid off the Direction, etc., etc.
24   Began to run the Line to be 56/2 feet South of the true **P**arallel at 10' West.
At 49 miles 7 chains crossed the lower Road leading from York to Joppa and Baltimore
at 49 miles 67 chains **M**r. John Lawson's House 4 chains to the South.
25   Continued the Line
At 50 miles 44 chains crossed the 1st branch of Gunpowder
    51 miles 17 chains crossed second Ditto
26   Continued the Line
At 52 miles 18 chains crossed the **M**ain Branch of Ditto
27   Continued the Line

	Miles	Chains	
	55	8	Crossed a small Branch of Gunpowder (river)
At	55	68	Crossed another of Ditto
	56	4	Crossed another of Ditto
	56	35	Crossed another of Ditto

28 Sunday

29   Continued the Line

At 57 miles 36 chains crossed a Branch of Gunpowder at half
a mile to the North of this is the Source of Codorus.

	Miles	Chains	
	57	66	A Branch of Gunpowder
At	58	58	**Mr.** Valentine Vant's House 50 links North
	58	66	Crossed the upper Road from York to Baltimore
	59	3	A Spring running into Gunpowder (river).

30   Continued the Line

At 60 miles 33 chains crossed the last branch of Gunpowder

Supposed to be in
the true **Parallel**
+ 28 feet North   { 60 miles   57 chains   18 links { Changed our direction 8' 18" to the Northwest
that is to be in the true **Parallel** 10' West =
11.37 miles

145

31   Continued the Line

	Miles	Chains	
	62	38	**Mr.** George Rinot's House 6 Chains to the South of the Line
	62	39	Crossed the 1st branch of Codorus.
At	62	47	**Mr.** Elias Hoarish's House 7 Chains South.
	62	57	Crossed a Road from Baltimore to **M'Allistor's** Town
	63	3	**Mr.** Peter Stophel's House 25 Links South
	63	15	A Branch of Codorus

August

1   Continued the Line

	Miles	Chains	
	63	76	Third and last Branch of Codorus
At	64	35	**Mr.** Henry Fight's House 7 Chains South
	64	60	**Mr.** Staphel Rinoman's House 2 Chains South

2   Continued the Line

	Miles	Chains	
	66	00	Crossed the 1st branch of Conewago
At	66	21	Crossed a 2nd Ditto
	67	18	**Mr.** Michael Worth's House 5 Chains South

3   Continued the Line

At 68 miles 28 links crossed a 3rd and last branch of Conewago

4 Sunday

5   Continued the Line

70.00 (miles) **Mr.** Henry Hiltibrand's House 6 Chains North

70.26 (miles) Crossed Piney Run: This runs into **Monocacy** which
           empties into the great River **Potowmack**

70.63 Crossed the Road leading from Baltimore to the Temporary Line.

146

6   Continued the Line

Crossed Piney Run six times in Running 46 Chains
from the last Road.
At 71 (miles) 42 (chains) 62 (links) a Board or Station.

7   Set up the Sector in our direction at the distance
of 71 miles 43 chains 19 links from the **Post** marked West, in **Mr.** Bryan's
field and made the following observations.

Star Name	Nearest Point on the Sector		Plane of the Sector East Revolutions and Seconds on the Micrometer		Difference		Apparent Zenith Distance		
	o	'	R	"	'	"	o	'	"
Gamma Cygni	0	15-	8	49	2	36.7	0	12	23.3
			5	48+					
Alpha Cygni	4	45-	6	42	1	21.5	4	43	38.5
			8	19.5					

99

8 At Noon a great storm of Thunder, Lightning, Hail and
Rain. The Hail intermixed with pieces of ice; one piece of
an irregular form measured one inch and six tenths in Length, one inch
two tenths in breadth and half an inch thick.

	Star Name	Nearest Point on the Sector		Revolutions and Seconds on the Micrometer		Difference		Apparent Zenith Distance		
		o	'	R	"	'	"	o	'	"
	Capella	6	0+	7	19+	0	26.8	6	00	26.8
				6	44.5					
9	Alpha Lyrae	1	10-	8	24+	1	21.6	1	08	38.4
				6	47-					
	Delta Cygni	4	50+	6	29-	0	44.0	4	50	44.0
				5	37-					
	Gamma Cygni	0	15-	7	03	2	40.0	0	12	20.0
				3	51					
	Alpha Cygni	4	45-	4	13	1	18.0	4	43	42.0
				5	39					
10	Capella	6	00+	9	26	0	28.7	6	00	28.7
				8	49+					147

Plane East

11 Sunday

	Star Name									
	Alpha Lyrae	1	10-	8	22	1	19.7	1	08	40.3
				6	46+					
	Delta Cygni	4	50+	5	33	0	43.0	4	50	43.0
				4	42					
	Gamma Cygni	0	15-	5	2	2	41.0	0	12	19.0
				1	49					
	Alpha Cygni	4	45-	2	17+	1	19.7	4	43	40.3
				3	45					
	Capella	6	0+	7	33+	0	29.3	6	00	29.3
				7	4					
12	Alpha Lyrae	1	10-	9	15+	1	21.8	1	08	38.2
				7	37.5					
	Gamma Cygni	0	15-	6	42-	2	42.2	0	12	17.8
				3	35.5					
	Alpha Cygni	4	45-	3	39+	1	15.7	4	43	44.3
				5	11					

13 Turned the Sector

Plane West

	Star Name									
	Alpha Lyrae	1	10-	7	9	1	27.0	1	08	33.0
				8	44					
14	Alpha Lyrae	1	10-	9	11.5	1	26.0	1	08	34.0
				10	45.5					
	Delta Cygni	4	50+	17	12	0	48.0	4	50	48.0
				18	8					
	Gamma Cygni	0	15-	9	25	2	46.0	0	12	14.0
				12	35					
	Alpha Cygni	4	45-	2	27+	1	16.3	4	43	43.7
				1	03					
	Capella	6	0+	6	32-	0	30.3	6	00	30.3
				7	10					

148

Date	Star Name	Nearest Point on the Sector °	'	Revolutions and Seconds on the Micrometer		Difference '	"	Apparent Zenith Distance °	'	"
15				Plane of the Sector West						
	Alpha Lyrae	1	10-	3	20.5	1	28.0	1	08	32.0
				5	4.5					
	Delta Cygni	4	50+	7	37	0	47.0	4	50	47.0
				8	32					
	Gamma Cygni	0	15-	7	48-	2	45.6	0	12	14.4
				11	05+					
	Alpha Cygni	4	45-	8	43+	1	16.8	4	43	43.2
				7	18.5					
	Capella	6	00+	4	31+	0	31.7	6	00	31.7
				5	11					
16	Alpha Lyrae	1	10-	4	43+	1	27.2	1	08	32.8
				6	26.5					
	Delta Cygni	4	50+	6	44+	0	50.7	4	50	50.7
				7	43					
	Gamma Cygni	0	15-	6	05-	2	47.0	0	12	13.0
				9	16-					
	Alpha Cygni	4	45-	9	11	1	17.0	4	43	43.0
				7	38					
	Capella	6	0+	9	45+	0	28.2	6	0	28.2
				10	21.5					
17	Alpha Lyrae	1	10-	7	38	1	26.8	1	08	33.2
				9	20.5					
	Delta Cygni	4	50+	10	31	0	48.0	4	50	48.0
				11	27					
	Gamma Cygni	0	15-	10	42	2	45.0	0	12	15.0
				13	51					
	Alpha Cygni	4	45-	14	00	1	15.0	4	43	45.0
				12	29					
18 Sunday	Capella	6	00+	5	28	0	31.5	6	00	31.5
				6	07.5					

19   Computing our observations. The results of which see following -   149

(Undated) NOTE: We laid off the angle of 8' 18" (recorded) in minutes of 30th of July thus, suppose AB, a Radius measured = 40 Chains

		log
Then as Rad =		10.
to AB 4000 links = 40 Chains =		3.6020600
: : Sine of 8' 18" BAC	=	7.3828038
: BC = 9.6575 Links	=	0.9848638

But the ground not admitting of a Mark to be seen 40 Chains but only 32.82 Chains. Then as 40: 9,657 Links : : 32.82 : 7.9 Links at the said distance of 32.82 Chains we laid off at Right Angles 7.9 Links and proceeded to run as on the 31st July etc., etc.

Figure
150

For the direction at our Station 71 Miles from the **Post Marked West** in **Mr.** Brian's Field.

h	m	s		
18	29	00	=	Right ascension Alpha Lyrae
20	33	27	=	Right ascension Alpha Cygni

				Alpha Arietis
21	53	03 ⎫		
23	39	19 ⎬ =	Right ascension Mid-Heaven ⎱	Eta Pleiades (Tauri)
23	43	46 ⎭		Aldebaran

h	m	s		h	m	s		h	m	s		
17	56	56.5		19	21	39		37	20	44		
	57	58.5			22	44			20	42.5		Equal Altitudes Alpha Lyrae
	59	05			23	46			20	42.5		
								18	40	21.5		
									29	00		
									11	21.5		Clock fast ⎱
				18	40	14						Alpha Lyrae ⎬ Passed the Meridian
				20	44	37						Alpha Cygni ⎭ by the Sector
20	02	04		21	25	08		41	29	52-		
	3	26			26	31.5			29	57.5		Equal Altitudes of Alpha Cygni
	4	44			27	47			29	51-		
								20	44	56		
									33	27		
									11m	29s	=	Clock fast

as 124m : 7.5s :: 80m : 5.5s   and as 124m : 7.5s :: 190m : 12s

	21	53	03		
	+	11	29		
	+	0	5.5		
	22	4	37		Alpha Arietis passes the direction, or Azimuth of 90° 04' 09"

				h	m	s
				23	43	46
23	39	19		+	11	29
+	11	29		+	00	12
+	00	12		23	55	27	Aldebaran Ditto
23	51	00	Eta Pleiades (Tauri) Ditto			

When Aldebaran passed, we placed a mark at the distance of ------ from the Instrument.   151

17   For the direction Continued

h	m	s		h	m	s		h	m	s		
17	54	37+		19	26	47+		37	23	34+		
	55	41+			27	52			23	33+		
	56	47			28	55			23	32+		
								18	41	47-		
								18	29	00		Right ascension of Star
									12	47-		Clock fast
				18	41	36						Alpha Lyrae ⎱ Passed the Meridian
				20	46	01						Alpha Cygni ⎰ by the Sector
20	07	22.5		21	22	40		41	32	44		
	08	42			24	1.5			32	43.5		
	10	04			25	20			32	42.5		
								20	46	21.5		
								20	33	37		
									12	44.5		Clock fast. As 124m : 7.8s :: 80m : 5s

	21	53	03		
	+	12	54.5		
	+		05		
	22	06	03	=	Alpha Arietis passes the Azimuth
	23	52	25.5		Eta Pleiades (Tauri) Ditto

	23	43	46		
		12	54.5		
	+	0	12		
	23	56	52.5	=	Aldebaran Ditto

When these three Stars passed the Azimuth (90° 04' 09" from the North) in the East, the wire bisected a candle placed at the mark we set last night so near that it could not be bettered.   152

Plane East

Alpha Lyrae

August	°	'	"
8			
9	1	08	38.4
10			
11	1	08	40.3
12	1	08	38.2
Mean (11d 1h)	1	08	38.97
Aberration			+12.24
Deviation			- 8.40
Precession			+ 4.06
Refraction			+ 1.20
Mean Zen. Dist.	1	08	48.07

Delta Cygni

August	°	'	"
9	4	50	44.09
11	4	50	43.0
Mean (10d 10h)	4	50	43.5
Aberration			- 9.24
Deviation			+ 6.90
Precession			-13.32
Refraction			+ 5.60
Mean Zen. Dist.	4	50	33.44

Gamma Cygni

August	°	'	"
9	0	12	20.0
11	0	12	19.0
12	0	12	17.8
Mean (11d 3h)	0	12	18.93
Aberration			+ 7.47
Deviation			- 5.90
Precession			+17.88
Refraction			+ 0.20
Mean Zen. Dist.	0	12	38.58

Alpha Cygni

August	°	'	"
9	4	43	42.0
11	4	43	40.3
12	4	43	44.3
Mean (11d 3.5h)	4	43	42.20
Aberration			- 6.28
Deviation			+ 5.30
Precession			-20.04
Refraction			+ 5.50
Mean Zen. Dist.	4	43	26.61

Capella

August	°	'	"
8	6	00	26.8
10	6	00	28.7
11	6	00	29.3
Mean (10d 11.5h)	6	00	28.27
Aberration			+ 7.80
Deviation			- 9.15
Precession			- 8.51
Refraction			+ 7.00
Mean Zen. Dist.	6	00	25.41

Plane East

Plane West

Alpha Lyrae

August	°	'	"
13	1	08	33.0
14		08	34.0
15		08	32.0
16		08	32.8
17		08	33.2
Mean (15d 9h)	1	08	33.0
Aberration			+13.14
Deviation			- 8.40
Precession			+ 4.09
Refraction			+ 1.20
Mean Zen. Dist.	1	08	43.03
Ditto East	1	08	48.07
True Zen. Dist.	1	08	45.55
1 Jan. 1764			
Ditto at the Post marked West	1	08	41.80
Distance from the true Parallel	0	00	3.75 North

Delta Cygni

August	°	'	"
13	4	50	48.0
14		50	47.0
15		50	50.7
16		50	48.0
Mean (15d 22h)	4	50	48.43
Aberration			-10.67
Deviation			+ 6.90
Precession			-13.44
Refraction			+ 5.60
Mean Zen. Dist.	4	50	36.82
Ditto East	4	50	33.44
True Zen. Dist.	4	50	35.13
Ditto at the Post marked West	4	50	40.40
Distance from the true Parallel	0	00	5.27 North

Gamma Cygni

August	°	'	"
14	0	12	14.0
15		12	14.4
16		12	13.0
17		12	15.0
Mean (15d 23h)	0	12	14.10
Aberration			+ 8.72
Deviation			- 5.90
Precession			+18.03
Refraction			+ 0.20
Mean Zen. Dist.	0	12	35.15
Ditto East	0	12	38.58
True Zen. Dist.	0	12	37.06
Ditto at the Post marked West	0	12	33.00
Distance from the true Parallel	0	00	4.06 North

Alpha Cygni

August	°	'	"
14	4	43	43.7
15		43	43.2
16		43	43.0
17		43	45.0
Mean (15d 23h)	4	43	43.73
Aberration			- 7.64
Deviation			+ 5.30
Precession			-20.21
Refraction			+ 5.50
Mean Zen. Dist.	4	43	26.68
Ditto East	4	43	26.68
True Zen. Dist.	4	43	26.68
Ditto at the Post marked West	4	43	31.20
Distance from the true Parallel	0	00	4.52 North

Capella

August	°	'	"
14	6	00	30.3
15		00	31.7
16		00	28.2
18	6	00	31.5
Mean (16d 13h)	6	00	30.42
Aberration			+ 7.94
Deviation			- 9.15
Precession			- 8.60
Refraction			+ 7.00
Mean Zen. Dist.	6	00	27.61
Ditto East	6	00	25.41
True Zen. Dist.	6	00	26.51
Ditto at the Post marked West	6	00	31.80
Distance from the true Parallel	0	00	5.29 North

3".75
5".27
4".06
4".52
5".29
—————
4".58 = Mean = 6 chains 94 Links that we are to the North of the true Parallel

Hence

153

(Undated) Hence the offsets at every Mile Post to where the Sector
was set up on the 12th of July as follows.
Here F (is) the Sector at the 48 Miles 64 Chains Station
N Ditto at this Station, that is 71 Miles 43 Chains from the Post marked West.
DF = 0 Chains 85 Links South of the Parallel
HN = 6.94 North of Ditto
Hence the offsets
Miles from the Post marked West

Miles	Chains	Links	For the circle GF and GH		For the Triangle dFD: dGL and the part (Indistinct)		True offsets to the Parallel	
			Chains	Links	Chains	Links	Chains	Links
48	64	5	0	0	0	85N	0	85N
49			0	3	0	78	0	75N
50			0	10	0	43	0	33N
51				18	0	8N	0	10S
52				22	0	26S	0	48S
53				25	0	60.5	0	85.5
54				27	0	95.5	1	22.5
55				27	1	30	1	57
56				25	1	65	1	90
57				21	2	00	2	21
58				15	2	34	2	49
59				10	2	69	2	79
60				3	3	04	3	07
60.71							3	23
61				7	3	29	3	36
62				14	3	63	3	77
63				20	3	98	4	18
64				24	4	34	4	58
65				26	4	69	4	95
66				27	5	03	5	30
67				26	5	38	5	64
68				23	5	73	5	96
69				19	6	08	6	27
70				13	6	42	6	55
71				5	6	76	6	81
71	43	19		0	6	94	6	94S

at 60.71 Miles the Angular Point, the offset = 3.23

154

(Undated)

Point		Miles					
	F =	48.806	F =	48.806	Error at F	0.85S
	N =	71.540	G =	60.710 changed at	Ditto at N	6.94N
Whole length		22.734	then	11.904 = FL	Sum	7.79

Then as 22.734 : 7.79 chains :: 11.904 : 4.08 chains; and then 4.08 - 0.85 (being S)
= 3 chains 23 links = LG = the distance of the true Parallel (or infinitely near) at the
Point of change. And as FL = 11.904 we have over run 11.37 by 0.534 of a mile
= QL at an angle of 8' 18" (vid) then as Rad: to QL :: Sine 8' 18" = LQR; LR = 10 Links
NO which we should have been more North, had we changed at 11.37 miles. Now
as the whole sum 7.89 chains : 22.734 :: 85 Links : 2.453 miles = Fd, the distance of the
point d from F where the Line crossed the chord DG : and it must cross the Parallel when
the offset from the chord DG is = to the offset in the Triangle dDF viz. at t. From the
whole the quantities of the Triangle dDE, dGL and LMN (to which add GL = HN constant)
corresponding to the intermediate miles are had by proportion.

From the foregoing computation of the stars we find we are 6 chains 94 links to the
Northward. Then to be in the true Parallel at 10' = 11.37 miles West
we change the direction found by the stars on the 16th and 17th August thus
as 11.37 miles : 6.94 chains :: 45.62 chains = Radius we measured : 34.7 Links. This
quantity we laid off to the Southward at Right Angles to the direction
found by the stars, and in this direction proceeded to run as follows.

Figure
155

20   Began to Run the Line in a direction to be in
the true **Parallel** at 10' = 11.37 **Miles** West.

	Miles	Chains	(Links)	
At	⎰71	61		Crossed **Piney** Run
	⎱71	61	70	Crossed Ditto
	71	62	25	Crossed Ditto
	71	63		**Mr.** Stephen Grise's House 7 Chains North of the Line
	72	38		Crossed **Piney** Run
	72	77		Crossed Ditto the last time

21   Continued the Line

At   ⎰73.58 Crossed **Monocacy** Road
      ⎨74.28 **Mr.** Michael Miller's House 4 chains North
      ⎱74.63 **Mr.** Henry Bower's House 2 chains North

22   Continued the Line

At   ⎰76.00 Crossed **Willollowey's** Creek
      ⎨76.5 **Mr.** William Davis's House 7 Chains North
      ⎱76.42 **Mr.** Thos. McCewn's House 50 Links South

23   Continued the Line

At   78.66 crossed **Rock** Creek. This creek here 2 chains wide,
two chains South where we crossed; Mash Creek joins Rock Creek.

24   Continued the Line

79.56 **Mr.** John McKenley's House 2 chains South
80.21 crossed **Mash** Creek. Breadth near two chains.   156

25   Sunday
26   Continued the Line

At 81 miles 32 chains **Mr.** John Everett's House 12 chains North
     81 miles 59 chains **Mr.** John Young's House   5 chains North
     82 miles 66 chains crossed **Middle** Creek
     82 miles 77 chains **Mr.** Matthew Elder's House 1 chain 50 Links South

Supposed to be in the   83 miles 13 chains 96 links changed our direction to be
true **Parallel**   again in the true **Parallel** 10' West as by the following computation.
Here BP, AP and DP = Computed true parallel = 50° 16' 40" (near enough for this purpose)
PS = Complement of the Latitude at the Sector = 50° 16' 35".42
SC the direction found by the Stars on the 16th and 17th of August, Instant.
SN = 45 chains 62 links = a Radius measured
which gives NM = 34.7 Links as by the leaf before.   (log)
Then as 45 chains 62 links   3.6591553
: Rad   10.
:: 34.7 Links   1.5403295
: Tangent angle NSM 26' 10"   7.8811742

     Angle PSC 89°55' 51"   (log)
     Angle PSA   = 90°22' 01"   Then as Sine AP 50° 16' 40"   =   9.8860120
                       (log)   To Sine Angle PSA 90° 22' 01"   =   9.9999911
As Rad   =10.   So is Sine PS 50° 16' 35".42   =   9.8860039.85
to 40 chains = 4000 links = 3.6020600   19.8859950.85
:: Sine dAo 34' 29".7   = 8.0015379   To Sine Angle SAP 89° 29' 39.3" =   9.9999830.85
to do 40.14 links   = 1.6035979   Add Angle PSA =
                                              Angle BAP 89° 55' 51"
                                       Sum 179° 25' 30".3   which
                              Subtract from 180° 00' 00".0
                                     Rest 00° 34' 29".7   Angle dAo which
                          we must lay off from our direction SAd
                          to give AB for to be again in the true
                          Parallel 10' West. This angle as 40 chains
                          Radius = Ad gives do = 40.14 Links which we laid
                          off, etc., etc. to the Northward, and   Figure
                          proceeded to run AoB as follows.   157

1765
August
27   Continued the Line in the direction last found.

84 miles 46 chains. **Mr.** Thomas Scot's House 5 chains South

28   Continued the Line

84 miles 74 chains crossed Flat Run

85 miles 51 chains Mr. James Stevenson's House 5 chains North.

29   Continued the Line

86 miles 41 chains. **Mr.** William Brown's House 2 chains North

86 miles 44 chains. Crossed Tom's Creek. The foot of the South Mountain.

86 miles 72 chains. **Mr.** Phineas Davidson's House 1 chain North.

30   Continued the Line

87 miles 75 chains. Crossed Friends Creek in the South Mountain.

88 miles 00 chains. **Mr.** John Chohorn's House one chain North in Ditto.

31   Continued the Line

September

1 Sunday

2   Continued the Line

3   Continued the Line

At 92 Miles 4 chains **Mr.** George Craft's House 6 chains North in the **Mountain.**

4   Continued the Line

At 93 (miles) 63 chains crossed the 1st spring running into Antietam.

94 (miles) 62 chains crossed a Spring running in to Ditto. This Spring
is at the foot of the South Mountain on the West side.

94 miles 62 chains 68 links. The **Post** on which the Transit Instrument was
fixed to Find the Direction.   158

5   Brought the Sector to the West Side of the Mountain.

6   Set up the Sector in our direction at the distance
of 94 miles 63 chains 10 links from the **Post** marked West in **Mr.** Bryan's field,
and made the following observations. Cloudy.

Plane of the Sector East

	Star Name	Nearest Point on the Sector		Revolutions and Seconds on the Micrometer		Difference		Apparent Zenith Distance		
		o	'	R	"	'	"	o	'	"
7	Delta Cygni	4	50+	5	14+	0	55.8	4	50	55.8
				4	10.5					
	Gamma Cygni	0	15-	5	10.5	2	54.0	0	12	06.0
				1	44.5					
	Alpha Cygni	4	45-	3	41.5	1	6.0	4	43	54.0
				5	3.5					
	Capella	6	00+	6	35.5	0	30.5	6	00	30.5
				6	5					
8 Sun.	Cloudy									
9	Alpha Lyrae	1	10-	6	50+	1	32.3	1	08	27.7
				5	10					
	Delta Cygni	4	50+	3	28-	0	56.0	4	50	56.0
				2	24-					
	Gamma Cygni	0	15-	4	39+	2	57.3	0	12	02.7
				1	18					
	Alpha Cygni	4	45-	6	21+	1	04.4	4	43	55.6
				7	34-					
	Capella	6	00+	7	23+	0	31.8	6	00	31.8
				6	43.5					

                                                   159

1765
September
9   For the direction at our Station 95 miles from the Post marked West
Time by the Clock

19h	19m	22s	20h	04m	50s	39h	27m	32s	
	20	59		6	37		27	36	Equal altitudes Delta Cygni
	22	42		8	13		27	35	

$$19h \quad 43m \quad 47.5s = \text{Star passed according to the clock}$$
$$19 \quad 37 \quad 39 \quad\;\; = \text{Right Ascension of Star}$$
$$6m \quad 8.5s \quad \text{Clock fast}$$

20h	17m	23s	20h	58m	17s	41h	19m	15s	
	19	6+	21	00	10		19	16+	= Equal altitudes of Alpha Cygni
	20	58	21	01	52		19	15+	

$$20h \quad 39m \quad 38s \quad = \text{Star passed by the clock}$$
$$20 \quad 33 \quad 27 \quad\;\; = \text{Right Ascension of Star}$$
$$6m \quad 11s \quad \text{Clock fast}$$

Now as   56m : 2.2 s :: 80m : 3s+
               Then   21h   53m   3s
                         +6   11-
                         +0   3+
                   21h   59m   17s   Alpha Arietis will be on the azimuth of
                                       9° 04' 09" from the North, Eastward

As   56m : 2.2s :: 190m : 7s+
               Then   23h   39m   19s
                         +6   11-
                         +0   7+
                   23h   45m   37s   Eta Pleiades (Tauri) will be on Ditto

               And   23   43   46
                       +6   11-
                       +0   7+
                       +0   1   = what the star's Right Ascension has
                                        gained since 1st June
                 23h   50m   05s   Aldebaran will be on the said azimuth

When Alpha Arietis passed, the middle wire of the Transit Instrument was brought
to it as usual, and a mark at the distance of 49 chains 10 links
placed; when the other two stars passed at the above times,
they bisected the mark 1st placed, that it could not be altered for the better.   160

	Star Name	Nearest Point on the Sector		Revolutions and Seconds on the Micrometer		Difference		Apparent Zenith Distance		
		°	'	R	"	'	"	°	'	"
10	Alpha Lyrae	1	10-	5	44	1	30.7	1	08	29.3
				4	5+					
	Delta Cygni	4	50+	2	11.5	0	57.2	4	50	57.2
				1	6+					
	Gamma Cygni	0	15-	5	30	2	53.0	0	12	07.0
				2	13					
	Alpha Cygni	4	45-	4	25.5	1	3.8	4	43	56.2
				5	37+					
	Capella	6	00+	11	7	0	32.3	6	00	32.3
				10	27-					
11	Gamma Cygni	0	15-	8	11.5	2	51.2	0	12	8.8
				4	48+					
	Alpha Cygni	4	45-	5	40+	1	6.2	4	43	53.8
				7	2.5					
	Capella	6	00+	10	47+	0	31.0	6	00	31.0
				10	16+					
12	Alpha Lyrae	1	10-	9	30	1	31.3	1	08	28.7
				7	43-					
	Delta Cygni	4	50+	7	32.5	0	55.8	4	50	55.8
				6	29-					
	Gamma Cygni	0	15-	6	50.5	2	51.5	0	12	8.5
				3	35					

1765
September
13

Turned the Sector Plane West

	Star Name	Nearest Point on the Sector		Revolutions and Seconds on the Micrometer		Difference		Apparent Zenith Distance		
		o	'	R	"	'	"	o	'	"
	Capella	6	0+	6	6+	0	37.7	6	00	37.7
				6	44					
14	Alpha Lyrae	1	10-	8	26+	1	36.2	1	08	23.8
				10	18.5					
	Delta Cygni	4	50+	10	25.5	1	00.5	4	51	00.5
				11	34					
	Gamma Cygni	0	15-	11	32+	2	57.0	0	12	03.0
				15	1+					
	Alpha Cygni	4	45-	13	33.5	0	56.5	4	44	03.5
				12	29					
	Capella	6	00+	8	51-	0	37.8	6	00	37.8
				9	36.5					
15 Sun.	Alpha Lyrae	1	10-	14	30.5	1	39.5	1	08	20.5
				16	26					
	Gamma Cygni	0	15-	13	28+	2	58.7	0	12	01.3
				16	51					
	Alpha Cygni	4	45-	15	35	0	58.5	4	44	01.5
				14	28.5					
	Capella	6	0+	10	40	0	39.0	6	00	39.0
				11	27					
16	Alpha Lyrae	1	10-	11	40	1	36.5	1	08	23.5
				13	32.5					
	Delta Cygni	4	50+	14	15-	1	02.3	4	51	02.3
				15	25					
	Gamma Cygni	0	15-	15	14	2	58.7	0	12	01.3
				18	37-					
	Alpha Cygni	4	45-	7	50.5	0	59.8	4	44	00.2
				6	43-					
	Capella	6	00+	8	12.5	0	37.5	6	00	37.5
				8	50					
17	Alpha Lyrae	1	10-	8	18-	1	36.0	1	08	24.0
				10	10-					
	Delta Cygni	4	50+	11	6	1	00.0	4	51	00.0
				12	14					
	Gamma Cygni	0	15-	10	46-	2	57.6	0	12	02.4
				14	15+					
	Alpha Cygni	4	45-	13	2	1	02.0	4	43	58.0
				11	44					
	Capella	6	00+	12	47	0	37.5	6	00	37.5
				13	32.5					

161

18   Computing our observations as follows.
19   Packing up the Instruments, etc., etc.   162

108

Plane East

	Alpha Lyrae (° ′ ″)			Delta Cygni (° ′ ″)			Gamma Cygni (° ′ ″)			Alpha Cygni (° ′ ″)			Capella (° ′ ″)		
	7			7			7			7			7	6 00	30.5
	9	1 08	27.7	10	4 50	55.8	9	0 12	6.0	9	4 43	54.0	9		31.8
	10		29.3	11		56.0	10		7.0	10		55.6	10		32.3
						57.2	11		8.8	11		56.2	11		31.0
	12		28.7	12		55.8			8.5			53.8			
Mean	10d 15h 1 08		28.56	10d 8h 4 50		56.20	9d 15h 0 12		07.57	9d 23h 4 43		54.90	6 00		31.40
Aberration			+16.96			−15.85			+14.18			−13.60			+ 7.75
Deviation			− 8.41			+ 6.87			− 5.81			+ 5.23			− 9.21
Precession			+ 4.26			−13.97			+18.80			−21.04			− 8.96
Refraction			+ 1.20			+ 5.60			+ 0.20			+ 5.50			+ 7.00
Mean Zen. Dist.	1 08		42.57	4 50		38.85	0 12		34.94	4 43		30.99	6 00		27.98

Plane West

	Alpha Lyrae (° ′ ″)			Delta Cygni (° ′ ″)			Gamma Cygni (° ′ ″)			Alpha Cygni (° ′ ″)			Capella (° ′ ″)		
	13			14			15			15			13	6 00	37.7
	14	1 08	23.8	15	4 51	00.5	16	0 12	03.00	16	4 44	01.5	14		37.8
	15			16		02.3	17		01.3	17	53	00.2	15		39.0
	16		23.5	17		00.0			01.3			58.0	16		37.5
	17		24.0						02.4				17		37.5
Mean	15d 23h 1 08		23.77	15d 22h 4 51		00.93	16d 0h 0 12		02.00	16d 0h 4 43		59.90	15d 17h 6 00		37.90
Aberration			+17.34			−16.74			+15.07			−14.85			+ 7.49
Deviation			− 8.41			+ 6.87			− 5.81			+ 5.23			− 9.25
Precession			+ 4.30			−14.12			+18.98			−21.28			− 9.01
Refraction			+ 1.20			+ 5.60			+ 0.20			+ 5.50			+ 7.00
Mean Zen. Dist.	1 08		38.20	4 50		42.54	0 12		30.44	4 43		34.50	6 00		34.13
Ditto Plane East	1 08		42.57	4 50		38.85	0 12		34.94	4 43		30.99	6 00		27.94
True Zen. Dist	1 08		40.38	4 50		40.69	0 12		32.69	4 43		32.74	6 00		31.03
Ditto at the Post 1st Jan. 1764	1 08		41.80	4 50		40.40	0 12		33.00	4 43		31.20	6 00		31.80
marked West			1.42 South			0.29 South			0.31 South			1.54 South			0.77 North

1″.42
0″.29
0″.31
1″.54
—————
3″.56
−0″.77
—————
2″.79 ÷ 5
average = 0″.56

(Average = 0″.56 = 56 feet) = 85 links that we are to
the South of the true Parallel.

Hence

109

Hence the offsets at every Mile Post, betwixt this Station and where the
Sector was set up August 7th, 1765, as follows.

Miles from the Post marked West	Offsets for the Circular part IPH and IPL Links	Offsets for the Triangle NdH		True offsets to the true Parallel	
		Chains	Links	Chains	Links
71.54	0+	6	94	6	94 South
72	4	6	65	6	69
73	12	6	00	6	12
74	18	5	37	5	55
75	22	4	74	4	96
76	25	4	11	4	36
77	27	3	48	3	75
78	27	2	85	3	12
79	25	2	21	2	46
80	21	1	57	1	78
81	16	0	94	1	10
82	9	0	31	0	40 South
82.495*	5	0	00	0	05 South
83	2	0	32	0	30 North
changed at 83.174	0-	0	43	0	43
84	6	0	46	0	40
85	14	0	50	0	36
86	20	0	53	0	33
87	24	0	57	0	33
88	26	0	61	0	35
89	27	0	64	0	37
90	26	0	68	0	42
91	23	0	72	0	49
92	19	0	75	0	56
93	13	0	79	0	66
94	5	0	83	0	78
94.789	0	0	85	0	85 North

(Offsets from dN to IH — for miles 71.54 through 82; Offsets from DK to IL — for miles 83 through 94.789)

*Crossed the chord IH at 82.495

164

Here HpIPL, the true Parallel of Latitude. N, the Sector at the last Station.
K at this and NDK the Line run. D, the Point changed at.

The Points $\begin{cases} N = 71.54 \text{ miles} \\ K = 94.789 \end{cases}$ NH = 6.94 chains North   Point$\begin{cases} D = 83.174 \text{ miles} \\ N = 71.540 \end{cases}$

Whole line   = 23.249   KL = 0.85   South   DN = 11.634 subtract 11.37 miles

rest = 0.264 mile what we have over run the usual change at an angle of 34' 29".7 (vid minutes
26th of August) Hence we are more South than we should have been if the ground would have admitted
us to have changed at the 10' West.

Points   K = 94.789
          D = 83.174
          DK = 11.615   Then as 23.249 miles : 85 links :: 11.615 miles : 42 links.   Then
          85 - 42 = 43 = DI the offset to the North at the change. Or as 23.249 : 85 :: 11.634 = ND : 43.
Now having KL = 0.85 chain and DI = 43 links, the intermediate offsets corresponding to the miles
are had from DK to IL by proportion as 11.634 miles : 6.94 chains + 85 links :: 43 links : 0.679 miles.
Then 11.634 miles less .679 miles = 10.955 miles=dN which corresponds to the error 6.94, hence the
offsets for the intermediate miles from dN to IH by proportion.

To the point   N = 71.54 miles
          add   dN = 10.955
Gives the point d_1 = 82.495 miles where the Line ND crossed the chord IH. Then
for the offset at   = 83.000
                          0.505
As 0.679 mile : 43 links :: 0.505 mile : 32 Links = bc = the offset at the 83 mile
to the chord IH from DN Northward. From the whole the separate parts of   Figure
the Triangle corresponding to the miles as by the Table.   165

20 Began to run the Line in the direction found by the stars on the 9th instant
Corrected by 9 links laid off to the North at the distance of 2 miles 32 chains
to account for the error at the Sector 85 links South, that is, to be in the
Parallel at 20' West.

21 Continued the Line.
95 miles 38 chains crossed a spring running into Antietam.
96 miles 3 chains. Mr. Staphel Shockey's House 7 chains North.

22 Sun. Went to see a cave (near the Mountain about 6 miles South of Mr. Shockey's.)
The entrance is an arch about 6 yards in length and four feet in height, when
immediately there opens a room 45 yards in length, 40 in breadth and 7 or 8
in height. (Not one pillar to support nature's arch): There divine service is
often (according to the Church of England) celebrated in the Winter Season.
On the sidewalls are drawn by the Pencil of Time, with the tears of the Rocks:
The imitation of Organ, Pillar, Columns and Monuments of a Temple; which, with
the glimmering faint light; makes the whole an awful, solemn appearance: Striking
its Visitants with a strong and melancholy reflection: That such is the abodes of
the Dead: Thy inevitable doom, O stranger; Soon to be numbered as one of them.
From this room there is a narrow passage of about 100 yards, at the end of which
runs a fine river of water: On the sides of this passage are other rooms, but not
so large as the first.

23 Continued the Line
99 miles 35 chains crossed Antietam Creek.

24 Continued the Line
101 miles 71 chains Mr. Samuel Irwin's Spring House, 2 chains North.
102 miles 34 chains Mr. Michael Walker's House 4 chains North.
102 miles 67 chains A great Spring running into Antietam.
102 miles 70 chains Mr. William Duglass' House 4 chains North.

25 Continued the Line
103 miles 69 chains Crossed a Road leading to Swaddingem's Ferry (or _____ Ferry)
on Potowmack.   166

26 Continued the Line
105 miles 78 chains 67 links changed our direction 8' 18" North by laying off
9.65 links at the distance of 33 chains 77 links.
106 miles 4 chains. Mr. Ludwig Cameron's House 4 chains North.

27 Continued the Line

28 Continued the Line
108 miles 5 chains Crossed the Road leading from Carlisle to William's Ferry on
Potowmack (near Watkin's Ferry)

29 Sun. At the River Potowmack. Forded it at the above Ferry; here Conecocheague falls
into the said River about seven miles to the South of our Line.
On the Virginia Side is a Log Fort and a Tavern. The River here is about 200 yards
wide.

30 Continued the Line.
108 miles 65 chains Mr. Thomas Meeks House 2 chains South
109 miles 14 chains Crossed Conecocheague Creek. Two chains in breadth.

October

1 Continued the Line

2 Continued the Line
112 miles 20 chains Crossed a Road leading from the Temporary Line to Frederick Town.

3 Continued the Line
114 miles 00 chains Mr. Philip Davis's House one mile and a half North by Estimation.   167

1765
October

4   Continued the Line
              115 miles 42 chains   Crossed a small spring at the foot of the North Mountain.

5   Continued the Line

6   Sunday

7   Set up the Sector in our Direction at the Distance of 117 miles 12 chains 97 links
              from the Post marked West in Mr. Bryan's Field and made the following observations.

Plane of the Sector East

	Star Name	Nearest Point on the Sector		Revolutions and Seconds on the Micrometer		Difference		Apparent Zenith Distance		
		o	'	R	"	'	"	o	'	"
	Capella	6	0+	10	33-	0	39.0	6	00	39.0
				9	46-				Very faint	
8	Cloudy									
9	Cloudy									
10	(Alpha) Lyrae	1	10-	10	45.5	1	37.5	1	08	22.5
				9	00					
	Delta Cygni	4	50+	8	7	1	7.5	4	51	7.5
				6	43.5					
	Gamma Cygni	0	15-	7	41	3	4.5	0	11	55.5
				4	12.5					
	Alpha Cygni	4	45-	5	31+	0	52.7	4	44	7.3
				6	32					
	Capella	6	00+	10	20	0	43.5	6	00	43.5
				9	23.5					
11	Alpha Lyrae	1	10-	9	0-	1	38.7	1	08	21.3
				7	5					
	Delta Cygni	4	50+	6	31	1	6.7	4	51	6.7
				5	16+					
	Gamma Cygni	0	15-	7	9.5	3	03.0	0	11	57.0
				3	34.5					
	Alpha Cygni	4	45-	4	0+	0	55.0	4	44	5.0
				5	3+					
	Capella	6	00+	6	10.5	0	42.8	6	00	42.8
				5	20-					
12	Alpha Lyrae	1	10-	9	26	1	38.0	1	08	22.0
				7	32					
13 Sun.	Alpha Lyrae	1	10-	10	14+	1	38.3	1	08	21.7
				8	20					
	Delta Cygni	4	50+	6	39	1	5.5	4	51	5.5
				5	25.5					
	Gamma Cygni	0	15-	4	40-	3	02.7	0	11	57.3
				1	13					
	Alpha Cygni	4	45-	7	49+	0	52.2	4	44	7.8
				8	49.5					
	Capella	6	00+	10	30+	0	43.3	6	00	43.3
				9	39					
14	Cloudy									
15	Cloudy									
16	Alpha Lyrae	1	10-	9	49+	1	36.3	1	08	23.7
				8	5					
	Delta Cygni	4	50+	6	37	1	6.3	4	51	6.3
				5	23-					

168

169

Turned the Sector Plane West when Alpha Lyrae passed the wire, it appeared by the clock to be within 20'' (of time) of the meridian. We therefore took Alpha Lyrae thus:

Star Name	Nearest Point on the Sector		Revolutions and Seconds on the Micrometer		Difference			Apparent Zenith Distance		
	o	'	R	''	o		''	o	'	''
Alpha Lyrae	1	10-	4	32.5	1		45.8	1	08	14.2
			6	34+						
Gamma Cygni	0	15-	6	49+	3		10.2	0	11	49.8
			10	31.5						
Alpha Cygni	4	45-	9	16.5	0		46.5	4	44	13.5
			8	22						

18 Cloudy

19 Alpha Lyrae	1	10-	5	36-	1		44.3	1	08	15.7
			7	36						
Alpha Cygni	4	45-	3	40+	0		48.0	4	44	12.0
			2	44+						
Capella	6	00+	3	33	0		49.5	6	00	49.5
			4	30.5						
20 Sun. Capella	6	00+	5	42-	0		50.6	6	00	50.6
			6	40+						
21 Alpha Lyrae	1	10-	8	10.5	1		42.5	1	08	17.5
			10	9						
Delta Cygni	4	50+	11	1-	1		12.8	4	51	12.8
			12	21.5						
Gamma Cygni	0	15-	13	24-	3		11.6	0	11	48.4
			17	7+						
Alpha Cygni	4	45-	15	30	0		46.7	4	44	13.3
			14	35+						
Capella	6	00+	8	40.5	0		51.2	6	00	51.2
			9	40-						

170

For the direction at our Station 117 miles from the Post marked West

	Time by Clock	Clock gains per day		
12	18h 46m 00s			
		1m 19s	}	Alpha Lyrae passed the meridian by the Sector
13 Sun.	18 47 19			
	19 55 33	1m 17s		Delta Cygni Ditto
	19 59 23			
20 Sun.	5 26 1.5	1m 16.5s		Capella Ditto
21	5 27 18			
	18 56 28			Alpha Lyrae Ditto
	20 5 3.5			Delta Cygni Ditto
	21 0 54			Alpha Cygni Ditto
22	18 57 42	1m 14 s		Alpha Lyrae Ditto
	20 6 17	1m 13.5s		Delta Cygni Ditto
	21 2 8-	1m 14 s		Alpha Cygni Ditto

21	20h 20m 33s	21h 39m 13 s	42h 02m 25s	}	
	21m 50s	40m 34 s	42h 02m 24s	}	Equal altitudes, Alpha Cygni
	23m 12s	41m 51s	2m 24s	}	
	mean		21h 01m 12s		
			20h 33m 28s		= Right Ascension Alpha Cygni
			27m 44s		Clock fast for sidereal time

21h 53m 03s = Right Ascension Mid-Heaven when Alpha Arietis on the Azimuth
+ 0   1 = Difference in Right Ascension Alpha Arietis from first day of June
+ 0   4.5
+27   44+
————————
22h 20m 52.5s = Time by the clock when Alpha Arietis will be on the Azimuth from the North of 90° 04' 09"

23h 39m 19 = Right Ascension Mid-Heaven Eta Pleiades (Tauri)
+ 0   1
+27   44
+ 0   10
————————
24h 07m 14.5s = Eta Pleiades (Tauri) on the Azimuth 90° 04' 09"

23h 43m 46s = Right Ascension Mid-Heaven when Aldebaran on Ditto
+ 0   01   for change in Right Ascension
+27   44+
+ 0   10+
————————
24h 11m 42s = Aldebaran will be on the Azimuth of 90° 04' 09" by the clock. When Alpha Arietis passed by the clock we placed a mark at the distance of 52 chains 68 links by the Transit instrument as usual, and when Eta Pleiades (Tauri) and Aldebaran came to the Azimuth it fell so near, that the mark could not be altered.   171

22   Proved the direction found last night thus

Time by clock

20h 23m 34s	21h 38m 39s	42h 04m 52s
24 52	40 00	04 52
26 13.5	41 19	04 53-

} Alt. of Alpha Cygni

21h 02m 26.5s)
20h 33m 28s   = Right ascension of star
————————
28m 58.5s   Clock fast
as 24h : 1m 14s :: 80m : 4s

21h 53m 04s = Right Ascension Mid-heaven when Alpha Arietis is on the Azimuth
+28m 58.5s
+00m 04s
————————
22h 22m 06.5s = Time by the clock when on the Azimuth

23h 39m 20s = Right Ascension Mid-Heaven when Eta Pleiades (Tauri) is on Azimuth
+28m 58.5s   as 24h : 1m 14s :: 190m : 10s
+ 0m 10s
————————
24h 08m 28.5s = Time by the clock when on Ditto (i.e., on the required Azimuth)

23h 43m 47s = Right Ascension Mid-Heaven when Aldebaran is on Azimuth
+28m 58.5s
+ 0m 10s
————————
24h 12m 55.5s = Time by the clock when on Ditto

At the above times the wire in the Transit Instrument was set to the star as usual and they all agreed within four inches of the mark placed last night.

N.B.   The mean of these two nights observations (that is the middle of the four inches) is five feet 11 inches South of the Notch in the tree made in our Line: From the Notch may be discovered next season whether the mark set by the stars is altered or not.   172

114

Plane of the Sector West

Star Name	Nearest Point on the Sector		Revolutions and Seconds on the Micrometer		Difference		Apparent Zenith Distance		
	o	'	R	''	'	''	o	'	''
Alpha Lyrae	1	10 –	9 11	13- 11.5	1	42.8	1	08	17.2
Delta Cygni	4	50+	11 13	51 19+	1	12.3	4	50	12.3
Gamma Cygni	0	15-	14 17	5+ 39	3	9.7	0	11	50.3
Alpha Cygni	4	45-	12 11	1.5 6+	0	47.2	4	44	12.8
Capella	6	00+	11 12	3.5 1	0	49.5	6	00	49.5
Alpha Lyrae	1	10-	10 12	27.5 28+	1	44.8	1	08	15.2

22 (Alpha Lyrae row)
23 Alpha Lyrae

24 Computing our observations as follows

25 Computing offsets, etc. Went to Captain Shelby's to desire him to go with us on the North Mountain for to show us the course of the River Potowmack Westward.

26 Packed up our Instruments and left them (not in the least damaged to our knowledge) at Captain Shelby's. Repaired with Captain Shelby to the Summit of the Mountain in the direction of our Line, but the air was so hazy prevented our seeing the course of the River.

27 Sun. Captain Shelby again went with us to the Summit of the Mountain (when it was very clear) and showed us the northernmost bend of the River Potowmack at the Conoloways; from which we judge the Line will pass about two miles to the North of the said River.

173

Plane of the Sector East

			Alpha Lyrae			Delta Cygni		
10			1h 08m 22.5s	10		4h 51m	7.5s
11			21.3	11			6.7
12			22.0				
13 Sunday			21.7	13			5.5
16			23.7	16			6.3
Mean	12d 15h		1h 08m 22.24s	12d 18h		4h 51m	6.50s
Aberration			+17.07				-18.37
Deviation			- 8.34				+ 6.70
Precession			+ 4.48				-14.72
Refraction			+ 1.20				+ 5.60
Mean Zenith Distance 1st January, 1764, Plane East			1h 08m 36.65s			4h 50m	45.71s
17			1h 08m 14.2s	17			
19			1h 08m 15.7s	19			
20 Sunday				20			
21			17.5	21		4h 51m	12.8s
22			17.2	22		51	12.3
23			15.2				
Mean	20h 15m		1h 08m 15.98s	21h 18m		4h 51m	12.55s
Aberration			+16.26				-18.05
Deviation			- 8.34				+ 6.70
Precession			+ 4.50				-14.90
Refraction			+ 1.20				+ 5.60
Mean Zen. Dist. 1 Jan. 1764, Plane West			1h 08m 29.60s			4h 50m	51.90s
Ditto Plane East			36.65s				45.71s
True Zen. Dist. 1 Jan. 1764			1h 08m 33.12s			4h 50m	48.80s
Ditto at Post Marked West			1h 08m 41.80s				40.40s
Difference			08.68 So.				08.40 So.
			8.40				
			8.14				
			9.00				
			8.15				
Mean			8.474 = 847.4 feet				

174

115

1765
October

		Gamma Cygni				Alpha Cygni				Capella	
		o ' "				o ' "				o ' "	
10		0 11 55.5	10		4 44 7.3		10		6 00 43.5	
11		57.0	11		5.0		11		42.8	
13 Sunday		57.3	13		7.8		13		43.3	
Mean	11d 15h	0 11 56.60	11d 15h	4 44 6.70		11d 23h	6 00 43.20	
Aberration		+17.33			-17.76				+ 5.46	
Deviation		- 5.62			+ 5.06				- 9.23	
Precession		+19.77			-22.14				- 9.41	
Refraction		+ 0.20			+ 5.50				+ 7.00	
Mean Zen. Dist.		0 12 28.28		4 43 37.36			6 00 37.02	
1st Jan. 1764, Plane East										

		Plane West									
17		0 11 49.8	17		4 44 13.5					
19			19		44 12.0		19		6 00 49.5	
20							20		6 00 50.6	
21		0 11 48.4	21		13.3		21		51.2	
22		50.3	22		12.8		22		49.5	
Mean	20d 7h	0 11 49.50	20d 1h	4 44 12.96		21d 23h	6 00 50.20	
Aberration		+17.35			-18.00				+ 4.45	
Deviation		- 5.62			+ 5.06				- 9.23	
Precession		+20.02			-22.41				- 9.53	
Refraction		+ 0.20			+ 5.50				+ 7.00	
Mean Zen. Dist., 1 Jan. 1764		0 12 21.45		4 43 43.05			6 00 42.89	
Ditto Plane East		28.28		37.36			37.02	
True Zen. Dist., 1 Jan. 1764		0 12 24.86		4 43 40.20			6 00 39.95	
Ditto at Post Marked West		33.00		31.20			31.80	
Difference		8.14S		9.00S			8.15S	

Mean for all stars = 8".474 = 847.4 feet = 12 chains 84 links = what we are to the South of the true Parallel.

175

(Undated) Hence the offsets at every mile post to where the Sector was set up on the 6th of
September as follows :

Miles from the Post Marked West	Distances from the chords AB and BC to the circle	Distances from SED to the chords AB and BC	True Offsets	
			Chains	Links
94.789	0-	0.85	0	85 North
95	3	0.96	0	93
96	12	1.50	1	38
97	18	2.04	1	86
98	22	2.57	2	35
99	25	3.11	2	86
100	27	3.64	3	37
101	27	4.18	3	91
102	25	4.72	4	47
103	21	5.26	5	05
104	16	5.79	5	63
105	9	6.32	6	23
Changed the direction 105.983	0	6.85	6	85
106	8	6.87	6	79
107	14	7.41	7	27
108	20	7.94	7	74
109	24	8.47	8	23
110	26	9.00	8	74
111	27	9.54	9	27
112	27	10.08	9	81
113	26	10.62	10	36
114	23	11.15	10	92
115	19	11.68	11	49
116	12	12.22	12	10
117	2	12.76	12	74
117.162	0	12.84	12	84 North

176

116

(Undated) Here AbC the true Parallel, AB and BC chords. S the Sector at the South Mountain
and D at the North. Spd a Parallel 85 Links South of the true Parallel SED the
line run from the South to the North Mountain.

E the point changed at = 105.983 miles		DC = 12 chains 84 links	
Point S	94.789	SA =	0 chains 85 links = pB = dC
SE	= 11.194 miles		11 chains 99 links = dD

Point D	= 117.162 miles	
S	= 94.789 miles	
Whole line	= 22.373 miles	

Then as 22.373 : 11.99 chains :: 11.194 : 5.99 chains = Ep to which add pB = 85 links gives
EB 6 chains 85 links the offset at the Change. Now having SA, EB and DC, the
offsets from SE to the chord AB and from ED to the chord BC corresponding to the
intermediate miles are had by proportion from which subtract all the way, the chord
from the circle; rest the true offsets from SED to the circle as by the Table.

NOTE: Here we changed so near 11.37 miles from S, and the angle changed being but   Figure
8' 18", there is nothing material to account for on that part.   177

1765
October
27 Sun.   From here we could see the Allegany Mountain
for many miles, and judge it by its appearance
to be about 50 Miles (in) distance in the direction
of our Line.
28   Set out on our return to the River Susquehanna to
make the offsets from our Visto to the True Line.
Set off the offsets to the 109 Mile Post.
29   Set off Ditto to the 96 Mile Post.
30   Set off Ditto to the 87 Mile Post.
31   Set off Ditto to the 74 Mile Post.

November
1   Set off Ditto to the 63 Mile Post.
2   Set off Ditto to the 50 Mile Post.
3 Sunday
4   Set off Ditto to the 38 Mile Post.
5   Set off Ditto to the 29 Mile Post.
6   Set off Ditto to the 27 Mile Post: which is near to
the River Susquehannah on the West Side.   178
7   At Peach Bottom Ferry
8   Discharged all hands in order to meet the Gentlemen Commissioners
on the 16th Instant at York.
9   At Peach Bottom Ferry
10 Sun.   At Ditto
11   Left Ditto
12   At York
13   At York
14   At York
15   At York
16   Attended the Gentlemen Commissioners
17 Sunday
18   Attended Ditto
19   Attended Ditto
20   At York
21   Left York and proceeded for the Middle Point to
set 50 Stones (one at each mile) in the Tangent Line

December
5   At Mr. Twifords on the River Nanticoke
17   Twenty stones arrived at Mr. Twiford's on the River Nanticoke; and about the
same time thirty were landed near the Bridge on the River Choptanck.

93

1766
January

1   The Stones all set. Left off for the winter season.

4   At Philadelphia

5 Sunday

6   Wrote to the Honorable Proprietors of Maryland and Pennsylvania.

7   At Brandywine

February

21   Left Brandywine and proceeded for curiosity to the Southward to see the country.

22   Crossed the River Susquehannah at Nelson's Ferry (about 7 miles North of the Line). The Ferry is about 100 yards wide, the River being pent in by two very lofty Hills. At 15 or 20 yards from the East Shore 170 Fathoms of Line with a very heavy weight, has been let down; but no bottom could ever be found.

23 Sun.   At Mr. William Lawson's near the Blue Ball in the Barrens (Borough) of York.

24   At Tawney Town.

25   At Frederick Town in Maryland near the South Mountain.

26   At Alexander (Alexandria) or Belheaven (Bell Haven) on the River Potowmack and crossed the said River at Ditto in to Virginia.

27   Passed through Colchester and Lodged at Dumfreys.

28   At Stafford Court House.

March

1   Near Port Royal on the River Rappahannock.

2 Sun.   Crossed the said River and lodged near the Fort Bridge. Saw green peas in the fields five or six inches high.

3   Crossed the River Pomonkey at Claybourn's Ferry. This is a beautiful situation on the Bank of the River: opposite the door in a Right Line over the River is a causeway of a Mile in Length, thro a mark (marsh) that is overflowed at High Tide about three feet, and if taken in, I think it would be very rich pasture. Reached the City of Williamsburg, the Metropolis of Virginia.

4   Wrote from hence to Mr. Williams: and left the City.

5   Near Tod's Bridge.

6   At Port Royal on Rappahannock at 3h 29m P. M. The Sun Shining in my face I saw a streak of Lightning from 10° altitude down to the Horizon.

7   Crossed Potowmack at Hoe's Ferry. The River here about 3 miles wide. Lodged near Port Tobacco.

8   Near Upper Marlborough.

9 Sun.   Near London Town. Rain and Snow.

10   Near London Town. Rain and Snow

11 & 12   At Annapolis, the Metropolis of Maryland.

13   At Ditto. Compared with his Excellency Horatio Sharpe, Esq. (Governor) a copy of our Journal.

14   Ditto.

April

9   The 9th April 1766. At 8h 06m P. M.
by the watch, a comet (meteor) (appeared.)
in a vertical with Beta Aurigae. At 8h 21m
a small star set over the trace as did
the comet at the above time.

NOTE: The small star set about 2 degrees to the
Northward of the comet.
    Captain Shelby's watch (set this Evening by the Sun)
16 m faster than mine.

10   10th at 9h 01m Captain Shelby's watch 18m
faster than mine.

(Undated: A page, mostly blank, containing some arithmetic.)

1766
March
15   Left Annapolis and proceeded for the North Mountain
to continue the Line.
17   At Frederick Town near the South Mountain in Maryland.
18   J. D. (Jeremiah Dixon) left Philadelphia to attend the Gentlemen Commissioners
the 20th Instant at Chestertown in Maryland.
21   Received our Instructions to proceed with the Line to
the Allegany Mountain.
29   At Capt. Shelby's near the North Mountain.
30 Sun.   At Capt. Shelby's near the North Mountain.
31   Messrs. Darby and Cope (Chain Carriers) with other Hands met at the North Mountain.

April
1   Changed the Direction found by the stars on the 21st and 22nd of October last,
to be in the true Parallel at 10' West. Thus
as 11.37 miles : 12.84 chains :: 52.68 chains : 74.36 links
This 74.36 Links we laid off to the South of the mark left according to the stars
(it being to the Eastward 52 chains 68 links from where we left off last season)
and continued the Line in the Direction so changed.
2   Continued the Line.
3   Continued Ditto. At 118 miles 63 chains crossed the Head of little Licking Creek
running into Conecocheage.
4   Continued the Line. At 119 miles 18 chains (The summit of the North Mountain) Fort
Frederick in Maryland nearly south Distant about 8 Miles, and Fort Loudon (under
Parnel's Nob in Pennsylvania) nearly North, Distant about 11 miles.
At 119 miles 47 chains crossed the first Spring running in the Big Licking creek which
is on the West side of the North Mountain.
5   Continued the Line.
6 Sun.   Snow
7   Rain ⎫
8   Rain ⎪
9   Rain ⎬   Waiting for the Waggons and Tents; which were
10   Rain ⎪   prevented arriving by Weather, etc.
11   Rain ⎪
12   Rain ⎭
13 Sunday
14   Mr. McLane came with the Waggons, Tents, etc.   183
15   Snow and Rain.
16   Continued the Line.
17   Continued the Line. At 121 miles 61 chains crossed a Road leading
from Fort Frederick to the little cove.
18   Continued the Line. At 122 miles 67 chains crossed Great Licking-creek, at the
foot of the North Mountain on the West Side.
At 123 miles 6 chains Mr. Brown's House 6 chains North.
19   Continued the Line.
20 Sunday
21   Continued the Line. At 126 miles 71 chains crossed the 1st branch
of the Conoloways. Snow fell all the afternoon.
22   Continued the Line. In the morning the Snow 4 inches deep in General.

23 Continued the line. At 128 miles 24 chains crossed the big Conoloway-creek.
At 129 miles 12 chains 04 links changed our direction to be again in the Parallel
at 10' West. Thus

			(log)
As SM = Sm = 52 chains 68 links (see 1st April)			= 3.721646
: Radius			=10.
:: NM = nm	74.36 Links		= 1.871339
: Tangent Angle nSm = MSN = 48' 32''			8.149693

     Angle PSC =   89° 55' 51''
     Angle PSA =   89° 07' 19'' Then
         (log)

As Sine AP	50° 16' 40''	= 9.8860120
: Sine PSA	89° 07' 19''	= 9.9999490
:: Sine PS	50° 16' 48''47	= 9.8860268
: Sine of	89° 15' 37''	9.9999638
Comp.	90° 44' 23''	= SAP = QAC
BAP =	89° 55' 51''	= PSC
Sum =	180° 40' 14''	
	-180° 00' 00''	
Rest	0° 40' 14''	= BAQ which must

Here P, the Pole : OAB
the true Parallel. S, the
Sector at the North Mountain
SCK the Parallel in at
the said Mountain, MSC the
direction we came in. MN
the said direction changed which
we went off in. MN the
Quantity changed = 74.36 Links
to the Eastward of S.

be laid off from the direction NSnAQ to the Southward, to give the direction or chord
AB, that is, to be again in the Parallel at 10' West.

       (log)

Now as Rad	10.
to 40 chains (4000 links)	3.6020600
:: Sine 40' 14''	8.0684811
: 46.8 Links	1.6705411

The ground admitting we measured a Radius = 48.23 chains = Ap
Then as 40 : 46.8 links :: 48.23 : 56.43 Links. This we laid off from p to b and continued Figure
the Line in the direction A to B as follows.   184

17 The Sun's Limbs 6h 11m 25s
       6 14 5
Set over the Allegany Mountain seen from the North
Mountain, distant about 50 miles
(indistinct) the apparent time.   185

24 Continued the Line. { At 129 3/4 miles by estimation the
       { Northernmost bend of the River Potowmack
       { Bore South distant about a mile and a half.

     { 130 miles 48 chains Mr. Edward Coomb's House 10 chains, North.
At   { 131 miles 20 chains Mr. Joseph Coomb's House 50 Links, North.
     { 132 miles 28 chains crossed the little Conoloway creek.

25 Continued the Line.
26 Continued the Line.
At 134 miles 54 chains The foot of Sidelong Hill (Here we could proceed no further with the waggons.)
  135 miles 29 chains The Top of Ditto.

27 Sunday
28 Continued the Line.
At 136 miles 27 chains crossed little Bear-creek at the foot of Sidelong Hill
on the West side.
  136 miles 50 chains crossed Big Bear Creek.
29 Continued the Line. At 138 miles 00 chains 40 links entered Sidelong Hill Creek.
Crossed the said creek three times and at 138 miles 50 chains left Ditto.
30 Sent for the Sector from Captain Shelby's.

May
1 (Blank)
2 The Sector brought to the East Side of Sidelong Hill.
3 Ditto brought to the foot of Town Hill on the East Side.
4 Sun. Set up the Sector (at Ditto) in our direction, at the distance
of 140 miles 15 chains 76 links from the Post marked West in Mr. Bryan's field
and made the following observations.   186

1766
May
5

Plane of the Sector East

Star Name	Nearest Point on the Sector		Revolutions and Seconds on the Micrometer		Difference		Apparent Zenith Distance		
	°	'	R	"	'	"	°	'	"
Alpha Lyrae	1	10-	5	23	1	5.0	1	08	55.0
			4	10					
Delta Cygni	4	50+	5	5	0	29.5	4	50	29.5
			4	27.5					
Gamma Cygni	0	15-	4	32-	2	29.7	0	12	30.3
			1	38					
Alpha Cygni	4	45-	1	38	1	29.0	4	43	31.0
			3	23					
6 Capella	6	00+	8	10-	0	47.7	6	00	47.7 faint
			7	14					
Alpha Lyrae	1	10-	8	47-	1	3.2	1	08	56.8
			7	35.5					
Delta Cygni	4	50+	6	15+	0	29.8	4	50	29.8
			5	37.5					
Gamma Cygni	0	15-	7	27.5	2	29.5	0	12	30.5
			4	34					
Alpha Cygni	4	45-	5	47.5	1	27.0	4	43	33.0
			7	30.5					
7 Capella	6	00+	8	43.5	0	46.5	6	00	46.5 faint
			7	49					
Alpha Lyrae	1	10-	8	1+	1	5.3	1	08	54.7
			6	40					
Delta Cygni	4	50+	7	36	0	28.5	4	50	28.5
			7	7.5					
Gamma Cygni	0	15-	8	47.5	2	29.5	0	12	30.5
			6	2					
Alpha Cygni	4	45-	7	37+	1	28.2	4	43	31.8
			9	21.5					

8

Turned the Sector Plane West

Star Name	Nearest Point on the Sector		Revolutions and Seconds on the Micrometer		Difference		Apparent Zenith Distance		
Delta Cygni	4	50+	8	12	0	36.0	4	50	36.0
			8	48					
Gamma Cygni	0	15-	8	40	2	36.0	0	12	24.0
			11	40					
Alpha Cygni	4	45-	11	16.5	1	23.0	4	43	37.0
			9	37.5					

9 Cloudy
10 Cloudy
11 Sun. Cloudy   The Oak and Hickory Buds just breaking into Leaf.

Star Name	Nearest Point on the Sector		Revolutions and Seconds on the Micrometer		Difference		Apparent Zenith Distance		
12 Alpha Lyrae	1	10-	8	34	1	9.5	1	08	50.5
			9	51.5					187
13 Alpha Lyrae	1	10-	5	50-	1	11.8	1	08	48.2
			7	17.5					
Delta Cygni	4	50+	5	28+	0	37.0	4	50	37.0
			6	13+					
Alpha Cygni	4	45-	6	47.5	1	24.5	4	43	35.5
			5	15					

For the Direction at our Station 140 miles from the Post marked West.
Time by the clock

11h 22m 31s	11h 56m 46s	23h 31m 22s	} Equal altitudes of Gamma Leonis
27 23	12 3 53	31 16	
34 36-	8 54	31 25	

11h 45m 41s	
11 37 08	= Right Ascension of Star
8 m 33s	= Clock fast for Sidereal Time

13 46 4 -	14 33 52 -	28 27 12 ::	} Equal altitudes of Arcturus
49 27.5	37 54	27 21.5	
53 20	41 15.5	27 19	

14 13 40	
14 5 2	= Right Ascension of Star
8 38	Clock fast

1766 May
Clock fast

14 51 15	= { Right Ascension Mid-Heaven when Gamma Leonis is on the azimuth
{ + 8 38	{ of 89° 55' 51" Westward from the North
{ + 0 1.5	
14 59 54.5	= Time by the clock when on Ditto.
16 17 28	= Right Ascension Mid-Heaven when Beta Leonis is on Ditto.
+ 8 38	
+00 04	
16 26 10	Time by the Clock when on Ditto
18 19 00	= Right Ascension Mid-Heaven when Arcturus on the Azimuth
+ 8 38	
+ 0 8.5	
18 27 46.5	Time by the clock when on Ditto.

When Regulus passed according to the clock we placed a mark as usual : its distance
from the Transit Instrument was 33 chains, 9 Links; and when Beta Leonis and Arcturus
passed we placed other marks. The extremes of the three were distant Eight Inches.   188

Star Name	Nearest Point on the Sector		Revolutions and Seconds on the Micrometer		Difference		Apparent Zenith Distance		
	°	'	R	"	'	"	°	'	"
Delta Cygni	4	50+	11	39.5	0	35.8	4	50	35.8
			12	23+					
Gamma Cygni	0	15-	11	31+	2	36.7	0	12	23.3
			14	32					
Alpha Cygni	4	45-	17	12	1	25.0	4	43	35.0
			15	31					
Alpha Lyrae	1	10-	12	0+	1	12.4	1	08	47.6
			13	21-					
Delta Cygni	4	50+	13	29+	0	38.4	4	50	38.4
			14	16-					
Gamma Cygni	0	15-	13	46.5	2	37.2	0	12	22.8
			16	48-					
Alpha Cygni	4	45-	1	2.5	1	24.5	4	43	35.5
			17	22					
Capella	6	00+	9	19	0	49.0	6	00	49.0
			10	16					

(row labels in left margin: 14, 15, 16)

Computing our observations as follows.   189

1766 May

Plane of the Sector East

	Alpha Lyrae (o ' ")	Delta Cygni (o ' ")	Gamma Cygni (o ' ")	Alpha Cygni (o ' ")	Capella (o ' ")
5	1 8 55.0	4 50 29.5	0 12 30.3	4 43 31.0	
6	1 8 56.8	4 50 29.8	0 12 30.5	4 43 33.0	6 00 47.7
7	54.7	28.5	30.5	31.8	46.5
Mean	6d 16h 1 8 55.50	6d 17h 4 50 29.27	6d 17h 0 12 30.43	6d 14h 4 43 31.93	6d 14h 6 00 47.10
Aberration	−13.16	+16.20	−16.02	+17.13	− 2.05
Deviation	− 7.05	+ 5.28	− 4.11	+ 3.43	− 8.48
Precession	+ 5.91	−19.41	+26.07	−29.21	−12.41
Refraction	+ 1.20	+ 5.60	+ 0.20	+ 5.50	+ 7.00
Mean Zen. Dist.	1 8 42.40	4 50 36.94	0 12 36.57	4 43 28.78	6 00 31.16

1st Jan. 1764 Plane East

Plane West

	Alpha Lyrae (o ' ")	Delta Cygni (o ' ")	Gamma Cygni (o ' ")	Alpha Cygni (o ' ")	Capella (o ' ")
8		4 50 36.0	0 12 24.0	4 43 37.0	
12	1 8 50.5				
13	1 8 48.2	50 37.0	23.3	43 35.5	
14		50 35.8	23.3	43 35.0	
15	1 8 47.6	50 38.4	22.8	43 35.5	
16					6 00 49.0
Mean	13d 4h 1 8 48.77	13d 1h 4 50 36.80	13d 0 12 23.37	13d 5h 4 43 35.75	16d 2h 6 00 49.0
Aberration	−11.60	+15.15	−15.20	+16.42	− 0.80
Deviation	− 7.05	+ 5.28	− 4.11	+ 3.43	− 8.48
Precession	+ 5.96	−19.57	+26.28	−29.45	−12.51
Refraction	+ 1.20	+ 5.60	+ 0.20	+ 5.50	+ 7.00
Mean Zen. Dist.	1 8 37.28	4 50 43.26	0 12 30.54	4 43 31.65	6 00 34.21

1st Jan. 1764 Plane West

	Alpha Lyrae	Delta Cygni	Gamma Cygni	Alpha Cygni	Capella
Ditto Plane East	1 8 42.40	4 50 36.94	0 12 36.57	4 43 28.78	6 00 31.16
True Zen. Dist.	1 8 39.84	4 50 40.10	0 12 33.55	4 43 30.21	6 00 32.69
1st Jan. 1764 Ditto at the Post	1 8 41.80	4 50 40.40	0 12 33.00	4 43 31.20	6 00 31.80
Marked West	1.96 South	0.30 North	0.55 North	0.99 North	0.89 South

Hence $\dfrac{1''.96 - 0'.30 - 0'.55 - 0'.99 + 0'.89}{5} = 0'.20 = 20$ feet $= 31$ links

that we are South of the true Parallel.

(Undated)   Hence the offsets at every mile Post to where the Sector was
set up on the 7th of October last as follows.

Miles from the Post marked West	Circle from the chords AB and BC	Triang. SRP hence PB = 44 Links must be added constant		True Offsets		
	Links	Chains	Links	Chains	Links	
117.162	0	12	40=SR	12	84	North
118	8	11	50	11	86	
119	16	10	40	10	68	
120	22	9	31	9	53	
121	25	8	25	8	42	
122	27	7	14	7	31	North
123	27	6	05	6	22	
124	26	4	96	5	14	
125	23	3	86	4	07	
126	18	2	76	3	02	
127	12	1	67	1	99	North
128	5	0	58	0	97	North
Changed the Direction 129	4	0	2N	0	2 S	For bd = 4 links = Circle
129m 12ch.04links	5	0	11S	0	16	from the chord and cb =
130	13	0	08	0	21	2 = Line from the chord
131	19	0	04	0	23	then cd = 2 = offset
132	23	0	00.5	0	23.5	from the Line.
133	26	0	03	0	23	
134	27	0	07	0	20	
135	27	0	11	0	16	
136	26	0	15	0	11	South
137	24	0	19	0	05	South
138	19	0	22	0	03	North
139	12	0	26	0	14	North
140	3	0	30	0	27	North
Sector 140.197	0	0	00	0	31	North

191

(Undated)   Here ABC the true Parallel
AB and BC chords of 11.37 miles nearly
S the Sector at the North Mountain
N Ditto at Town Hill
SLN the Line run. P the point we should have changed at
if the ground would have permitted: L the Point we did change at
Then L = 129.150 miles where we did change

P = 128.532 = 117.162 + 11.37 miles

rest PL= 0.618 = What we have over run at an angle of 40' 14" (see minutes
of the 23rd April) = KPL hence KL = 58 Links = MN : for LN and PM are Parallel
Then if we had changed at P our error would have been 58 + 31 = 89 Links = MC: Hence
as the whole length of the Line 23.035 miles : 89 links :: 11.37 miles : 44 links = PB.
And as 23.035 : 89 :: 11.988 (= SP + PL) : 47 links = Kg
or as PM = 11.665 miles : (89 - 44) (= MC - PB) :: PL = .618 miles = PK : 3 links nearly.
Then 44 + 3 = 47 = Kg as before.
Now KL - Kg = 58 - 47 = 11 = gL = what we run to the North of the chord BC,
before we changed.   Then as NC + gL = 42 links : LN = 11.047 miles ::
gL = 11 links : 2.9 miles = LQ.
Then the point L = 129.150 miles + 2.9 miles = 132.050 miles, the point Q where we passed
the chord BC. and where we passed the true parallel will be at D, where the offset
from the chord is = the offset in the Triangle NQC which falls at 137.625 miles
As LK = 58 : PK = 0.618 miles :: gL:0.117 = pg, then 129.150 miles - 0.117 = 129.033 miles
the point p, where the Visto crossed the chord BC.
From the whole, the Quantity of the Triangle NQC, gQL, gpL and pBP
corresponding to the intermediate miles, are had by proportion, as by the second column.

Figure
192

124

17   Placed a mark to the Eastward (in the direction found by the stars on
the 13th Instant) so as to be seen from the Summit of Town Hill.

18 Sun.   Packing up Instruments.

19   Continued the Line in the direction found by the stars, that is, to
be in the Parallel we are now in at 10' West.
At 140 miles 54 chains. The top of Town Hill.

20   Continued the Line.
At 143 miles 77 chains crossed 15 Mile Creek.

21   Continued the Line.
At 146 miles 52 chains. The top of Ragged-Mountain.

22   Continued the Line.
At 148 miles 21 chains crossed Old Town Creek.

23 }   Brought the Sector etc., from the Town Hill to the
24 }   Warrior Mountain

25 Sunday

26   Continued the Line
At 149 miles 17 chains the top of little Warrior Mountain.

27   Continued the Line. At 151 miles 48 chains the summit of
the great Warrior Mountain. Here we changed our
direction 8' 18" to the Northward, that is, to be in the Parallel
we are now in at 10' West : thus
as 40 chains : 9.6575 links (corresponding to the angle 8' 18") :: 1 mile 53 chains 87 links =
(Radius we measured) : 32.31 links. This we laid off to the Northward from our
direction on Flintstone Mountain.
At 151 miles 67 chains, crossed Flintstone Creek.
    153 miles 21 chains 87 links, the top of Flintstone Mountain.   193

28   Continued the Line.
At 154 miles 28 chains crossed a Run between Flintstone Mountain
and Evits Mountain

29   Continued the Line.
At 155 miles 33 chains. The Summit of Evits Creek Mountain
At 156 miles 69 chains, crossed the 1st Branch of Evits Creek.} These (last two) join about
At 156 miles 79 chains, crossed the 2nd Branch of Ditto.   } 1/4 mile South.

30   Continued the Line.
At 157 miles 64 chains, The top of Nobbley Mountain.
At 157 miles 75 chains, crossed the Road leading from Fort Cumberland
to Bedford.

31   Continued the Line.
At 159 miles 71 chains The summit of Wills' Creek Mountain:
Here by the estimation of some who live near the place, Fort
Cumberland bears South, distant between 5 and 6 miles.
At 161 miles 25 chains crossed Wills' Creek: This creek in general about 30 yards
in breadth, and at this time 1.5 or 2 feet nearly in depth.

June

1 Sunday

2   Continued the Line.

3   Continued the Line.

4   Continued the Line.
At 163 miles 57 chains The Summit of the little Allegany Mountain.

5   At 165 miles 28 chains crossed the North Branch of Jennings' Run.

6 }   Brought the Sector etc., from the Warrior Mountain to the foot
7 }   (on the East side) of Savage Mountain : (the 2nd Ridge of the
8 Sun. } Allegany Mountains).   194

Set up the Sector in the Direction of our Line
at the distance of 165 miles 54 chains 88 links from the Post marked West
in Mr. Bryan's field, and made the following observations:

Plane of the Sector EAST

Star Name	Nearest Point on the Sector		Revolutions and Seconds on the Micrometer		Difference		Apparent Zenith Distance		
	o	'	R	''	'	''	o	'	''
Alpha Lyrae	1	10-	5	12-	1	16.4	1	8	43.6
			3	39+					
Delta Cygni	4	50+	7	2-	0	39.7	4	50	39.7
			6	14					
Gamma Cygni	0	15-	6	27	2	42.5	0	12	17.5
			3	20.5					
Alpha Cygni	4	45-	3	31.5	1	17.5	4	43	42.5
			5	5					

10

Alpha Lyrae	1	10-	7	38-	1	15.0	1	08	45.0
			6	15-					
Delta Cygni	4	50+	6	9-	0	40.7	4	50	40.7
			5	20					
Gamma Cygni	0	15-	5	39+	2	41.3	0	12	18.7
			2	34					
Alpha Cygni	4	45-	2	18	1	18.3	4	43	41.7
			3	44+					

11

Alpha Lyrae	1	10-	5	44	1	16.0	1	8	44.0
			4	20					
Delta Cygni	4	50+	3	39	0	41.3	4	50	41.3
			2	50-					
Gamma Cygni	0	15-	4	31-	2	41.7	0	12	18.3
			1	25					
Alpha Cygni	4	45-	17	40.5	1	17.5	4	43	42.5
			1	14					

195

12 Turned the Sector: Plane WEST

Star Name	Nearest Point on the Sector		Revolutions an and Seconds on the Micrometer		Difference		Apparent Zenith Distance		
	o	'	R	''	'	''	o	'	''

13

Alpha Lyrae	1	10-	1	14	1	20.7	1	8	39.3
			2	43-					
Delta Cygni	4	50+	2	18	0	45.7	4	50	45.7
			3	12-					
Gamma Cygni	0	15-	3	21	2	45.5	0	12	14.5
			6	30.5					
Alpha Cygni	4	45-	6	15-	1	14.2	4	43	45.8
			4	44.5					

14

Alpha Lyrae	1	10-	6	14+	1	21.4	1	8	38.6
			7	44-					
Delta Cygni	4	50+	9	3- ::	0	49.6	4	50	49.6 ::
			10	0+					
Gamma Cygni	0	15-	10	16-	2	46.8	0	12	13.2
			13	26.5					
Alpha Cygni	4	45-	5	42.5	1	13.5	4	43	46.5
			4	21					

15 Sun.

Alpha Lyrae	1	10-	5	10+	1	21.7	1	08	38.3
			6	40					
Delta Cygni	4	50+	7	31.5 ::		51.8			
			8	31+					
Gamma Cygni	0	15-	8	17	2	46.5	0	12	13.5
			11	27.5					
Alpha Cygni	4	45-	9	4-	1	14.4	4	43	45.6
			7	33+					

16 }
17 }

Computing our observations, offsets, etc., as follows:
Ditto

N.B. Capella passing the Meridian with the Sun, and the weather
in general a little hazy in the day time, prevented our
making any observations of that Star.

Plane of the Sector EAST

		Alpha Lyrae			Delta Cygni			Gamma Cygni			Alpha Cygni		
		o	'	"	o	'	"	o	'	"	o	'	"
June	9	1	08	43.6	4	50	39.7	0	12	17.5	4	43	42.5
	10		08	45.0		50	40.7		12	18.7		43	41.7
	11		08	44.0		50	41.3		12	18.3		43	42.5
Mean	10d 13h	1	08	44.20	4	50	40.57	0	12	18.17	4	43	42.23
Aberration				− 4.52			+ 8.69			− 9.62			+11.22
Deviation				− 6.86			+ 5.03			− 3.85			+ 3.19
Precession				+ 6.15			−20.18			+27.08			−30.35
Refraction				+ 1.20			+ 5.60			+ 0.20			+ 5.50
Mean Zen. Dist. the 1st Jan. 1764		1	08	40.17	4	50	39.71	0	12	31.98	4	43	31.79

Plane WEST

		Alpha Lyrae			Delta Cygni			Gamma Cygni			Alpha Cygni		
June	13	1	08	39.3	4	50	45.7	0	12	14.5	4	43	45.8
	14		08	38.6					12	13.2		43	46.5
	15		08	38.3					12	13.5		43	45.6
Mean	14d 13h for Alpha Lyrae	1	08	38.73	4	50	45.70	0	12	13.73	4	43	45.97
Aberration				− 3.38			+ 7.59			− 8.63			+10.26
Deviation				− 6.86			+ 5.03			− 3.85			+ 3.19
Precession				+ 6.18			−20.27			+27.20			−30.48
Refraction				+ 1.20			+ 5.60			+ 0.20			+ 5.50
Mean Zen. Dist. the 1st Jan. 1764		1	08	35.87	4	50	43.65	0	12	28.65	4	43	34.44
Ditto Plane East		1	08	40.17	4	50	39.71	0	12	31.98	4	43	31.79
Mean Zen. Dist. the 1st Jan. 1764		1	08	38.02	4	50	41.68	0	12	30.31	4	43	33.11
Ditto at Post marked West		1	08	41.80	4	50	40.40	0	12	33.00	4	43	31.20
				3.78			1.28			2.69			1.91
				South			South			South			South

(Average of four values) = 2.ʺ41 = 241 ft. = 3.66 chains
That we are to the South of the true Parallel.

(Undated) Hence the offsets at every Mile Post to where the
Sector was set up, the 4th of May as follows:

Miles from the Post marked West	Circle from the Chord	Triangle taking the whole length of the Line. Then 31 Links = AT = OP must be constantly added.		True offsets	
	Links	Chains	Links	Chains	Links
140. 197 miles	− 0	0	00	0	31 North
141	− 8	0	10	0	33
142	−15	0	22	0	38
143	−21	0	33	0	43
144	−25	0	45	0	51
145	−27	0	57	0	61
146	−27	0	69	0	73
147	−25	0	80	0	86
148	−22	0	92	1	01
149	−18	1	05	1	18
150	−12	1	17	1	36
Changed ⎫ 151	− 4	1	30	1	57
the ⎬ 151 mi. 48 ch. 0 li.	− 0	1	35	1	66
Direction ⎭ 152	− 5	1	42	1	68
153	−12	1	53	1	72
154	−18	1	65	1	78
155	−22	1	77	1	86
156	−25	1	88	1	94
157	−27	2	00	2	04
158	−27	2	12	2	16
159	−25	2	24	2	30
160	−21	2	36	2	46
161	−15	2	47	2	63
162	− 8	2	58	2	81
163	+07 ⎫Triangle	2	71	3	03
164	+12 ⎪LBc south	2	83	3	26
165	+24 ⎬of the	2	95	3	50
Sector 165. 686 miles	+32 ⎭Parallel	3	03	3	66 North 198

(Undated)   Here TGP the true Parallel. ADMO the Parallel we were in at
Town Hill. Then AT = DG = OP = 31 Links.
ACLB the course run from the Town Hill. AC = CL= 11. 37 miles

Then   165. 686 miles
          −140. 197
AB =   25. 489
AL =   22. 74
BL =   2. 749 = What we have over run the usual distance, at an
angle (with the chord Ld) of 8' 18" (the constant change supposing we had changed
at L to have been again in the Parallel at 10' West). Hence as Rad : BL ::
Sine 8' 18" = Angle BLd : Bd = 53 Links. And since cd = 21 links (= the distance of the
chord from the circle at 2. 749 Miles from L) 53 − 21 will be = Bc = 32 links = the
distance of the Parallel we were in at L.
Now   32 links = Bc
          +31   = OP
Sum   63 which subtract from BP = 3. 66 chains (= Distance from the true Parallel found
by the Sector remains 3. 03 = co. And then as AB: Co :: AL : LM = 2. 70 chains =
the distance from the Parallel we were in at Town Hill, when we had run
22. 74 Miles.
From the whole the different parts of the Triangle cLCADMo corresponding to
the intermediate miles is found (they being similar straight lines) by proportion : To
which apply the small triangle BcL*, the chord from the circle, and the constant Quantity
31 Links, that we were to the South at A; gives the true offsets from BLCA, as
by the Table.

*The right line Lc and the circle Lpc differ so little may be estimated the same.

Figure
199

128

Saturday the 14th of June, 1766. Went to the top of Savage Mountain,
about 2 miles from the Tents. From hence; to the Summit of the next
Ridge called the little Meadow Mountain:
I judge by appearances to be about 5 or 6 miles: Between this, (Savage or Allegany Mts.)
and the said little Meadow Mountain, runs Savage River; which empties into
the North Branch of Potowmack: This is the most Westernmost
Waters, that runs to the Eastward in these parts.
Beyond the Dividing Mountain (Savage), the waters all run to the Westward;
The first of Note (which our Line would cross if continued) is the little Yochio
Geni, running into the Monaungahela, which falls into the Ohio or
Allegany River at Pitsbourg (about 80 miles West, and 30 or 40 North from hence) called
by the French Fort Duquesne.
The Ohio is Navigable for small craft by the accounts I have had from
many that have passed down it; and falls in to the River Mississippi
(about 36.5 degrees of North Latitude; Longitude 92 degrees from London); which empties
itself in to the Bay of Florida.
The Lands on the Monaungahela and Ohio are allowed to be
the best of any in the known parts of North America: The
Rivers abound with variety of Fish, and quantity almost incredible.
At present the Allegany Mountains is the Boundary
between the Natives and strangers; in these parts of his
Britanic Majesties Collonies.
From the solitary tops of these mountains, the Eye
gazes round with pleasure; filling the mind with
adoration to that prevading spirit that made them.

200

18   Set a post (18 Inches square, 3 feet in the ground and 5 above) at the
distance of 3.66 chains, North of the Sector, marked M, on the South
Side, P on the North Side, and W on the West: and began to cut a
Visto in the true Parallel or Line between Maryland and Pennsylvania:
By drawing it through points, laid off from the Line we have run, at
every 10 chains.

19   Continued the Visto or Line, toward the Post marked West in Mr. Bryan's field.
20   Carried the Instruments to Mr. Stumblestones in Wills Creek Valley.
21   Continued the Line to the 162 Mile post.
22 Sun.   Went to see Fort Cumberland: It is beautifully situated on a rising
ground, close in the Northwest fork made by the falling in of Wills
Creek into Potowmack; The Fort is in bad repair; has in it at present
only 10 Six Pounders.   Going to the Fort I fell into General Braddock's Road,
which he cut through the Mountains to lead the Army under his command
to the Westward in the year 1755, but fate; how hard: made through
the desert a path, himself to pass; and never; never to return.
23   Continued the Line. Sent three men with the Telescope
of the Sector to Captain Shelby's.
24   Continued the Line.
25   Continued the Line.
26   Continued the Line.
27   Continued the Line.
28   Continued the Line to the 154th Mile Post.
29 Sunday
30   Continued the Line.
July
1   Continued the Line.
2   Continued the Line.
3   Continued the Line.
4   Continued the Line.
5   Continued the Line to the 140th Mile Post.
From the summit of Town Hill, the Visto shows itself to be the Arch of a lesser circle
of the Sphere, or Parallel of North Latitude: That part of the visto passing over the
Ragged Mountain, being apparently to the South of a right line extended to the visto
at the top of Evits Mountain.

201

July

  6 Sun.   At Town Hill: Measured three leaves on one Stem of a Hickory,
            Each of which was 17 Inches in length and 12 inches in breadth.

  7   Continued the Line. This day from the Summit of Sidelong Hill I saw the Line still
            formed the arch of a lesser circle very beautiful, and agreeable to the Laws of a Sphere.

  8   Continued the Line.

  9   Continued the Line.

10   Continued the Line.

11   Continued the Line.

12   Continued the Line to the 127th Mile Post.

13 Sunday

14   Continued the Line.

15   Continued the Line.

16   Continued the Line.

17   Continued the Line.

18   Continued the Line.

19   Continued the Line to the 118th Mile Post.

20 Sun.   (19th, 20th and 22nd) I went to the Summit of the North
            Mountain when the air was so hazy I could not see the Visto over Evit's
            Mountain: But the chain carriers told me they saw it very plain on Friday the 18th;
            and that the Visto over Sidelong Hill appeared to the South of a right line
            (or arch of a great circle) extending to the Visto on Evit's Mountain. The quantity I
            intended to have measured but was prevented for the reason above.

21   Continued the Line.

22   Continued the Line.

23   Continued the Line.

24   Continued the Line.

25   Continued the Line.

26   Continued the Line to the 107th Mile Post.

27 Sunday

28   Rain.

29   Continued the Line.

30   Continued the Line.

31   Continued the Line.

August

  1   Continued the Line.

  2   Continued the Line to the 96th Mile Post.

  3 Sunday

  4   Continued the Line. A great Storm of Thunder and Lightning: The
            Lightning in continued streams or streaks, from the
            Cloud to the ground all round us; about 5 minutes before
            the hurricane of wind and Rain; the Cloud from the
            Western part of the Mountain put on the most Dreadful
            appearance I ever saw: It seemed to threaten an
            immediate dissolution to all beneath it.

  5   Continued the Line.
            The Sun Eclipsed
            Time by the Clock   Time by the Clock   Sun's Lower Limb

202

h	m	s	h	m	s	o	'
8	7	5	16	0	47	68	16
	9	42	15	58	15	69	18
	11	7				69	50
	12	47				70	30
	13	56				70	57
	15	37				71	33-
	18	6				72	32.5
	19	4				72	51
	20	12				73	17
8	21	58				73	36

Equal altitudes of Sun's Lower Limb: Hence the Sun's center passed the Meridian by the mean of these two observations at 12h 3m 57s by the clock.

Clouds prevented observing these corresponding altitudes

11 12   The Eclipse had not begun

11 18   The Eclipse began within about one minute of this time

Clouds during almost all the morning: and flying so quick we could seldom have sight of the sun two minutes at a time

1766
August

5   Afternoon

h	m	s		°	′	
2	20	17	The Eclipse Ended			
2	20	12	Ditto by Mr. Dixon			
3	23	9		83	36	⎫
	24	44		83	3	⎬ Altitudes double. Sun's Upper Limb
	26	47		82	15.5	
	28	48		81	32	⎭
4	2	35		67	31	⎫
	6	37		65	57.5	⎬ Altitudes double. Sun's Lower Limb
	8	38		65	15	
	9	32		64	51	
	11	39		63	56	⎭
4	14	58		62	45	⎫
	18	00		61	39	⎬ Ditto for Mr. Dixon
	21	15		60	26	
	22	46		59	41	
	24	1		59	16	
	25	33		58	41	⎭

The altitudes were taken with a Hadley's Quadrant (of 18 Inch Radius) by reflection
in Quicksilver. The adjustment of the Quadrant one minute 20 seconds to be
subtracted from the observed angles: We had no Instrument with us that we
could use to find time with besides this, or any micrometer, but by appearance
the digits eclipsed were about seven*: the light was greatly diminished,
and at the middle very heavy, gloomy darkness took place.
The End of the Eclipse was observed with Reflecting Telescope
that magnified about 70 Times.
*(This evidently refers to proportion of totality.)

203

6   Time by Clock

      Forenoon

h	m	s	°	′	
7	53	28	60	57	⎫
	54	44	61	28	
	56	7	61	58	
	57	38	62	31.5	⎬ Double Altitudes of the Sun's Lower Limb
7	59	37	63	19	
8	1	11	63	56.5	
	3	14	64	43.5	
	4	28	65	10	⎭

In these the adjustment of the Quadrant is one Minute and a half
to be added to the observed angles. I could wish the adjustment
                 of these 20 seconds were not so subject to change

These observations were made in the South-Mountain
768*yards North of the Line and 92 Miles 20 chains from the Post
marked West in Mr. Bryan's field.
  *Latitude = 39° 43′ 41″ North

               This day went to the Summit of the
Continued the Line.   South Mountain, but there was
               such a thick Blue mist in the Valley I
               could not see the Visto to the North Mountain.

7   Continued the Line.
8   Continued the Line.
9   Continued the Line to the 85th Mile Post.
10 Sunday
11   Continued the Line.
12   Continued the Line.
13   Continued the Line.
14   Continued the Line.
15   Continued the Line.
16   Continued the Line to the 73rd Mile Post.
17 Sunday
18   Continued the Line.
19   Continued the Line.
20   Continued the Line.

204

August

20   Eclipse of the Moon

Time by the Watch

h	m	s		
2	55	30		in the Morning the Eclipse ended.

                                o   '

h	m	s	o	'	
3	13	55	31	12	⎫
3	16	50	30	23-	⎬ Altitudes of Alpha Lyrae taken double.
3	20	40	29	15.5	⎭

by reflection with a Hadley's Quadrant to which was applied
a Telescope that magnified about 4 times: Adjustment
of the Quadrant one minute to be added to the observed angles.
Digits eclipsed about 5, the edge of the shade was
not near so well defined as that which happened the
17th of March 1764.
These were observed about 2 Miles North of the Line and
opposite the 67th Mile Post

21   Continued the Line.

22   Continued the Line.

23   Continued the Line to the 61st Mile Post. From near this place the Visto at the top of the
South Mountain is seen; and shows the Line still forms a true Parallel of North Latitude

24 Sunday

25   Continued the Line.

26   Continued the Line.

27   Continued the Line.

28   Continued the Line.

29   Continued the Line.

30   Continued the Line to the 44th Mile Post.

31 Sunday   205

September

1   Continued the Line.

2   Continued the Line.

3   Continued the Line.

4   Continued the Line.

5   Continued the Line.

6   Continued the Line to the 30th Mile Post. From the top of Slate
Ridge (at the 31 Mile Post). I saw the Visto still formed the natural Parallel.

7 Sunday

8   Continued the Line.

9   Rain.

10   Continued the Line.

11   Continued the Line.

12   Continued the Line. Sent Expresses to Annapolis, and Philadelphia to acquaint
the Gentlemen Commissioners we should finish with the Line the 27th of this Month.

13   Continued the Line to the 21st Mile Post.

14 Sunday

15   Continued the Line.

16   Rain.

17   Continued the Line.

18   Continued the Line.

19   Continued the Line.

20   Continued the Line to the 13th Mile Post.

21 Sunday

22   Continued the Line.

23   Continued the Line.

24   Continued the Line.

25   Continued the Line to the intersection of the Meridian
from the Tangent point with the Parallel which finished
our Instructions.   206

N. B. From any Eminence in the Line where 15 or
20 Miles of the Visto can be seen (of which there are many): The said Line
or Visto, very apparently shows itself to form
a Parallel of Northern Latitude.
The Line is measured Horizontal; the Hills and Mountains measured with a 16 1/2 feet
Level and besides the Mile Posts; we have set Posts in the true Line,
marked W, on the West side, all along the Line opposite
the Stationary Points where the Sector and Transit Instrument
stood. The said Posts stand in the Middle of the
Visto; which in general is about Eight yards wide.
The number of Posts set in the West Line is 303.

26   (No entry was made)

27   Received a letter from the Gentlemen Commissioners for Pennsylvania
acquainting us, that the next meeting of the Commissioners
for both Provinces; is to be held at Christiana Bridge
in Newcastle County; the 28th of next Month.

30   Discharged all Hands

October
1

At Newark in Newcastle County   207
In the letter mentioned last, the Commissioners informed us,
they had no objection of our employing the interval of
time to the 28th Instant, in executing our instructions from
the Royal Society of London; towards determining the
Length of a Degree of Latitude (of which Instructions the
commissioners of both Provinces had received notice from the
Honorable: the Proprietors: To whom we wrote in June 1765 for leave to use their Instruments;
and the indulgence to do it in their Provinces.)
Accordingly from this information, we this day set out
with the Sector* etc. for the Middle Point, or South end
of the Tangent Line; To execute the following Instructions from the Royal Society.

   * The Telescope part, carried by three Men.   208

                    October 24, 1765
At a Council of the Royal Society

Resolved that the precise measure of a degree of Latitude in
America in the neighborhood of Pennsylvania appears to the Council
and to the Astronomer Royal who was pleased to assist on this
occasion, to be a work of great use, and importance: and, that the
known abilities of Messrs. Mason and Dixon, the Excellence of the
Instruments with which they are furnished, the favorable level
of the Country, and their having assistants well practised in Measuring;
do all concur in giving good Ground to hope, that this
business may soon be executed with greater precision, than had ever
yet been done; and at a much less charge than the Society can expect
an opportunity of doing it hereafter.

Resolved to employ Messrs. Mason and Dixon in the said
admeasurement of a degree of latitude and to allow them the
whole of their demand, being the sum of two hundred Pounds Sterling
for the said Work: and also in case, the Proprietors of Maryland and
Pennsylvania should refuse their stipulated allowance for their
passage home, but not otherwise, the further sum of forty Pounds
for the said Passage.

Resolved that it is the sense of the Council, that Messrs. Mason
and Dixon measure the whole space required, without regarding
what they have done on a former occasion: and that they be instructed
to compare frequently their fir rods with their brass standard; and
note down the degree of the Thermometer, at each time of such   209

comparison. also that they take a particular care of the brass standard;
and bring it home with them, in order to it being compared
with the french standard, if thought necessary and that the
Secretary communicate these Resolutions to Messrs. Mason and Dixon.

Resolved, that Mr. Maskelyne, Astronomer Royal, be requested
to draw up such further instructions as he thinks necessary for
Messrs. Mason and Dixon, in the work now ordered.

Resolved, that the Right Honorable Lord Baltimore and Mr. Penn
the Proprietors of Maryland and Pennsylvania, be applied to, for
the use of their instruments now there, and that C. Morton, Secretary
be desired to write to them accordingly.

Copies of the Letters from the Right Honorable Lord Baltimore and
Mr. Penn to Charles Morton Secretary.

Thursday Evening
November 7, 1765

Sir,
 I beg the favor of you to present my Complements to the Council
of the Royal Society and to acquaint them that after Messrs. Mason
and Dixon have finished they are engaged to by Messrs. Penn and
Myself, I can have no sort of objection to their being otherways
employed they are extremely welcome to make use of the Instruments
already there, and I will send order to them to bring back
the Brass Rule or standard, to be compared with the french one
according to the Society's Intention. Their staying a few months
in America after they have finished Mr. Penn's and My Lords business
will make no alteration in the allowance Stipulated to be paid them
for their passage

I am
 Sir,
      With great Regards
      and Esteem
      Your Most Obedient
      humble Servant
      Baltimore

210

Dr. Morton S. R. S.

Sir

I have this morning seen My Lord, Baltimore, and we both agree,
that Messrs. Mason and Dixon, after they are discharged by our
Commissioners from running the Line between Maryland and Pennsylvania,
shall be at liberty to attend the Service of the Royal Society, and
shall be allowed the same passage money, as they would
have been entitled to had they returned to England as soon as they had been
discharged by our Commissioners.

We also agree that they may make use of any Instruments belonging
to the Proprietors of Pennsylvania, provided that Lord Sterling, on the
part of the Proprietors of New Jersey, has not present occasion for
them, as the Proprietors of Pennsylvania have before promised to let
him have them. I am,

   Sir

      Your most humble Servant
      Tho. Penn

Spring Garden, Nov. 7, 1765
Dr. Morton S. R. S.

211

August 8, 1766

At a Council of the Royal Society

The Council taking into Consideration the Supposed Wreck of the
Ship Egdon wherein the Instruments were sent to Messrs. Mason and
Dixon; and it appearing, that the said observers are already furnished
sufficiently for the Work ordered by the Society.
Ordered, that a copy of the instructions drawn up by Mr. Maskelyne, be transmitted to Messrs. Mason and Dixon, and that half an
ounce of silver wire be enclosed, therewith; and that they be directed
to proceed with their business, with the Instruments of the Proprietors
now in their hands.

Messrs. Mason and Dixon.

> The enclosed are duplicates of letters sent
> you from the Royal Society last year: and they
> are now repeated, because your not writing
> to us has occasioned a suspicion that the
> former letters have miscarried. I have nothing
> to add except what you will perceive,
> that you are not to expect any other instruments
> than what you already have: and that we
> shall be glad to hear from you as soon as may be:
> I am, Gentlemen.
>
>> Your most obedient, and
>> humble servant.
>
>> C. Morton, S. R. S.

212

Instructions sent by Mr. Maskelyne, Astronomer Royal
to Messrs. Mason and Dixon

Messrs. Mason and Dixon

> Greenwich, November
> 8th, 1765

I have the pleasure to acquaint you that the Council of the Royal
Society, to whom I have communicated your Proposals for measuring
a degree of Latitude and a degree of Longitude, in North America,
have resolved that you should carry the first into Execution upon
the terms you offered. But to prevent any mistake, I must observe
that the Council understand your Proposals that you are to measure
all the lines over again, or at least the two principal lines, namely
the line AB, according to your Scheme which makes an angle of
4 degrees with the Meridian, and the line BC, which is due north. This
they direct should be done with four fir rods of 10 foot each, tipped with
brass at the ends, with which you will be furnished by Mr. Bird,
together with a brass standard of five foot to examine the rods
by from time to time, and one or two Thermometers to note the
temperature of the Air, whether the room or open Air, where the
rods are compared, at the time. Hence an allowance may be made
hereafter for any change the rods may Undergo. You are also desired
to bring back the rods and standard to England, as they may be
hereafter compared with the french Measures.
The Council have desired me to send you some Instructions about
the Method you should pursue in your Operations. I rely a great
deal upon your own judgment and attention, nevertheless I will
point out to you those circumstances which seem to me most
necessary you should attend to.

213

135

You propose setting up the sector at the point (A) the Southern extremity
of your Meridian, and observing the Zenith distances of the
same stars with it as you have already taken at (P) and (N). As you
turned the Sector at both those stations, I take it for granted you
intend to do so at (A) which I would strongly recommend to you, as it
will greatly conduce to the accuracy of the Celestial Measure.
Be very careful to trace your line strait. You might first fix stakes or
posts in the ground from distance to distance, and then stretch a long
rope by the side of them, or parallel to them as a Guide for the
direction of the rods in measuring. If the nature of the Ground is any
where very difficult, take an off sett directly at right angles, noting
how much, and go on parallel to your former course, till the
Ground allows you by another off sett or off setts to return into the
Line again. There are two Methods of measuring, either of which
may be used, or sometimes one and, sometimes the other as circumstances
vary. The one is by always laying the rods truely horizontal
by means of a carpenter's level, or Spirit level, and as the Ground
rises or falls, instead of bringing the rods to touch at the ends,
connecting them by means of a plumb line, (string silver Wire would be
best with the plummet immersed in Water) defended as much as
possible from the wind. In pursuing this Method you will find it useful
to carry stakes or Wedged pieces of wood with you to
drive into the Ground for a support of one or both ends of the
rods in levelling them. But the most convenient Method as
well   of levelling the rods as of bringing their ends to meet   214
exactly would be supporting the ends by stands which rise and
fall by a screw. It is not necessary to have a very nice spirit level for
this purpose, nor a long one, as the rods are plained strait. I shall
send you one with the rods, which you will take care to adjust or
verify as you use it. The other method of measuring is by laying the
rods upon the ground itself, but this it is evident should only be
done where the ground is very even. In this method it will be necessary
to level the ground as you go along, to find how much it rises
and falls, in order to reduce the direct measure to a Horizontal line
and here note, that the common tables of the difference between the
true and apparent level are very erroneous, because they take no
account of the terrestrial refraction of the rays of Light, whose curvature
near the surface of the Earth is one fifth of the curvature of the
Earth's Surface, on which account the numbers in all the common
tables should be diminished in the proportion 5 to 4.
The following expression gives the difference of the apparent and
true level including the effect of Refraction 0.534 of the square of
the distance expressed in English Miles of 5280 feet, is the difference
required in English feet. Keep the rods as dry as you can, for if any
thing alters their length it is to be supposed to be changes of
moisture and dryness, as metals are affected by those of heat and
cold. Always take care to bring the ends of the rods to meet, without
any shock, and don't trust this to your Labourers. It will be better
to use three rods at once, and always leave two on the Ground at a
time, while you carry the third or hindermost forward to put before
the rest, and while this rod is taken up or put down let the other
rods which remain on the Ground be either held down by the hand   215
or pressed down by a weight, that they may not be liable to be
moved from their place.

You will doubtless think proper to fall on some Method that may
prevent or discover mistakes in counting the number of rods laid
down, either by having several to count, or any other device usual
among Surveyors. It is very necessary and important to know with
precision the direction of your line, with respect to the Meridian (which
by the bye, is not the same at both extremities) in order to reduce it
to the distance of the Parallels of Latitude passing through the two extremities.
Though you mention that you have the direction of the Line (AB)
very exact from the time of the star in the Little Bear next the Pole star
passing its Azimuth, yet as you have not particularly described how
you traced the Line forward in this direction, I cannot help at present
entertaining some doubts on the subject, which probably you may

hereafter clear up. However in any case I think it would be very expedient and proper, to verify the direction of this line, which may easily be done in the following Method.

Set up Signals at a great distance from each other as the curvature of the earth or other obstacles will allow you to see them through the telescope of the transit Instrument. These signals may be either along the line or out of it, and it signifies but little how much. The first must be observed from the South extremity of the line at (A) and the last must be at the Northern extremity of the line at (B). The best choice of places for the signals will be of those which will conduct you most readily that is to say with the fewest number from one extremity of the line to the other. If there were any hills or eminences in the country, which I am afraid by the accounts given of it, there are not, it would facilitate this business very much, as two or three, might then carry the connection from one end of the line to the other. With the help of the transit Instrument determine the bearing or Azimuth of each Signal, from the preceding one, beginning at the Southern Extremity (if convenient) till from the last signal but one you observe the bearing of the signal, at the Northern extremity of the line at (b). Then if the Signals lie all along the Line AB, their bearings and known distances from each other (which last are not required very accurate for this particular purpose) will give the true direction of the line (AB) with respect to the Meridian though the line traced for it and supposed a strait line be an irregular line formed of several right lines making Angles with One another. But if the Signals lie out of the line (AB) and their distances from the line can be easily measured the same thing may be done as before. But if the Signals be considerably out of the Line AB, the distances between their parallels of Latitude may be found by setting up the Sector at each Signal and taking a few Zenith Distances of Stars, for great accuracy is not necessary for this purpose. The distance between the parallels of Latitude compared with their bearings will determine the direction of the line (AB) as before. The readiest way of finding the bearing of any Signal from another is by directing the transit Instrument to it, fixed and adjusted as such, and observing the interval of time between the transits of two known stars across its vertical, one of which shall be as near to, and the other as far from the pole as possible. If your clock is good and its rate of going well determined, it is immaterial whether the Interval of time between the transits of the two stars over the given vertical be great or small. As I do not find that you have a clock with you, I shall make a proposal to the Council of the Royal Society, that their clock, which I took to St. Helena and Barbados may be sent to you, with the help of which joined to your transit Instrument you may determine the bearings of your Signals many different ways, and make any other Astronomical observations. Always fix the clock up firm, and adjust the pendulum to the same length, and it will always keep the same rate of going very nearly. If the interval of the transits of the two Stars is small, it is not necessary to be so very nice about the rate of the clocks going. Should this clock be sent to you adjust the Pendulum to the Upper Scratch No. 3 standing against the Index which answered to Sidereal time at St. Helena, and keep the clock going in the same place for some days, in order to determine its rate of going. Note the height of the thermometer at the time. This Experiment will show the force of Gravity, where you set it up, compared with the force of Gravity here, At Saint Helena, the Cape of Good Hope and Barbados. Endeavor to Estimate your Elevation above and distance from the Sea where you set the clock up, also note the Latitude of the place. You ought to determine the direction of your line within five minutes, and the whole length within the ten thousandth part of the whole or fifty feet.

Preserve all your Measures and Observations as they may be revised At leisure. I am etc.

N. Maskelyne, Astronomer Royal

216

217

218

To Messrs. Mason and Dixon in Pennsylvania

Instructions for Measuring a degree of Latitude
there.

Sorjts Inn London   22 March 1766

Gentlemen:

By tne death of Mr. Calvert it falls to my lot to
acknowledge the receipt of your letter of Sixth of January last, addressed to
him which I have communicated to Lord Baltimore, and his Lordship
has directed me to express his satisfaction in your Proceedings, and the
happy prospect of bringing your great work to a conclusion in the
ensuing summer.

His Lordship, from a due Sense of your Services, and a
desire of showing his approbation of them has in concurrence with
Messrs. Penn agreed to your Entering upon the Important charge
Proposed to be Delegated to you by the Royal Society, as soon
as the business of his commission is ended and to Indulge you the use
of the Instruments for that Work, with a Continuance of the same
Allowance for your return as was first agreed, in the same manner
as if you had engaged in no new Undertaking.

When you renew your Operations I shall be glad to be
favored with accounts of your further Proceedings, as opportunities
offer, and in the meantime remain

Gentlemen

Your most Obedient and Humble Servant

Hugh Homersley

Messrs. Charles Mason and Jeremiah Dixon

Gentlemen

We are to inform you that the Time of our
Meeting the Maryland Commissioners has been postponed by our
mutual agreement to the Twenty Eighth of the next Month.
You will therefore discharge your Workmen as soon as you
Return to the East End of the East and West Lines. If you think
the Season is proper for you to measure a Degree of Latitude
agreeable to your Instructions from the Royal Society, we have
no objections to your employing yourselves in that Business
till the time of our Meeting, but we shall then expect you will
attend us at Christiana Bridge in New Castle County to lay
your Books before us and make report of your Work.   We are

Gentlemen

Your humble Servants

Will Allen
Benjamin Chew
John Ewing

Philadelphia, September 19th, 1766

P. S. I had sealed the Letter before I had
filled up a Blank left at first Writing for
the Day of our Meeting which obliged me
to break it open again.
B. C.

(Undated. ᵗHere we have an envelope addressed as follows
and to which other comments are annexed as shown.)

To Messrs

Charles Mason & Jeremiah Dixon

New Castle County

(On back) This letter was broke open and resealed by me.

B. Chew

(Also on back at end) Betsy Little
Opposite the Butanes
Philadelphia

222

Messrs. Mason and Dixon:

I have received your letter of the 6th of January
with a particular account of your proceedings, since your last, and we
are very well satisfied with the account you give of them; We apprehend that
you cannot have put stones to every Mile of the Line from Cape Henlopen to
the Middle of the Peninsula, or in the Tangent Line, unless you had many
made in Pennsylvania, the particular place you have noted down where
the parallel of Latitude has crossed, we are very well pleased with; as we
are that you made use of your time when not employed by us to run the
Degree of Latitude for the Royal Society about which my Lord Morton often
Speaks to me.

I am at a loss to know what was the Commissioners reason for ordering
you to run the parallel of Latitude from the place where the Meridian Line
intersects it to the River, as I have not received from them their minutes, and
when you write next let me know them lest they should omit it.

I shall expect to hear from you if you proceed to extend the Line
further westward in the mean time remain.

Your affectionate Friend

London, June 17, 1767   Tho. Penn

223

Editorial Note:

(Undated.   Here is an envelope addressed as follows)

For

Messrs. Mason & Dixon

in Pennsylvania

(On the back of the envelope is the following notation)

To the care of John Montgomery, Esq. at Carlisle,
who is devised to put this Letter under a Cover and to
forward it by the first opportunity to Fort Cumberland
or wheresoever Mr. Mason or Mr. Dixon may be.

Joseph Shippen, Jr.

224

8 — Set up the Sector at the Middle Point (in a West Line) between Cape Henlopen and Chesapeak Bay: and made the following observations.

Star Name	Nearest Point on the Sector		Plane of the Sector EAST — Revolutions and Seconds on the Micrometer		Difference		Apparent Zenith Distance		
	°	'	R	"	'	"	°	'	"
Gamma Andromedae	2	45-	5	31-	0	31.3	2	44	28.17
			6	10					
Beta Persei	1	35-	7	8	0	6.0	1	34	54.0
			7	14					
Delta Persei	8	35-	7	32+	1	25.0	8	33	35.0
			9	13+					
Capella	7	15+	6	16	1	21.3	7	16	21.3
			4	39-					
Beta Aurigae	6	25+	3	34-	1	3.2	6	26	03.2
			2	22.5					
Castor	6	05-	1	10	0	9.5	6	04	50.5
			1	0.5					

9 — Cloudy

Star Name	°	'	R	"	'	"	°	'	"
10 Alpha Lyrae	0	05+	3	26.5	2	19.0	0	7	19.0 N
			0	43.5					
Gamma Cygni	1	05-	4	42	1	7.7	1	3	52.3 N
			6	6-					
Alpha Cygni	6	00-	5	41	0	4.7	5	59	55.3 N
			5	46-					
Gamma Andromedae	2	45-	7	12	0	30.0	2	44	30.0 N
			7	42					
Beta Persei	1	35-	8	15.5	0	06.5	1	34	53.3 N
			8	22					
Delta Persei	8	35-	5	51.5	1	25.5	8	33	34.5 N
			7	33					
Capella	7	15+	6	48.5	1	20.0	7	16	20.0 N
			5	20.5					
Beta Aurigae	6	25+	3	29.5	1	4.0	6	26	4.9 N
			2	17.5					
Castor	6	05-	15	25	0	9.5	6	04	50.5 S
			15	15.5					

225

Star Name	°	'	R	"	'	"	°	'	"
11 Alpha Lyrae	0	5+	8	26	2	20.7	0	7	20.7
			5	41					
Delta Cygni	6	5+	5	44-	1	51.0	6	6	51.0 N
			3	37-					
Gamma Cygni	1	5-	3	37	1	8.0	1	3	52.0
			5	1					
Alpha Cygni	6	0+	4	32	0	5.5	6	0	5.5
			4	37.5					
Gamma Andromedae	2	45-	6	14-	0	29.3	2	44	30.7
			6	43					
Beta Persei	1	35-	7	42-	0	4.3	1	34	55.7
			7	46					
Delta Persei	8	35-	5	38.5	1	23.0	8	33	37.0
			7	17.5					
Capella	7	15+	8	51	1	20.3	7	16	20.3
			7	23-					
Beta Aurigae	6	25+	7	20.5	1	4.0	6	26	4.0
			6	8.5					
Castor	6	5-	4	31	0	10.5	6	4	49.5
			4	20.5					

12 Sun.	Star Name	Nearest Point on the Sector		Revolutions and Seconds on the Micrometer		Difference		Apparent Zenith Distance		
		o	'	R	"	'	"	o	'	"
	Alpha Lyrae	0	5+	5	29-	2	22.0	0	7	22.0
				2	43-					
	Delta Cygni	6	5+	4	31.5	1	51.0	6	6	51.0
				2	24.5					
	Gamma Cygni	1	5-	6	26	1	9.0	1	3	51.0
				7	43					
	Alpha Cygni	6	0+	13	8	0	3.5	6	0	3.5
				13	11.5					
	Gamma Andromedae	2	45-	2	37+	0	32.4	2	44	27.6
				3	18-					
	Beta Persei	1	35-	3	46	0	5.0	1	34	55.0
				3	51					
	Delta Persei	8	35-	1	43	1	27.0	8	33	33.0
				3	26					
	Capella	7	15+	6	28	1	22.0	7	16	22.0
				4	50					
	Beta Aurigae	6	25+	1	33+	1	4.0	6	26	4.0
				0	21+					
	Castor	6	5-	15	37.5	0	8.0	6	04	52.0
				15	29.5					

226

Turned the Sector Plane WEST

13	Gamma Andromedae	2	45-	6	2+	0	24.8	2	44	35.2
				5	29.5					
	Beta Persei	1	35+	5	43	0	0.7	1	35	0.7
				5	44-					
	Delta Persei	8	35-	6	2.5	1	22.5	8	33	37.5
				4	24					
	Capella	7	15+	7	4.5	1	27.5	7	16	27.5
				8	40					
14	Alpha Lyrae	0	5+	14	12	2	21.0	0	7	21.0
				16	49					
	Alpha Cygni	6	00	13	16	0	00.0	6	0	00.0
				13	16					
	Gamma Andromedae	2	45-	2	46	0	24.0	2	44	36.0
				2	22					
	Beta Persei	1	35+	2	5-	0	0.6	1	35	0.6
				2	5+					
	Delta Persei	8	35-	3	27+	1	19.6	8	33	40.4
				2	0-					
	Capella	7	15+	1	50+	1	29.7	7	16	29.7
				3	36					
	Beta Aurigae	6	25+	2	51	1	11.5	6	26	11.5
				4	18.5					
	Castor	6	05-	7	17	0	12.0	6	04	48.0
				7	29					

Wound up the clock; in which it was stopped about 23 seconds.

	Star Name	Nearest Point on the Sector		Revolutions and Seconds on the Micrometer		Difference		Apparent Zenith Distance		
		°	'	R	"	'	"	°	'	"
15	Alpha Lyrae	0	5+	3	33	2	22.7	0	07	22.7
				6	20-					
	Delta Cygni	6	5+	6	18	1	58.0	6	06	58.0
				8	32					
	Gamma Cygni	1	5-	7	4	1	5.3	1	03	54.7
				5	43-					
	Alpha Cygni	6	0+	6	36+	0	1.2	6	00	1.2
				6	37.5					
	Gamma Andromedae	2	45-	6	40.5	0	24.5	2	44	35.5
				6	16					
	Beta Persei	1	35	5	48-	0	0.0	1	35	0.0
				5	48-					
	Delta Persei	8	35-	8	2	1	22.0	8	33	38.0
				6	24					
	Capella	7	15+	7	21.5	1	27.5	7	16	27.5
				9	5					
	Beta Aurigae	6	25+	9	25-	1	11.8	6	26	11.8
				10	44.5					
	Castor	6	5-	12	45+	0	12.7	6	4	47.3
				13	6					
16	Alpha Lyrae	0	5+	4	48+	2	22.7	0	07	22.7
				7	35					
	Delta Cygni	6	5+	2	20.5	1	55.2	6	06	55.2
				4	32-					
	Gamma Cygni	1	5-	0	25	1	4.5	1	03	55.5
				17	12.5					
	Alpha Cygni	6	0+	0	8.5	0	0.5	6	00	0.5
				0	9					
	Gamma Andromedae	2	45-	4	31.5	0	28.0	2	44	32.0
				4	3.5					
	Beta Persei	1	35	3	25	0	0.0	1	35	0.0
				3	25					
	Delta Persei	8	35-	4	4	1	23.5	8	33	36.5
				2	24.5					
	Capella	7	15+	1	20-	1	29.3	7	16	29.3
				3	5					
	Beta Aurigae	6	25+	5	29.5	1	10.5	6	26	10.5
				6	48					
	Castor	6	5-	8	5	0	10.5	6	04	49.5
				8	15.5					
17	Alpha Lyrae	0	5+	5	18-	2	23.3	0	07	23.3
				8	5					
	Gamma Cygni	1	5-	8	1.5	1	04.0	1	03	56.0
				6	41.5					
	Alpha Cygni	6	0-	6	48.5	0	0.5	5	59	59.5
				6	48					
	Capella	7	15+	8	43	1	27.5	7	16	27.5
				10	26.5					
	Beta Aurigae	6	25+	10	39-	1	11.3	6	26	11.3
				12	0.6					
	Castor	6	5-	12	14-	0	11.6	6	04	48.4
				12	25+					
18	Alpha Lyrae	0	5+	6	49	2	25.3	0	7	25.3
				9	38+					
	Delta Cygni	6	5+	7	45-	1	59.3	6	6	59.3
				10	0.8					
	Gamma Cygni	1	5-	5	15	1	04.0	1	3	56.0
				4	0.3					
	Alpha Cygni	6	00+	16	47-	0	2.3	6	0	2.3
				16	49					

227

228

Observations made at the Middle Point for determining the Angle of our 1st Line with the Meridian, etc.

Apparent Right Ascension of Stars the 12th October 1766

°	′	″	h	m	s		h	m	s	
308	22	33	20	33	30	Alpha Cygni				
222	53	30	14	51	34	Beta Ursae Minoris	2	51	34	
161	54	9	10	47	37	Beta Ursae Majoris	22	47	37	
162	16	54	10	49	8	Alpha Ursae Majoris	22	49	08	
175	22	47	11	41	31	Gamma Ursae Majoris	23	41	31	Under the
359	5	32	23	56	22	Alpha Andromedae				Pole
180	56	17	12	3	45	Delta Ursae Majoris	0	3	45	
190	55	4	12	43	40	Epsilon Ursae Majoris (Alioth)	0	43	40	
11	29	49	0	45	59.5	Polaris	12	45	59.5	
198	36	47	13	14	27	Epsilon Ursae Majoris	1	14	27	

These reduced by both hands

11

Time by the Clock

h	m	s
18	31	17.5
20	16	10
20	25	40

Alpha Lyrae ⎫
Gamma Cygni ⎬ Passed the Meridian by the Sector
Alpha Cygni ⎭

			h	m	s	h	m	s	h	m	s	
19	51	27	21	17	10+	41	11	23	20	35	41.5	
	52	49-		18	35+		11	24		35	42	Equal Altitudes of Alpha Cygni
	54	13		19	56		11	23			41.5	

20h 35m 42s
20h 33m 30s
2m 12s Clock too fast for sidereal time

22	18	59	Alpha Ursae Majoris passed our 1st Line: upper star
22	22	34	Beta Ursae Majoris passed our 1st Line: lower star

23	34	19+	0	18	14	47	57	31	29	58	45.5	
	36	37		20	54		57	31	23	58	45.5	Equal Altitudes of Alpha
	39	17		23	13		57	32		18	46	Andromedae

23 58 46
23 56 22 Right Ascension
2m 24s Clock too fast

12 Sun.

18	32	23
20	17	13
20	36	45-

Alpha Lyrae ⎫
Gamma Cygni ⎬ Passed the Meridian by the Sector
Alpha Cygni ⎭

22	20	13	Alpha Ursae Majoris passed our 1st Line: upper star
	23	26	Beta Ursae Majoris passed our 1st Line: lower star

			h	m	s	h	m	s	h	m	s	
20	0	16	21	10	22							
	1	42		11	47-	41	13	29-	20	36	44.5	
	3	15		13	14	41	13	30		36	45	Equal Altitudes of Alpha Cygni

20 36 45- Passed according to the clock
20 33 30 = Right Ascension
3m 15s - Clock fast   229

1766
October
13

Time by the Clock

h	m	s	h	m	s	h	m	s	h	m	s	
							Sum			Half-Sum		
19	50	41	21	22	12+	41	15	33	20	37	46.5	⎞
	51	58		23	35.5		15	33.5		37	47-	⎬ Equal Altitudes of Alpha Cygni
	53	20.5		24	52		15	33		37	46.5	⎠
									20	37	46.5	Passed the Meridian by the Clock
									20	33	30.0	Right Ascension
										4	16.5	Clock too fast

| 22 | 21 | 16 | Alpha Ursae Majoris passed our 1st Line |
| 22 | 24 | 21 | Beta Ursae Majoris passed our 1st Line |

Hence by Alpha Cygni the Clock gains 61.5 seconds per day (of Sidereal Time), then

22	49	8
	+ 4	16.5
	+ 0	5+
22	53	30	= The time by the clock when Alpha Ursae Majoris will pass the Meridian under the Pole

23	41	31
	+ 4	16.5
	+ 0	8
23	45	55.5	= The Time by the Clock when Gamma Ursae Majoris will pass the Meridian under the Pole

0	46	00
	4	16
	0	11
0	50	27	= The Time when the Pole Star will be on the Meridian: and at the Instant

when the Clock showed 22h 53m 30s, the vertical wire in the Equal Altitude Instrument was brought to bisect the star Alpha Ursae Majoris and there made fast.
(The Level showing the Horizontal Position of the Axis of the Telescope: and the
Line of Collimation in the Evening made good). The Telescope was then brought
parallel to the Horizon and by a candle through a small hole, a mark at the distance of 21 chains was placed opposite the above mentioned wire as a meridian: Northwards
at the Distance of 21.42 Chains. When Gamma Ursae Majoris, and the Pole Star passed according
to the Clock, they were both run down to the Horizon in the same manner, and the wire
Bisected the 1st Mark as near as could be judged.   230

14   Time by the Clock

h	m	s	h	m	s	h	m	s	h	m	s	
20	2	21	21	12	15	41	17	35	20	38	47.5	⎞
	3	48		13	47		17	35		38	47.5	⎬ Equal Altitudes Alpha Cygni
	5	20+		15	14		17	35+		38	47.5	⎠
									20	38	47.5	
									20	33	30	
										5	17.5	Clock fast

23	37	44.5	0	20	49	0	3	36	0	1	48	⎞
	40	06.5		23	32		3	38.5		1	49+	⎬ Equal Altitudes of Alpha
	42	47		25	54		3	38.5		1	49+	⎠ Andromedae
									0	1	49-	
									23	56	22	
										5	27-	Clock fast

Hence		0	45	59.5
			+ 5	17.5
			+ 0	13
		0	51	30	Time by the Clock when the Pole Star will be on the Meridian.
		2	51	34	Right Ascension Beta Ursae Minoris.
			+ 5	17.5
			+ 0	19
		2	57	10.5	Time by the Clock when Beta Ursae Minoris will be on the Meridian.
At		2	3	40	Beta Ursae Minoris passed our 1st Line.
					Cloudy when the Pole Star passed the Meridian.
At		2	47	10.5	Ran down Beta Ursae Minoris for a Meridian, and by a
					Candle at the distance of a mile, being brought opposite

the vertical wire we there placed a Mark. After these Observations, wound up the
Clock, in doing which it was stopped about 23 seconds.

144

						Sum					
h	m	s	h	m	s	h	m	s	h	m	s
19	52	14+	21	23	47	41	18	42.5	20	39	21+
	53	32.5		25	10		18	42.5		39	21+
	54	55.5		26	28		18	42+		39	21

}Equal Altitudes Alpha Cygni

20	39	21+
20	33	30
5	51+	Clock too fast

22 31 56   Delta Ursae Minoris passed our 1st Line.
Allowing the Clock to go as before then

0	45	59.5
+ 5	51	
+ 0	13	
0	52	3.5 Pole Star on the Meridian

At 0h 52m 3.5s the Pole Star was Observed for a Meridian. It was rendered dubious
by Clouds, but a mark was placed at the distance of a mile, and it fell 5 inches
East of the mark placed by Beta Ursae Minoris last night. At 2h 4m 18s Beta
Ursae Minoris passed 1st Line.

231

16   Time by the Clock   Sum   Half-Sum

h	m	s	h	m	s	h	m	s	h	m	s
20	0	17	21	17	24	41	20	32	20	40	16
	1	41		18	51.5		20	32.5		40	16+
	3	8		20	16		20	33		40	16.5

}Equal Altitudes of Alpha Cygni

20	40	16+
20	33	30
6	46+	Clock too fast

22 23 46   Alpha Ursae Majoris passed our 1st Line.
22 26 45.5   Beta Ursae Majoris passed our 1st Line.

22 32 45   Delta Ursae Minoris passed our first Line. This is the Star whose
                passage over the Line is so often taken in 1764.

23	41	16	0	19	46	0	6	37	0	3	18.5
	43	51.5		22	46		6	37.5		3	19-
	46	51		25	22		6	38		3	19

} Equal Altitudes of Alpha Andromedae

0	3	19-
23	56	22
6	57-	Clock too fast. Hence by

the going of the clock in the interval between Alpha Cygni and Alpha Andromedae
passing the Meridian we have

0	45	59
+ 6	46	
+ 0	14	
0	53	00 = Time when by the Clock the Pole Star will be on the Meridian.

and

2	51	34
+ 6	46	
+ 0	21	
2	58	41 = Time when Beta Ursae Minoris will be on the Meridian.

At
0 53 00   Brought the wire to the Pole Star as usual, and by the Candle at the
                distance of a Mile, placed a mark, which fell as near as could be
                judged on the Mark placed the 14th.
At
2 5 10   Beta Ursae Minoris passed our 1st Line.
At
2 58 41   Brought the wire to Ditto for a Meridian as before, and by a
                Candle at the distance of a Mile placed a mark, which fell three inches East
                of that placed 14th. In this last Observation I turned the axis of
                the Telescope end for end; that is the Telescope itself was turned
                upside down: This proved the Ends of the Cylinders to be good.

232

17   In the Evening by a Candle placed behind a board with a small hole in it, right
over the Mark placed the 13th, the line was extended to the marks at a Mile Distance
and there a Mark was placed which fell one-fourth of an Inch East of the Mark placed
the 14th.

From the whole there is 6 Observations all within three Inches at the distance of a
Mile; The mean was taken as a point in the Meridian from the Middle Point: over
which said Middle Point, the Axis of the Equal Altitude instrument was placed when
the Observations were made.

At the above Meridian Point, we laid off a Line (pg) at Right Angles, and by a Candle
being placed at the distance of about a mile and a quarter in our 1st Line over a
Notch in a peg left in our 1st Line in the ground; another Candle was brought in
to the 1st Line, Under which a mark was set at the intersection of the Line at right
Angles with the meridian and our 1st Line.

18   The ground being made smooth (level as a floor by nature) the distance was measured
(twice) between the Meridian Point, and the above 1st Intersection in our 1st Line,
and found to be five Chains 14 feet and three tenths of an Inch.

With this same Chain (made by a Brass Statute Yard) the distance from the above
mentioned Meridian Point, to the Middle Point was measured, and found exactly 80
chains. This had been measured several times before in the year 1760; when a
North Line was run from the Middle Point: and their Meridian Mile Post; is nine
feet and 10 Inches East of ours.

233

Observations for determining the Moon's Right Ascension made at the Middle Point
or the South End of the Tangent Line.

Method: Over the Point in the Meridian at the distance of a mile north a Candle was
placed: to which the vertical wire in the Equal Altitude Instrument was brought
and in that position the vertical axis of the said instrument was made fast;
Then the Telescope was turned to the Southward; and the passage of the Moon and
Star taken: Always just before, and after each observation turning the Telescope
to the North to see that the wire still bisected the Candle.

N.B.   Time would not admit of our cutting a Visto, and placing a Mark in the Meridian
Southward.

17   Time by the Clock

h	m	s	h	m	s	
23	40	40				
	43	04	0	25	27	Equal Altitudes of Alpha Andromedae
	45	51		27	50	Hence passed at 0h 4m 15s
						Right Ascension of Star 23h 56m 22s
						Clock too fast 7m 53s+
1	36	32		1st Wire		
	37	23		Meridian		The Moon's first or Western Limb passed the Meridian.
	38	15		3rd Wire		
1	38	50		1st Wire		
	39	41.5				Moon's last or Eastern Limb passed the Meridian.
	40	34				
1	49	46.5				Beta Arietis passed the Meridian: a Star about 3 or 4° N of Moon
2	02	02				Alpha Arietis passed the Meridian: a Star about 8° N of Moon
4	30	39-				Aldebaran passed the Meridian:
4	48	10				
	49	23.5	5	51	42)	Equal Altitudes of Beta Aurigae
	50	42		52	56)	

234

18   Time by the Clock

h	m	s	h	m	s		
23	48	52	0	12	56	} Equal Altitudes of **Alpha Andromedae**	
	52	22		18	4		
	57	27		21	33.5		
2	35	47	1st wire				
	36	40				Moon's Eastern Limb passed the Meridian	} Mr. Dixon
	37	33	3rd wire				
6	18	12	7	9	40	Equal Altitudes of Sirius	

19 Sun.

h	m	s	h	m	s	
23	26	17.5	0	42	34	} Equal Altitudes of Alpha Andromedae
	27	52		44	18	
	29	35		45	52	
2	3	52				Alpha Arietis passed the Meridian (the upper star mentioned 17th)
3	34	32.5	1st wire			
	35	28				Moon's Eastern Limb passed the Meridian.
	36	22	3rd wire			

h	m	s	
3	40	54	
	41	12	
	41	50	
	42	22	} Stars in the Pleiades passed the Meridian.
	43	30	The brightest star Eta Pleiades (Tauri)
	45	11	
	45	11	
4	32	26	Aldebaran passed the Meridian.
5	13	15	Rigel passed the Meridian.

                  Sum   Or a Star

h	m	s	h	m	s	h	m	s		
5	36	56.5	7	27	33.5	13	8	21.5	} Equal Altitudes of Gamma Geminorum	by itself about 25° Zenith Distance South
	38	48+		29	34		8	22		
	40	48		31	26		8	22.5		
						6	34	11	} This Star passed by the clock	

When Twilight began I saw (with a small Reflector) some of the Stars in the Pleiades
very near the Moon's Limb.

    N.B.   The three wires in the Telescope of the Equal Altitude Instrument have not
           been proved to be of equal distance from each other; Though they seem to be
           very nearly so.

                                                                         235

20   Packing up the Instruments.
21   Left the Middle Point.
24   At Newark.
26   The Waggon; and three men with the Telescope part of the Sector arrived at Newark.
27   Examined the Instruments and found that they had not received any damage.
28   At Christiana Bridge in Newcastle County.
29   One of the Commissioners for Pennsylvania came to the Christiana Bridge in Newcastle
        County and acquainted us, the Gentlemen Commissioners were not to meet at this Time;
        And that we were to proceed immediately to set 100 Stones (one at each mile) in the
        Line.

November
17   The Gentlemen Commissioners of both Provinces met at Christiana Bridge.
18   Attended the meeting of the Gentlemen Commissioners of both Provinces at Christiana
        Bridge.
19   Attended the meeting of the Gentlemen Commissioners of both Provinces at Christiana
        Bridge.
20   Attended the meeting of the Gentlemen Commissioners of both Provinces at Christiana
        Bridge. The Stones all Set; which finished the Tangent Line: from the Tangent Point
        to the West Line: and 65 Miles of the said West Line, or Boundary between Maryland and
        Pennsylvania, the 64th Mile from the beginning of the West Line excepted, at which
        there is no Stone.
        One of the Gentlemen Commissioners of each Province attended this work.   236

20   N. B. The Stones in the West Line are Set 73 Links Eastward of the Mile Posts; so that they stand at even Miles from the North-East end of the Province of Maryland, or the Beginning of the West Line.

21   Attended the Gentlemen Commissioners.

At this Meeting the Commissioners agreed we should immediately proceed to extend the West Line (from the Post Marked West in Mr. Bryan's field) Eastward to the River Delaware. And also Resolved that General Johnson (his Majesty's Agent for Indian Affairs) should be applied to (if they will not sell their Land) for to gain the consent of the Six Nations to let us continue the West Line to the extent of the Provinces.

22
23 Sun.   Preparing a Post for the Transit (or equal altitude) instrument; Boards for Mark, finding a Point in the west line, etc.
24

25   Changed the Direction found by Stars on the 20th of March and 4th of April 1765; to be in the true Parallel of the West Line, at the distance of 12 Miles 25 Chains Eastward of the Post marked West in Bryan's field. Thus: if we had run WB, the true chord*, then 9' 00" is the Angle for a Chord of 12 miles 25 chains which being changed would give the true chord WE for 12 miles 25 chains the direction: But as we found on setting up the Sector at S we were 1 chain 95.5 links north of the parallel the changing of 9' 00" only; will carry us to N, making NE = BS = 1 Chain 95.5 Links. To account for which: As 12 Miles 25 Chains : 1 Chain 95 Links :: 0.5 Mile : 7.92 Links to the error in .5 mile. And at 0.5 Mile Rad 9' 00"   10.5 Links
Sum to be laid off from WS southward, that is from a to c at a   18.42 Links
Radius of 0.5 Mile in order to run the true chord WE Eastward

We measured a Radius Westward from W to a = 45.5 Chains, and laid off from a to c 20.16 links and in this direction cWE (W being the Post Marked West) we ran Eastward for the Delaware as follows.

Figure
237

* When we set out on April 5th 1765 to run the West Line.

At 0 miles 23 chains Mr. Culbertson's House about one chain North.
    1 mile 06 chains crossed a road leading from Christiana Bridge toward new Garden Meeting House.

26   Continued the Line: At 1 mile 64 chains crossed Pike Creek.

27   Continued the Line.
At 3 miles 42 chains crossed Mill Creek.
At 4 miles 02 chains crossed a Road leading from Newport to Lancaster.
At 5 miles 24 chains crossed Red Clay Creek.
At 5 miles 68 chains crossed a Road leading from Newport to Lancaster.

28   Continued the Line.
At 6.5 miles Newport Bore south: distant one-half mile.
At 7 miles 27 chains crossed a Road leading from Newport to Willingstown, or Wilmington.

29   Continued the Line. At 9 miles 7 chains 17 links the West Bank of Christiana Creek.
    Measured the breadth of the Creek thus

        B a point on the East Bank.
        A a point on the West Bank.
        AC a base at nearly right angles to the Line AB = 6 Chains;
        the angles as by Trigonometry measured with a Hadley's Quadrant
                      (log)
        As Sine B (25° 17') =   9.630524
         : Ac or 6   =   0.778151
         :: Sine C (61° 51') =   9.945328
      : AB 12 chains 38 links =   1.092955

         at A 9 miles 7 chains 17 links
            9 miles 19 chains 55 links = the measure at B

At 9 miles 79 chains crossed a Road leading from Newcastle to the Lower Ferry on Christiana Creek.

30 Sun.   Placed a Mark in the Line on the Bank of the Delaware.
    Measured Christiana Creek a second time, in the direction of the Line thus.

Figure
238

30 Sun. Thus BC a Base on the East Side of the Creek = 13 Chains 55 Links. AC the Line.
A, a point on the West Side, and B, a point on the East Side. The Angles Measured
as by Trigonometry: then 81° 33' + 45° 3' = 126° 36'   complement = 53° 24' = the angle A

		(log)
As sine A 53° 24'	=	9.904617
: AB 13° 55'	=	1.131939
:: Sine B 81° 33'	=	9.995260
		11.127199
		9.906617
: AC 16 chains 69.5 links		1.222582

Note: There we passed the
creek very oblique.

10 miles 52 chains 87 links = the measure at A.
10 miles 69 chains 56 links = the measure at C, on the east side of the creek.
At 10 miles 52 chains 87 links the west bank of Christiana Creek the second time.
    11 miles 11 chains The North Side of a House belonging to Mr. Wm. Pewsey is
                     south 2 chains 10 links.
    11 miles 14 chains The most southernmost part of a Marsh called Cherry Island;
                  is South, three chains and 57 links.
At 11 miles 20 chains 88 links, the top of the Bank of the River Delaware.
This distance falling short of 12 miles 25 chains by 1 mile 4 chains 12 links the
true Parallel is Seven feet South of the Line or Mark placed on the Bank of the
Delaware yesterday.

December
1 Placed a post (marked E, on the east side) on the Bank of the River Delaware in the
Parallel of 15 statute Miles South of the Southernmost Point of the City of Philadelphia.
This Post is distant from the Post marked West in Mr. Bryan's field 11 miles 20
chains 88 links; And at the time of Setting the said Post; the water of the Delaware
was nearly five feet to the eastward.
From the Post marked E on nearly a South Course (south course a little Westerly)
to a Corner of a Marsh in which it stands, is one chain 80 links: This Corner and
its opposite Land to the Southward we judge to be the Mouth of Christiana Creek.
The said post marked E stands on the Bank of a marsh belonging to Mr. Wm. Pewsey   Figure
of Philadelphia, very near the Southernmost part of Cherry Island.   239
N. B. We set Posts in the Line (marked E, on the East Side, with the number of Miles)
    at the End of each Mile, from the Post marked West in Mr. Bryan's field.

1767
January
6 Wrote to the Honorable Proprietors of Maryland, and Pennsylvania.
Wrote also to the Reverend Nevil Maskelyne, Regius Professor of Astronomy; and   240
Dr. Morton, Secretary of the Royal Society.

1766
December
2 } At Newport. Snow fell all these two days.
3 }
4   Left Newport.
5   At Brandywine.
11   The Sector set up at Mr. Harland's in the same Parallel that it stood in; in the year
1764 and made the following Observations.
Here we also set up the clock, sent us by the Royal Society of London: and also
the Proprietors Clock, to which I applied a Pendulum made with Walnut that had
lain dry for about 40 years.

1766 December	Star Name	Nearest Point on the Sector		Revolutions and Seconds on the Micrometer		Difference		Apparent Zenith Distance		
		°	'	R	"	'	"	°	'	"
13	Gamma Andromedae	1	15+	5	20.5	0	54.8	1	15	54.8
				4	18-					
	Beta Persei	0	5+	4	46+	1	20.3	0	6	20.3
				3	18					
	Delta Persei	7	5+	4	8	0	2.0	7	5	2.0
				4	6					
	Capella	5	50-	5	35	2	18.0	5	47	42.0
				8	17					
14 Sun.	Cloudy									
15	Gamma Andromedae	1	15+	7	32	0	55.0	1	15	55.0
				6	29					
	Beta Persei	0	5+	8	3-	1	21.7	0	6	21.7
				6	25					
	Delta Persei	7	5+	6	27	0	3.0	7	5	3.0
				6	24					
	Capella	5	50-	4	46.5	2	19.0	5	47	41.0
				7	29.5					
	Beta Aurigae	4	55+	9	20.5	2	27.0	4	57	27.0
				6	29.5					
	Castor	7	35-	9	14.5	1	23.5	7	33	36.5
				7	35					

At 2h 53m 56s Star passed the meridian by the Sector: Beta Persei

Note: This day we set the Pendulum of the Royal Society's Clock to the upper scratch with Number 3 at the index as desired by Mr. Maskelyne.

241

16	Gamma Andromedae	1	15+	9	37-	0	55.7	1	15	55.7
				8	33					
	Beta Persei	0	5+	7	45.5	1	21.0	0	6	21.0
				6	16.5					
	Delta Persei	7	5+	5	21.5	0	2.0	7	5	2.0
				5	19.5					
	Capella	5	50-	7	11	2	18.7	5	47	41.3
				9	46-					
	Beta Aurigae	4	55+	9	39	2	27.7	4	57	27.7
				6	47+					
	Castor	7	35-	6	34.5	1	21.8	7	33	38.2
				5	5-					

2h 50m 40s   Passed the Meridian by the Sector, Beta Persei

4h 50m 37s   6° 32' 34".5
4 51 50   33' 52"   Equal altitudes of Beta Aurigae by the Royal Society's
     53   8   35' 5"   Clock which I call P.
11 26   00   The first Satellite of Jupiter Immerged. Fahrenheit Thermometer, in the Tent 14°, in the Air 10°. This Day the Proprietor's Clock was cleaned by the maker, Mr. Jackson; which clock I call Q.

17	Alpha Lyrae	1	20+	5	44-	1	42.0	1	21	42.0
	Cloudy all the day after			7	42-					
18	Cloudy									
19	Alpha Lyrae	1	20+	5	1.5	1	43.5	1	21	43.5
				7	1					Windy
	Beta Persei	0	5+	8	42.5	1	20.2	0	6	20.2
				7	14+					
	Delta Persei	7	5+	7	4	0	3.7	7	5	3.7
				7	0+					
	Capella	5	50-	5	42.5	2	16.0	5	47	44.0
				8	22					
	Beta Aurigae	4	55+	8	.6+	2	27.3	4	57	27.3
				5	15					
	Castor			4	45+	1	21.3	7	33	38.7
				3	16					
20	Cloudy									
21	Alpha Lyrae	1	20+	3	2	1	41.7	1	21	41.7
				5	0-					242

150

Turned the Sector Plane WEST

Star Name	Nearest Point on the Sector		Revolutions and Seconds on the Micrometer		Difference		Apparent Zenith Distance		
	°	'	R	''	'	''	°	'	''

At 22h 20m P before Q 1m 22s

Star Name	°	'	R	''	'	''	°	'	''
Beta Persei	0	5+	6	4+	1	29.7	0	6	29.7
			7	42					
Delta Persei	7	5+	7	50-	0	10.3	7	5	10.3
			8	8					
Capella	5	45+	4	5-	2	56.8	5	47	56.8
			7	25.5					
	5	50-	4	5-	2	07.2	5	47	52.8
			1	33.5					
Beta Aurigae	4	55+	7	0-	2	35.3	4	57	35.3
			9	51					
Castor	7	35-	10	0+	1	30.0	7	33	30.0
			11	38+					

(left margin: Dry fair weather)

At 5h 49m P before Q 1m 19s Thermometer in the Tent = 24°.
  7h 10m P before Q 1m 18s   in the open Air = 22°.

22 Cloudy At 20h 52m P before Q 1m 11s Thermometer in the Tent 44°.
  Moist Weather 14h 26m P before Q 1m 2s Thermometer in the Tent 38°.
23 Cloudy   in the Air 38°.

At 20h 00m P before Q 0m 59s Thermometer in the Tent 44°.
               Thermometer in the Air 45°.
And the Vibration of the Pendulum 1° 35' on each side of 0.
At 14h 37m P before Q 48.5s Thermometer in the Tent = 40°. Rain great part
                 Out = 44°. of the Night
At 17h 35m P before Q 47.0s

24 Moist Weather At 20h 00m P before Q 45.5s Thermometer in the Tent 43°.
                out in the Air 45°.
And the Vibration of the Pendulum = 1° 40'

Star Name	°	'	R	''	'	''	°	'	''
Alpha Lyrae	1	20+	6	44-	1	36.0	1	21	36.0
			5	00-					
Gamma Andromedae	1	15+	4	41-	1	4.8	1	16	4.8
			6	1.5					
Beta Persei	0	5+	4	16.5	1	30.2	0	6	30.2
			6	3-					
Delta Persei	7	5+	6	16.5	0	10.5	7	5	10.5
			6	27					
Capella	5	50-	9	19-	2	7.7	5	47	52.3
			6	47					
Beta Aurigae	4	55+	6	2	2	35.0	4	57	35.0
			9	1					
Castor	7	35-	6	31+	1	29.2	7	33	30.8
			8	16.5					

(right margin: 243)

4h 28m 40s
  30m 18s+ 5h 25m 3s 9h 55m 21s ⎫
  32m 5.5s   26m 40s   55m 20s-⎭ Equal Altitudes of Capella
At 7h 30m P before Q 38s; Ther. 27° Hence passed the Meridian
  14h 00m Ther. in the Tent 22°. by the Clock at 4h 57m 40s+
      in the Air·20°.
At 15h 21m P before Q 35s.+

25 Christmas
 Cloudy At 18h 35m P before Q 33s. Ther. 43°.
     At 20h 00m P before Q 33s. Ther. in the Tent 44°.
                out 46°.
     At 3h 00m P before Q 29.5s. Ther. in 36°. ⎫ Moist weather
              out 36°. | with a little rain:
     At 14h 00m   Ther. in the Tent 38°. | The Snow that fell
              out 37°. ⎭ 2nd & 3rd nearly gone.

1766
December

26   Cloudy

18h 30m P before Q 22s

20h 00m P before Q 21s+   Ther. in the Tent 45°.   Vibrations
                         out 47°.   1° 40'

Moist Weather   21h 00m   Ther. in the Tent 45°.
                           in Air 48°.

15h 00m   Ther. in the Tent 38°.
                           in Air 41°.   P before Q̇ 11s.

27   At 18h 40m P before Q 9s   Ther. in Tent 40°.
                               out 44°.

20h 00m P before Q 8.5s   Ther. in 40°.
                           out 42°.

Star Name	Nearest Point on the Sector		Revolutions and Seconds on the Micrometer		Difference		Apparent Zenith Distance		
	°	'	R	''	'	''	°	'	''
Alpha Lyrae	1	20+	5	13+	1	35.3	1	21	35.3
			3	22					
Gamma Andromedae	1	15+	8	19	1	4.0	1	16	4.0
			9	31					
Beta Persei	1	5+	9	17.5	1	29.5	0	6	29.5
			11	3					
Delta Persei	7	5+	12	16+	0	9.7	7	5	9.7
			12	26					
Capella	5	50-	6	32	2	9.0	5	47	51.0
			4	7					

Fair and dry all day (left margin, beside Gamma Andromedae–Delta Persei rows)

244

After these, by Accident Occasioned by a strong gust of wind the Plane was moved
out of the Meridian.

At 7h 44m P before Q 3s   Thermometer in the Tent 20°.
                               out 17°.

15h 00m Q before P 0s   Thermometer in the Tent 21°.
                             out 18°.

28 Sun.   At 20h 00m Q before P 2s+   Thermometer in the Tent 31°.   Vibration
                               out 26°.   1° 35'.

Fair and dry   Wound up both Clocks

At 21h 00m P before Q 1m 15.5s

Star Name									
Alpha Lyrae	1	20+	7	16::					
			5	29					
Gamma Andromedae	1	15+	4	14	1	3.7	1	16	3.7
			5	26-					
Beta Persei	0	5+	2	42.5	1	28.5	0	6	28.5
			4	27					
Beta Aurigae	4	55+	8	14-	2	35.6	4	57	35.6
			11	13+					

In the Evening Brought the Plane in to the
Meridian and made the following Observations.

   4h 28m 41s   5h 20m 59s   9h 53m 9s   Equal Altitudes of
         30   22+   22   47-   53   9   Capella. Hence passed
         32   10   24   30.5   53   11.5   the Clock at
At 5   57   00 P before Q 1m 12s   4h 56m 35s
                               Ther. in the Tent 20°.
                               out in Air 15°.

29   Snow. Packed up the Sector.

At 21h 00m P before Q 1m 5.5s   Ther. in Tent 28°.
                               in Air 28°.

4h 55m P before Q 1m 1.5s   Ther. in Tent 29°.
                               in Air 28°.

30   At 21h 00m P before Q 53.5s   Ther. in Tent 32°.
     4h 5m 52.5s   5h 43m 24s+ ⎫   in Air 32°.
       7   12   44   46.5 ⎬ Equal Altitudes of Capella. Hence passed

Fair and dry: The Snow a foot deep. (left margin)

       8   34   46   4.5 ⎭ by the Clock at 4h 55m 59s.
At 6h 00m P before Q 49s   Ther. in Tent 17°.
                             in Air 14°.

14h 30m Thermometer in the Tent 5° above 0. P before Q 47.5s.
               in the Air 3° below 0.

At 16h 53m P before Q 48s

245

1766
December
31

           At 21h 00m P before Q 48s   Thermometer in the Air 18°.
                                            in the Tent 20°.
           At 3h 00m   Thermometer in the Air 7° below zero.
                                            in the Tent 0°.
           Found Q stopped, or at Rest: Q pointed at 2h 51m: I set Q going again.

fair
weather

           At 5h 00m P before Q 17m 5s Thermometer in the Tent 3° below zero.
                                      in the Air 13° below zero.
           At 13h 50m (before sunrise)   Thermometer in the Tent 10° below zero.   froid
                                      in the Air 20° below zero.

           found Q at rest again

1767
January
1

           At 19h 30m   Thermometer in the Tent 21° above zero.
                                        in the Air 17° above zero.
                                        Vibration 1° 12'

        4h 10m 33s   5h 37m 45s
           11 55   39 10   Equal altitudes, Capella. Hence passed

fair and
clear
weather

           13 19.5   40 31- at 4h 55m 32s.
           At 5h 50m   Thermometer in the Tent 3° below zero.
                                        in the Air 12° below zero.
                                        Vibration 1° 10'
           At 13.5 (before sunrise)   Thermometer in the Tent 9° below zero.
                                      in the Air 22° below zero.
           At 17h Vibration 1° 5'   The Pendulum swings a little farther from zero
           on the West Side, than the East: The Clock faces the North. In
           rectifying the Instrument for the Equal Altitude; the immediate touch
           of the Brass was like patting one's Fingers against the points of
           Pins and Needles; the cold was so intense.

2   At 21h 25m Thermometer in the Tent 21°.   Vibration 1° 7'
                                  in the Air 15°.
             3h 45m Thermometer in the Tent 9°.
                                 out 5°.
             14h (before sunrise) Thermometer in the Tent 11°.
                                   in the Air 9°.

3   Thermometer before sunrise in the Air 34°.
4 Sunday   At 22h 30m Thermometer in the Tent 39°.   Vibration 1° 20'. Rain
                                  in the Air 39°.

Very wet   At 16h   Thermometer in the Tent 37°.
                   Thermometer in the Air 37°.   246

5   At 21h   Set Q agoing
Rain   21h 57m P before Q 8m 47s+ Vibrations P 1° 35'. The Pendulum
Snow   rather swings now farthest on the East Side. Thermometer in the Tent 48°.
all gone   Air 49°.

           14h 00m Thermometer in the Air 49°.
6   At 21h 00m Thermometer in the Tent 53°. Rain all the Morning.
Very   in the Air 54°.
much   At 5h 30m Thermometer in the Tent 43°. Vibration 1° 40'.
rain   out in the Air 44°.
7   At 22h 8m P before Q 8m 26s Thermometer in the Tent 46°.
                                Sum

        3h 50m 26s   5h 55m 8.5s   9h 48m 05s
Clear   51m 39s+   56m 27s   9h 48m 6s+ } Equal Altitudes of Capella.
weather   52m 56.5s   57m 41.5s   48m 7.5s) Hence the star passed at 4h 54m 3s.
          At 6h   Thermometer in Tent 25°.
                                 Air 26°.
             14.5 (before sun rise Thermometer in the Air 28°.)
                                Sum

8   4h 4m 48s   5h 40m 3s   9h 47m 33s } Equal Altitudes of Capella: Hence
fair   6m 7.5s   41m 24s   47m 35s } star passed at 4h 53m 46s.
weather: 7m 30s-   42m 44.5s   32.5s)
fair   At 5h 43m Thermometer in Tent 23°.
and   At 12h 59m 30s The first Satellite of Jupiter Immerged.
clear   At 12h 59m 30s Thermometer in the Tent 20°.
           At 14h 30m   Thermometer in the Air 17°.

1767
January

9   At 22h 00m   P before Q 8m 7s Th ermometer in Tent 40° Vibration
                                                          Air 40°   1° 35'+

The Pendulum swings 8' more East than West

10   At 23h 11m   Thermometer in the Tent 43°
fair   6h 21m 28s   8h 2m 45s ⎫
and   22m 43s   4m 3s ⎬ Equal Altitudes of Castor
moderate   24m 00s   5m 18s-⎭
weather   At 7h 34m 18s   The first Satellite of Jupiter Immerged
         7h 38m   Thermometer in the Tent 25°   247

11 Sunday   At 22h 14m   P before Q 7m 50s Thermometer in the Tent 50°
            14h 30m   Thermometer in the Air--cloudy in the Air 47°

12   At 23h 25m   P before Q 7m 43s Thermometer in the Tent 42°
                                                 in the Air 44°

I now wound up Q

13   At 21h 50m   P before Q 8m 2s Thermometer in the Tent 42°
fair weather   in the Air   45°

Vibration 1° 40' The Pendulum swings to the Eastward as
on the 9th day

At 16h 00m   Thermometer in the Air 23°   in the Tent 23°

14   At 21h 45m   P before Q 7m 53s thermometer in the Tent 33°
Cloudy with   in the Air 33°
snow and rain   16h 30m   Thermometer in the Air 33°

15   At 21h 35m   P before Q 7m 44s Thermometer in the Tent 39°
cloudy   in the Air 41°

At 16h 00m   Thermometer in the Tent 30°
                              in the Air 30°

16   At 21h 34m   P before Q 7m 33.5s thermometer in the Tent 39°
                                         in the Air 37°
fair   Vibration 1° 35' and the Pendulum swings to the East as before

      4h 5m 4s+   5h 35m 23s   9h 43m 13s⎫   Equal Altitudes of Capella. Hence star
        6   25   36   47   9 43   12⎬   passed at 4h 51m 36s
        7   50   38   7   43   11+⎭

At 5h 40m   Thermometer in the Tent 24°
                              in the Air 21°

17h 00m   Thermometer in the Tent 28°
                              in the Air 25°

17   At 22h 4m   P before Q 7m 26s Thermometer in the Tent 43°
Cloudy   in the Air 39°
most of   At 16h 30m   Thermometer in the Tent 33°
the night   in the Air 31°

18 Sunday   At 23h 37m   P before Q 7m 18s Thermometer in the Tent 39°
                                      in the Air 39°

At 16h 20m   Thermometer in the Tent 25°
                              in the Air 26°   248

19   At 22h 25m   P before Q 7m 11s Thermometer in the Tent 39°
                                      in the Air 36°
fair   Now wound up Q
weather   4h 4m 8.5s   5h 34m 44s   9h 41m 36s ⎫   Equal Altitudes of Capella. Hence
         5   27.5   36   8   9 41   35.5⎬   star passed at 4h 50m 48s
         6   52   37   29   41   37.5⎭

At 5h 40m   Thermometer in the Tent 21°
                            in the Air 18°

20   Cloudy   At 23h 40m   Thermometer in the Tent 39°   P before Q 7m 36s
                                in the Air 40°

At 16h 00m   Thermometer in the Tent 39°
                              in the Air 39°

21   Fine   At 22h 33m   P before Q   7m 27.5s   Thermometer   in the Tent 40°
     temperate   in the Air   40°
     weather in   At 15h 20m   Thermometer   in the Tent 23°
     the Afternoon   in the Air 21°   Began to snow

22   At 23h 00m   P before Q 7m 21.5s   Thermometer   in the Tent 27°
                                    in the Air 27°   Snow

Vibration 1° 30' and the Pendulum swings 8' or 10' more East than
West as before

At 15h 30m   Thermometer   in the Tent 25°
                            in the Air   23°   Snowing still

1767
January

23   At 23h 20m   P before Q 7m 17s   Thermometer   in the Tent 32°   Snow
     in the Air 32°

At 16h 00m   Thermometer   in the Tent 32°
     in the Air 32°

24   Cloudy   At 23h 00m   P before Q 7m 9s   Thermometer   in the Tent 43°
     in the Air 40°

Vibration 1° 30' and the Pendulum swings as before.
Wound up P.
At 15h 30m   Thermometer   in the Tent 32°   Rain freezing.
     in the Air 32°

25 Sun.   At 23h 15m   P before Q 6m 59s+   Thermometer   in the Tent 31°   Cloudy with
     in the Air 30°   rain--

At 15h 30m   Thermometer in the Tent 28°   freezing
     in the Air 27°   Rain freezing.   249

26   At 1h 00m   P before Q 6m 49.5s   Thermometer   in the Tent 32°   Rain and
     in the Air 32°   freezing

Wound up Q
At 1h 25m   P before Q 7m 30s
15h 23m   Thermometer   In the Tent 21°
     in the Air 20°

27   At 0h 40m   P before Q 7m 19.5s   Thermometer   in the Tent 27°
     in the Air 25°

3h 32m 53s   6h 2m 7s   9h 37m 26.5s)   Equal Altitudes of Capella. Hence
   34m 5s-   3m 21.5s   9h 27m 26s- }   star passed at 4h 48m 43s
   35m 19.5s   4m 34.5s   37m 27.5s)

At 6h 7m   Thermometer   in the Tent 15°
     in the Air 12°
At 15h 40m   Thermometer   in the Air 11°
     in the Tent 14°

Clear weather but these three days past, rain and froze the moment it fell on the
trees or ground; such that the limbs of the Trees broke in a surprising manner,
with the weight of clear Ice upon them.

28   At 23h 15m   P before Q 7m 11s   Thermometer   in the Tent 36°
     in the Air 32°

Vibration 1° 20' and Pendulum swings as before.
At 15h 43m   Thermometer   in the Tent 15°
     in the Air 13°

29   At 0h 5m   P before Q 7m 2s   Thermometer   in the Tent 35°
     in the Air 34°

At 16h 26m   Thermometer   in the Tent 16°
     in the Air 16°

30   At 23h 40m   P before Q 6m 54s   Thermometer   in the Tent 31°
     in the Air 35°   Snow

Vibration 1° 20' and Pendulum swings as before.
At 17h 15m   Thermometer   in the Tent 32°
     in the Air 35°   Rain

31   At 1h 5m   P before Q 6m 44s   Thermometer   in the Tent 36°
     in the Air 36°   Rain

At 15h 40m   Thermometer   in the Tent 36°
     in the Air 35°

February
 1 Sunday   At 23h 20m   P before Q 6m 34.5s   Thermometer   in the Tent 36°
     in the Air 37°   Clouds

At 15h 40m   Thermometer   in the Tent 15°
     in the Air 13°   Clear weather   250

 2   At 23h 30m   P before Q 6m 28s   Thermometer   in the Tent 40°
     in the Air 34°   clear

Wound up Q
At 15h 40m   Thermometer in the Tent 16°
     in the Air 15°

1767
February
3

At 23h 55m   P before Q 7m 3s   Thermometer in the Tent 41°
                                                in the Air 38°

          Vibration 1° 30' and the Pendulum swings to the East as before
4h 21m 12.5s   6h 36m 10.5s⎫
   22   22   37   24 ⎬ Equal Altitudes of Beta Aurigae.
   23   35+   38   34 ⎭ Windy
At 6h 40m   Thermometer in the Tent 26°
                         in the Air 25°
At 15h 44m   Thermometer in the Tent 14°
                         in the Air 10°

4

At 23h 10m   P before Q 6m 56s   Thermometer in the Tent 34°
                                                in the Air 32°

          Vibration 1° 30' and Pendulum swings as before
3h 34m 52s- 5h 56m 0.5s   Sum: 9h 33m 20.5s⎫
   36   5   57   16+   33   21+⎬ Equal Altitudes of Capella: hence this
   37   20   58   29   33   21-⎭ star passed at 4h 46m 40.5s by the clock
At 6h 0m   Thermometer in the Tent 24°
                         in the Air 23°
    16h 0m   Thermometer in the Tent 30°
                         in the Air 32°

5

At 0h 20m   P before Q 6m 48s   Thermometer in the Tent 45°
                                                in the Air 41°

    15h 57m   Thermometer in the Tent 13°
                         in the Air 12°

    19h 00m   Vibration 1° 30' Pendulum swings as before

6

At 0h 15m   P before Q 6m 4s+ Thermometer in 28°   Cloudy
                                             out 24°

    16h 54m   Thermometer in the Tent 13°, in the Air 12°

7

At 0h 0m   P before Q 6m 39s   Thermometer in 34°
                                             out 36°   Cloudy

    16h 54m   Thermometer in the Tent 25°; in the Air 24°   251

8 Sunday

At 22h 10m   Thermometer in the Tent 54°   Hazy
                         in the Air 52°

    23h 15m   P before Q 6m 33s
3h 55m 32s   5h 33m 5.5s   17.5s⎫
   56   50+   34   26   16.6 ⎬ Equal Altitudes of Capella, hence this star
   58   12   35   45.5   17.5 ⎭ passed at 4h 45m 38.5s
At 5h 40m   Thermometer in the Tent 33°, in the Air 32°
          Vibration 1° 35' and Pendulum swings East as before
At 16h 30m   Thermometer in the Tent 32°, in the Air 32°

9

At 0h 0m   P before Q 6m 25.5s Thermometer in 42°
                                             out 41°   Cloudy

    16h 30m   Thermometer in Tent 41°, in the Air 41°.   Thunder
              and Lightning in the Night
At 18h 40m   Wound up Q which had been let go down and stop for some Hours.

10

At 23h 56m   P before Q 2m 45s   Thermometer in 34°   Cloudy and hazy
                                             out 35°   weather

    16h 37m   Thermometer in the Tent 25°, in the Air 25°

11

At 23h 35m   P before Q 2m 37s   Thermometer in the Tent 40° Vibration
                                                in the Air 38°   1° 40'

          Pendulum swings East as before
          This afternoon took down Q.
At 16h 25m   Thermometer in the Tent 30°, in the Air 29°   Cloudy

12

At 23h 25m   Thermometer in the Tent 38°, in the Air 41°
At 16h 23m   Thermometer in 31°, out 31°

13

At 0h 20m   Thermometer in the Tent 32°, out 33°   Cloudy
    17h 22m   Thermometer in the Tent 28°, out 24°

14

At 17h 00m   Thermometer in the Tent 26°, in the Air 27°

15 Sunday

At 1h 45m   Thermometer in 34°, out 33°
    16h 42m   Thermometer in 18°, out 10°

16

At 23h 55m   Thermometer in Tent 39° in the Air 48°, Hazy.
At 13h 44m 50s   The first Satellite of Jupiter not immerged.   Flying
    13h 46m 25s   The first Satellite of Jupiter was immerged.   Clouds
    16h 48m   Thermometer in the Tent 28°, out 17°   252

Going of P

					Per day loses
December	24	4h	57m	40s	
					16.3s
	28	4	56	35	
					18.0
	30	4	55	59	
					13.4
January	1	4	55	32+	
					11.8
	7	4	54	3	
					17.0
	8	4	53	46	
					16.30
	16	4	11	36	
					16.0
	19	4	50	48	
					15.63
	27	4	48	43+	
					15.34
February	4	4	46	40.5	
					15.50
	8	4	45	38.5	
					15.9
	25	4	41	8-	

Note: When the Clock was stopped and the Point of Pendulum at rest
it hung over at 8' or 10' to the East of zero. It's my opinion
the arch was not altered, but that the Post of the Clock settled after
the extreme cold so much Eastwards.

C. Mason

253

Apparent Times of the Eclipses at Paris

December 16   22h 58m 13s
January   8   22 55   50
          10   17 23   21

Right Ascension of Sun 16d = 17h 36m 39s
                        17d = 17   41   05
                                      4   26

As 24h : 4m 26s :: 1h : 11m
Then 17h 41m 5s - 11s = 17h 40m 54s = Right Ascension of Sun at the Eclipse

  5h 42m 51s = Beta Aurigae passed
  5 42   26 = Right Ascension of Star
    0m 25s = Clock slow when star passed
        + 4
    0m 29s = Clock slow at the Eclipse

Then 24h : 16s :: 5h 43m : 4s

11h 26m 00s   the Eclipse according to the clock
   + 0   29
11h 26m 29s = Right Ascension Mid Heaven at the Eclipse
17h 40m 54s = Right Ascension Sun then

December 16,   17h 45m 35s Apparent Time
December 16,   22h 58m 13s
                5h 12m 38s Difference according to the Eclipse, 16d

4h 41m 37s Complement = 19h 18m 23s = Sun's Right Ascension 8d
4h 37m 15s Complement = 19h 22m 45s = Sun's Right Ascension 9d
                           4m 22s

24h : 4m 22s :: 1h 4m : 11s
Then 19h 22m 45s - 11s = 19h 22m 34s = Sun's Right Ascension
  4h 53m 46s+   Capella passed by the clock
  <u>4h 59m 33s</u> = Right Ascension of Capella
     5m 47s = Clock slow
        <u>+ 3s</u>
     5m 50s = Clock slow at the eclipse
As 24h : 16s :: 8h : 5s
12h 59m 30s Eclipse by the clock
  <u>+ 5   59</u>
13h 5m 29s = Right Ascension Meridian at the Eclipse
<u>19 22 34</u>   = Right Ascension of Sun
17h 42m 46s = Apparent time at Brandywine
<u>22 55 50</u>
 5h 13m 04s = Difference in Meridian by that 8d.

4h 32m 54s Complement = 19h 27m 6s = Sun's Right Ascension 10d.
4h 28m 34s Complement = <u>19h 31m 26s</u> = Sun's Right Ascension 11d.
                         4m 30s
As 24h : 4m 20s :: 6h 37m : 1m

4h 53m 46s
   <u>0m 32s fast</u>
4h 53m 14s = Capella passed by the clock

4h 53m
<u>7   34</u>
2h 41m
As 24h : 16s :: 2h 41m : 2s

7h 34m 18s
  <u>+ 6   19</u>
7h 40m 37s = Right Ascension Mid Heaven at the Eclipse
<u>19h 30m 15s</u> = Right Ascension of Sun
12h 10m 22s = Apparent Time at Brandywine
<u>17h 23m 21s</u>
 5h 12m 59s = Difference Meridian by that on the 10d.

254

1767
February

17	At	0h 15m	Thermometer	in the Tent 28°
				in the Air Ditto
19	At	1h 30m	Thermometer	in the Tent 39°
				in the Air 44°
		21h 25m	Thermometer	in the Tent 46°, in the Air 55°
20	At	23h 45m	Thermometer	in the Tent 48°, in the Air 59°
21	At	17h 30m	Thermometer	in the Tent 14°, in the Air 12°
22 Sun.	fair and clear			
23	Snow			
24	Ditto		Sum	

25   4h 11m 43s-   5h 7m 9s   9h 22m 16s-⎫
         13   21   8 55.5   22   16.5⎬ Equal Altitudes of Capella
         15   7   10 32+   22   15 ⎭ Hence the star passed the Meridian at
                                             4h 41m 8s- by the Clock

         At 10h 42m 50s   the 1st Satellite of Jupiter Immerged, very
                        dubious by its near approach to Jupiters Limb.

        N. B. The Eclipses of the Satellites of Jupiter were observed
               with a Reflecting Telescope that magnified it about 70Times.

26   Fair and pleasant weather
27   Fair and pleasant weather

1767
February
28 Took down and Packed up the Clock belonging to the
Royal Society. The Pendulum swings
to the Eastward as before. Vibration 1° 40'. The Index
stands at 3, or rather about a line minus of 3. The
point of the Pendulum swings something farther back from the arch
(showing the degrees and minutes) than it did when it was set up.
The Clock was fixed to a piece of Sawed* Timber 22 Inches
in breadth and 5 1/4 inches thick. The said piece of Timber was;
four feet into the ground, which was composed of a very firm,
dry, hard clay.

* Sawed on all sides forming an oblong square.   255

At 2h P.M. The Thermometer in the Air 69°

March
1 Sun.   At 2h P. M. Thermometer in the Air 56°
2   At Ditto   46°
3   At Ditto   57°
4   At Ditto   49°
5   At 3h 30m P. M.   51°
6   At 1h P. M.   51° Rain
7   At 2h Ditto   48° Rain
8 Sun.   At 3h Ditto   56°
9   At 2h P. M. Ditto   51°
10   At 3h Ditto   50°
11
12   At about Sunrise   11°
            2h P. M.   26°
13   At about Sunrise   7°
            2 P. M.   28°
14   At 3h Ditto   36°
15 Sun. At 2h P. M.   47°
16   At 2h 30m Ditto   71°
17   At 2h Ditto   67°
18   In the Morning Snow

22 Sun. Left Brandywine and proceeded to New Town on
Chester River in Maryland to attend the Gentlemen
Commissioners the 24th Instant according to their
appointment made at Christiana Bridge in November last
24   At Ditto
25   At Ditto: The Commissioners not arriving we
set out for Annapolis

Note: The Thermometer in the Air was placed on the North
         side of a House (suspended from the end of a stick) about
         two feet from the wall.
         That in the Tent, by the outside of a Clock Case with a
         Blanket around it, which surrounded the Clock.   256

159

Aberration of stars observed at the Middle Point in October 1766.

		h	m	s		
Alpha Lyrae mean 17".6						
	k	2	24	55		
Sun Oct. 11d 11h		6	10	37		
		9	13	35	17.6°	1.2455
		2	16	25	Sine	9.9877
					-17".11	1.2332
Alpha Lyrae	k	2	24	55		
Sun 15d 22h		6	23	3		
		9	17	58		1.2455
		2	12	2	Sine	9.9783
					-16".74	1.2238

		h	m	s		
Delta Cygni	k	2	11	35		
Sun 12d 0h		6	19	9	18".4	
		9	0	44		1.2648
		2	29	16	Sine	9.9999
Delta Cygni	k	2	11	35		
Sun 16d 23h		6	24	5		1.2648
		9	5	40	Sine	9.9979
		2	54	20	-18".31	1.2527

		h	m	s		
Gamma Cygni	k	2	6	11		
Sun 11d 12h		6	18	40	mean 17".4	1.2405
		8	24	51	Sine	9.9982
					-17".33	1.2387
Gamma Cygni		2	6	11		
Sun 17d 00h		6	24	7		1.2405
		9	0	18	Sine	9.9999
					-17".40	1.2404

		h	m	s		
Alpha Cygni	k	2	1	10	mean 18".0	1.2553
Sun 12d 1h		6	19	12	Sine	9.9938
		8	20	22	-17".75	1.2491
Alpha Cygni		2	1	10		
Sun 16d 12h		6	23	38		1.2553
		8	24	48	Sine	9.9982
					-17".93	1.2535

		h	m	s		
Gamma Andromedae	k	5	0	1		
		0	2	5		
Sun 11d 0h		6	18	10	mean 11".8	1.0719
		6	20	15	Sine	9.5392
					-4".08	0.6111
Gamma Andromedae	k	0	2	5	11".8	1.0719
Sun 14d 17.5h		6	21	51	Sine	9.6082
		6	23	56	-4".79	0.6801

		h	m	s		
Beta Persei	k	11	18	20		
Sun 11d 1h		6	18	12	mean 9".6	0.9823
		6	6	32	Sine	9.0561
					-1".09	0.0384
Beta Persei		11	18	20		
Sun 15d 7h		6	52	24	mean 9".6	0.9823
		6	10	44	Sine	9.2701
					-1".79	0.2525

		h	m	s		
Delta Persei	k	11	0	55		
Sun 10d 20h		6	18	00	10".4	1.0170
		5	18	55	Sine	9.2838
					+2".00	0.3008
Delta Persei		11	0	55		
Sun 15d 7.5h		6	22	27		
		5	23	22		1.0170
		0	6	38	Sine	9.0626
					+1".20	0.0796

		h	m	s		
Capella	k	9	28	50		
Sun 11d 0h		6	18	17		
		4	16	67	mean 8".0	0.9031
		1	13	10	Sine	9.8355
					+5.48	0.7386
Capella		9	28	30		
Sun 15d 21h		6	23	0	8".0	0.9031
		4	21	30	Sine	9.7941
					+4".98	0.6972

		h	m	s		
Beta Aurigae	k	9	8	40		
Sun 11d 4h		6	18	20	mean 7".35	0.8663
		3	27	00	Sine	9.9499
		2	3	00	+6".55	0.8162
Beta Aurigae		9	8	40		
Sun 16d 9h		6	23	31	7".35	0.8663
		4	2	11	Sine	9.9275
		1	27	49	+6".22	0.7938

		h	m	s		
Castor		7	4	45		
Sun 11d 5.5h		6	18	23	4".4	0.6434
		1	23	8	Sine	9.9031
					-3".52	0.5465
Castor		7	4	45		
Sun 16d 11h		6	23	35	4".4	0.6434
		1	28	20	Sine	9.9300
					-3".75	0.5734

Sun's Longitude

	d	h		h	m	s	
Paris	11	11	Alpha Lyrae	6	18	37	
1766	12	00	Delta Persei	6	19	9	
October	11	12	Gamma Persei	6	18	40	Plane East
	12	1	Alpha Cygni	6	19	12	
	11	0	Gamma Andromedae	6	18	10	
	11	1	Beta Persei	6	18	12	
	10	20	Delta Persei	6	18	00	
	11	3	Capella	6	18	17	
	11	4	Beta Aurigae	6	18	20	
	11	5.5	Castor	6	18	23	

Sun's Longitude

	d	h		h	m	s	
Paris	15	29	Alpha Lyrae	6	23	3	
1766	16	23	Delta Cygni	6	24	5	
October	17	00	Gamma Cygni	6	24	7	
	16	12	Alpha Cygni	6	23	38	
	14	17.5	Gamma Andromedae	6	21	51	Plane West (Indistinct)
	15	7	Beta Persei	6	22	24	
	15	7.5	Delta Persei	6	22	27	
	15	21	Capella	6	23	00	
	16	9.5	Beta Aurigae	6	23	31	
	16	11	Castor	6	23	35	

Time at Paris of the Observations.
Solar Longitudes from the Conaissance
(des Temps.)

257

160

The Aberration of Stars Observed at Brandywine in December 1766

		h	m	s		
Alpha Lyrae	k	2	24	55	17."6	
Sun 19d 6h		8	27	55		
		11	22	50		1.2455
		0	7	10	Sine	9.0961
					+2."20	0.3416
k		2	24	55		
Sun 25d 17.5h		9	4	35		1.2455
		11	29	30	Sine	7.9408
					+0."15	9.1869

Gamma Andromedae	k	0.25				
		h	m	s		
Sun 19d 5.5h		8	22	50	14."8	1.0319
		8	24	55	Sine	9.9983
					11."76	1.0702
		0	2	5		
Sun 26d 21h		9	5	43		1.0719
		9	7	48	Sine	9.9960
					-11."63	1.0679

		h	m	s		
Beta Persei		11	18	20	9."6	0.9823
Sun 16d 8.5h		8	54	59	Sine	9.9813
					-9."20	0.9636
		11	18	20		
Sun 25d 14h		9	4	24		0.9823
		8	22	44	Sine	9.9982
					-9."56	0.9805

		h	m	s		
Delta Persei	k	11	0	55	10."4	1.0170
Sun 16d 9h		8	20	00	Sine	9.9181
		7	25	55	-8."61	9.9351
Sun 24d 1h		11	0	55		
		9	3	23		1.0170
		8	4	18	Sine	9.9548
					9."37	0.9718

		h	m	s			
Capella	k	9	28	30	mean	8"	0.9031
Sun 16d 10.5h		8	25	4		Sine	9.6019
		6	23	34		-3."20	0.5050
		9	28	30			
Sun 24d 16h		9	3	28			0.9031
		7	1	58		Sine	9.7238
						-4."24	0.6269
		h	m	s			
Beta Aurigae		9	8	40		7."35	0.8663
Sun 17d 9h		8	26	2		Sine	8.9135
		6	4	42		0."60	9.7798
		9	8	40			
Sun 25d 2h		9	3	54			0.8663
		6	12	34		Sine	9.3376
						-1."60	0.2039
		h	m	s			
Castor	k	7	4	45		4."4	0.6434
Sun 17d 11h		8	26	7		Sine	9.9337
		4	0	52		-3."78	0.5771
		7	4	45			
Sun 23d 6h		9	2	2			
		4	6	47			0.6434
		1	23	13		Sine	9.9036
						3."52	0.5470

	Plane East						Plane West		
	d	h		Sun's Longitude			d	h		Sun's Longitude
Paris	19	6	Alpha Lyrae	8 27 55	Paris	25	17.5	Alpha Lyrae	9 4 35
1766	14	5.5	Gamma Andromedae	8 22 50	1766	26	21	Gamma Andromedae	9 5 43
December	16	8.5	Beta Persei	8 24 59	December	25	14	Beta Persei	9 4 24
	16	9	Delta Persei	8 25 0		24	14	Delta Persei	9 3 23
	16	10.5	Capella	8 25 4		24	16	Capella	9 3 28
	17	9	Beta Aurigae	8 26 2		25	2	Beta Aurigae	9 3 54
	17	11	Castor	8 26 7		23	6	Castor	9 2 2

258

161

(Undated)

Nutations at the Middle Point by the Table I computed before. The following are the Nutations computed at large from the Maximum of 19" for the deviation of the Obliquity of the Ecliptic, the same as the table before was computed from 17"8 = Equa. of the Precession of the Equinoxes.

Right Ascensions Stars 1766		Annual Precession in Declination 1766	Nutations
Gamma Andromedae	27° 26'	17"80	-7"52
Beta Persei	43° 16'	14"60	-8"21
Delta Persei	51° 36'	12"46	-8"35
Capella	74° 52'	5"24	-7"75
Beta Aurigae	85° 35'	1"54	-7"10
Castor	109° 55'	6"83	+4"60
Alpha Lyrae	277° 15'	2"53	+6"05
Delta Cygni	294° 25'	8"29	+3"95
Gamma Cygni	303° 30'	11"07	+2"83
Alpha Cygni	308° 22'	12"45	+2"18

Ascending node of moon's orbit from the sun = 10 - 15 - 39
from Vernal Equinox   1 - 14 - 21
                                               h   m   s

	(log)		And as Rad		(log)
As Rad	10.		: Cos DdaV 44° 21' *		10.0000
S Da V 44° 21' *	1.25042		:: Mn 9"5		9.8543
:: Mean Precession 17"8			: Nutation 6.79		0.8320
: Precession 12"44	1.09492				0.9777

	Alpha Lyrae	Delta Cygni	Gamma Cygni	Alpha Cygni	Gamma Andromedae	Beta Persei	Delta Persei
Cos Star's Right Ascension	9.1010	9.6163	9.7419	9.7929	9.9482	9.8622	9.7932
Precession 12"44	1.0949	1.0949	1.0949	1.0949	1.0949	1.0949	1.0949
Sum	10.1959	10.7112	10.8368	10.8879	11.0431	10.9571	10.8881
Cosine Obliquity 23° 28'	10.3999	10.3999	10.3999	10.3999	10.3999	10.3999	10.3999
Equinoctial precession	9.7960	0.3113	0.4369	0.4879	0.6432	0.5572	0.4882
	-0"62	+2"05	-2"74	-3"08	-4"40	-3"61	-3"08

	Alpha Lyrae	Delta Cygni	Gamma Cygni	Alpha Cygni	Gamma Andromedae	Beta Persei	Delta Persei
As Rad	1.0000	1.0000	1.0000	1.0000	1.0000	1.0000	1.0000
: Sine Right Ascension	9.9965	9.9593	9.9211	9.8943	9.6634	9.8359	9.8941
:: Nutation 6"79	0.8320	0.8320	0.8320	0.8320	0.8320	0.8320	0.8320
-Equa. Obliq.	0.8285	0.7913	0.7531	0.7263	0.4954	0.6679	0.7261
	+6.74	+6.19	+5.66	+5.33	-3.13	-4.66	-5.32
	-0.62	+2.05	-2.74	-3.08	-4.40	-3.61	-3.08
Combined	+6"12	+4"14	+2"92	+2"25	-7"53	-8"27	-8"40

	Capella	Beta Aurigae	Castor
Cos Star's Right Ascension	9.4167	8.8865	9.5323
Precession	1.0949	1.0949	1.0949
Sum	10.5116	9.9814	10.6272
Cosine Obliquity	10.3999	10.3999	10.3999
(Sum)	0.1117	9.5815	0.2273
Equinoctial precession	-1"29	-0"38	-1"69

	Capella	Beta Aurigae	Castor
As Rad	1.0000	1.0000	1.0000
: Sine Right Ascension	9.9847	9.9987	9.9732
:: Nutation 6"79	0.8320	0.8320	0.8320
-Equa. Obliq.	0.8167	0.8307	0.8052
	-6.56	-6.77	+6.39
	-1.29	-0.38	-1.69
Combined	-7"85	-7"15	+4"70

* Editorial note: This probably denotes the angle from the vernal equinox to the ascending node of the moon's orbit.

(Undated)   For the Nutations at Brandywine in December, 1766

Longitude of Ascending Node of Moon = 10s 12° 6'
a' Vernal Equinox   =   37° 54'   Sine   (log)
                                                          9.8704
:: Mean Precession 17."8   1.2504
 : Precession 13."21   1.2208 and
As Rad : cosine 37° 54'   9.8263
:: Mn 9."5   0.9777
 : Nutation 6."37   0.8040

	Alpha Lyrae	Gamma Andromedae	Beta Persei	Delta Persei	Capella	Beta Aurigae	Castor
Then Cosine star's R. A.	9.1080	9.9482	9.8622	9.7932	9.4167	8.8865	9.5323
Precession 13."21	1.1208	1.1208	1.1208	1.1208	1.1208	1.1208	1.1208
Sum	10.2218	11.0690	10.9830	10.9140	10.5375	10.0073	10.6531
Cosine Obliquity	10.3999	10.3999	10.3999	10.3999	10.3999	10.3999	10.3999
Equi. Precession	9.8219	0.6691	0.5831	0.5141	0.1376	9.6074	0.2532
	+0."66	-4."67	-3."83	-3."29	-1."37	-0."40	-1."79
As Rad	10.0000	10.0000	10.0000	10.0000	10.0000	10.0000	10.0000
: Sine Star's R. A.	9.9965	9.6634	9.8359	9.8941	9.9847	9.9987	9.9732
:: Nutation 6."07	0.8040	0.8040	0.8040	0.8040	0.8040	0.8040	0.8040
:: Equi. Nutation	0.8005	0.4674	0.6399	0.6981	0.7887	0.8027	0.7772
Obliquity	-6.32	-2.93	-4.36	-4.99	-6.15	-6.35	+5.99
Equi. Precession	+0.66	-4.67	-3.83	-3.27	-1.37	-1.40	-1.79
Combined	-5.66	-7.60	-8.19	-8.26	-7.52	-6.75	+4.20
By the Table Computed before	-5."66	-7."60	-8."18	-8."24	-7."48	-6."77	+4."18

260

1766
October

Plane of the Sector EAST

		Alpha Lyrae o ' "	Delta Cygni o ' "	Gamma Cygni o ' "	Alpha Cygni o ' "	Gamma Andromedae o ' "
						8 2 44 28.7
	10	0 7 19.0		10 1 3 52.3		10 2 44 30.6
	11	0 7 20.7	11 6 6 51.0	11 1 3 52.0	11 6 0 5.5	11 2 44 30.7
	12	0 7 22.0	12 6 6 51.0	12 1 3 51.0	12 6 0 3.5	12 2 44 27.2
Mean	11d 11h	0 7 20.57	6 6 51.0	1 3 51.77	6 0 4.5	2 44 29.2
Aberration		-17.11	-18.40	-17.33	-17.75	- 4.0
Nutation		+ 6.12	+ 4.14	+ 2.92	+ 2.25	- 7.5
Prec. 11d 1766		0.00	0.00	0.00	0.00	0.00
Refraction		+ 0.12	+ 6.11	+ 1.06	+ 6.00	+ 2.75
Mean Zen. Dist. 11 Oct. 1766		0 7 9.70	6 6 42.85	1 3 38.42	5 59 55.00	2 44 20.39

Plane of the Sector WEST

	Alpha Lyrae o ' "	Delta Cygni o ' "	Gamma Cygni o ' "	Alpha Cygni o ' "	Gamma Andromedae o ' "
13					13 2 44 35.3
14	0 7 21.0			14 6 0 0.0	14 44 36.0
15	0 7 22.7	15 6 6 58.0	15 1 3 54.7	15 6 0 1.2	15 44 35.5
16	0 7 22.7		16 1 3 55.5	16 6 0 0.5	
17	0 7 23.3		17 1 3 56.0	17 5 59 59.5	
18		18 6 6 59.3	18 1 3 56.0	18 6 0 2.3	
Mean	0 7 22.42	6 6 58.65	1 3 55.55	6 0 0.70	2 44 35.57
Aberration	-16.74	-18.31	-17.40	-17.93	- 4.79
Nutation	+ 6.12	+ 4.14	+ 2.92	+ 2.25	- 7.53
Precession	- 0.03	- 0.14	- 0.18	- 0.19	- 0.19
Refraction	+ 0.12	+ 6.11	+ 1.06	+ 6.0	+ 2.75
Mean Zen. Dist. October 11, 1766	0 7 11.89	6 6 50.45	1 3 41.95	5 59 50.83	2 44 25.81
Ditto Plane East	0 7 9.70	6 6 42.85	1 3 38.42	5 59 55.00	2 44 20.39
Mean Zen. Dist. Oct. 11, 1766 at Middle Point	0 7 10.79	6 6 46.65	1 3 40.18	5 59 52.92	2 44 23.10
Ditto at Brandywine	1 21 36.42S				1 15 38.19
Difference between Brandywine and Middle Point	1 28 47.21				1 28 44.91

261

163

Plane of the Sector EAST

	Beta Persei (o ′ ″)	Delta Persei (o ′ ″)	Capella (o ′ ″)	Beta Aurigae (o ′ ″)	Castor (o ′ ″)
8	1 34 54.0	8 33 35.0	7 16 21.3	6 26 3.2	6 4 50.5
10	1 34 53.5	8 33 34.5	7 16 20.0	6 26 4.0	6 4 50.5
11	1 34 55.7		7 16 20.3	6 26 4.0	6 4 49.5
12	1 34 55.0	8 33 33.0	7 16 22.0	6 26 4.0	6 4 52.0
Mean 11d 11h	1 34 54.55	8 33 34.7	7 16 20.90	6 26 3.80	6 4 50.62
Aberration	- 1.09	+ 2.00	+ 5.48	+ 6.55	- 3.52
Nutation	- 8.27	- 8.40	- 7.85	- 7.15	+ 4.70
Prec. 11d 1766	0.00	0.00	0.00	0.00	0.00
Refraction	+ 1.58	+ 8.55	+ 7.26	+ 6.43	+ 6.08
Mean Zen. Dist. 11 Oct. 1766	1 34 46.77	8 33 36.32	7 16 25.79	6 26 9.63	6 4 57.88

Sector WEST

	Beta Persei (o ′ ″)	Delta Persei (o ′ ″)	Capella (o ′ ″)	Beta Aurigae (o ′ ″)	Castor (o ′ ″)
13	1 35 0.7	8 33 37.5	7 16 27.5		
14	35 0.6	33 40.4	16 29.7	6 26 11.5	6 4 48.0
15	35 0.0	33 38.0	16 27.5	26 11.8	4 47.3
16	35 0.0	33 36.5	16 29.3	26 10.5	4 49.5
17			16 27.5	26 11.3	4 48.4
Mean	1 35 0.33	8 33 38.10	7 16 28.30	6 26 11.38	6 4 48.30
Aberration	- 1.79	+ 1.20	+ 4.98	+ 6.22	- 3.75
Nutation	- 8.27	- 8.40	- 7.85	- 7.15	+ 4.70
Precession	- 0.16	- 0.14	- 0.07	- 0.02	- 0.10
Refraction	+ 1.58	+ 8.55	+ 7.26	+ 6.43	+ 6.08
Mean Zen. Dist. Oct. 11, 1766	1 34 51.69	8 33 39.31	7 16 32.62	6 26 16.76	6 4 55.23
Ditto Plane East	1 34 46.77	8 33 36.32	7 16 25.79	6 26 9.63	6 4 57.88
Mean Zen. Dist. Oct. 11, 1766 at Middle Point	1 34 49.23	8 33 37.82	7 16 29.20	6 26 13.20	6 4 56.56
Ditto at Brandywine	0 6 4.83	7 4 53.84	5 47 40.60	4 57 28.11	·7 33 40.90
Difference between Brandywine and Middle Point	1 28 44.40	1 28 43.98	1 28 48.60	1 28 45.09	1 28 44.34

262

Plane of the Sector EAST

	Alpha Lyrae (o ′ ″)	Gamma Andromedae (o ′ ″)	Beta Persei (o ′ ″)
13		1 15 54.8	0 6 20.3
15		1 15 55.0	0 6 21.7
16		15 55.7	0 6 21.0
17	1 21 42.0		
19	1 21 43.5		0 6 20.2
21	1 21 41.7		
Mean	1 21 42.40	1 15 55.17	0 6 20.80
Aberration	+ 2.20	-11.76	- 9.20
Deviation	- 5.66	- 7.60	- 8.19
Precession	+ 0.48	- 3.12	- 2.64
Refraction	+ 1.36	+ 1.26	+ 0.10
Mean Zen. Dist., 11th Oct. 1766 Plane East	1 21 40.78	1 15 33.95	0 6 00.87

Plane of the Sector WEST

	Alpha Lyrae			Gamma Andromedae			Beta Persei		
	o	'	''	o	'	''	o	'	''
21							21	0	6	29.7
24	1	21	36.0	24	1	16	4.8	24	0	6	30.2
27		21	35.3	27		16	4.0	27		6	29.5
28				28		16	3.7	28		6	28.5

	Alpha Lyrae			Gamma Andromedae			Beta Persei		
Mean	1	21	35.65	1	16	4.17	0	6	29.48
Aberration			+ 0.15			-11.63			- 9.56
Nutation			- 5.66			- 7.60			- 8.19
Precession			+ 0.53			- 3.76			- 3.05
Refraction			+ 1.36			+ 1.26			+ 0.10
Mean Zen. Dist., 11 Oct. 1766	1	21	32.03	1	15	42.44	0	6	8.78
Ditto Plane East	1	21	40.78	1	15	33.95	0	6	0.87
True Mean Zen. Dist. Oct. 11, 1766	1	21	36.42	1	15	38.19	0	6	4.83
True Zen. Dist. Observed at Brandywine in Jan. & Feb. 1764 reduced to 1st Jan. 1764	1	21	44.2	1	14	50.8	0	5	25.5
Precession to Oct. 11, 1766			- 7.03			+49.45			+40.56
Reduced to Oct. 11, 1766	1	21	37.17	1	15	40.25	0	6	6.06

	Alpha Lyrae			Delta Cygni			Gamma Cygni		
True Zen. Dist. Observed in Mr. Bryan's field reduced to 1st Jan. 1764	1	8	47.00	4	50	35.19	0	12	38.20
Precession to 11 October 1766			- 7.03			+23.03			-30.75
True Zen. Dist. 11 October 1766	1	8	39.97	4	50	58.22	0	12	07.45
Ditto Observed at the Middle Point	1	7	10.79	6	6	46.65	1	3	40.18
Celestial Arch between the Observatory in Mr. Bryan's field and the Middle Point	1	15	50.76	1	15	48.43	1	15	47.63

263

Plane of the Sector EAST

	Delta Persei			Capella			Beta Aurigae			Castor		
	o	'	''	o	'	''	o	'	''	o	'	''
13	7	5	2.0	13	5	47	42.0						
15		5	3.0	15		47	41.0	15	4	57	27.0	15	7	33	36.5
16		5	2.0	16		47	41.3	16		57	27.7	16	7	33	38.2
19		5	3.7	19		47	44.0	19		57	27.3	19	7	33	38.7
Mean	7	5	2.67	5	47	42.08	4	57	27.33	7	33	37.80
Aberration			- 8.61			- 3.20			- 0.60			- 3.78
Deviation			- 8.26			- 7.52			- 6.75			+ 4.20
Precession			- 2.26			- 0.95			- 0.29			- 1.25
Refraction			+ 7.08			+ 5.80			+ 4.95			+ 7.55
Mean Zen. Dist. 11th Oct. 1766 Plane East	7	4	50.62	5	47	36.21	4	57	24.64	7	33	44.52

165

Plane of the Sector WEST

	Delta Persei	Capella	Beta Aurigae	Castor
	o ' "	o ' "	o ' "	o ' "
	21 7 5 10.3	21 5 47 52.8	21 4 57 35.3	21 7 33 30.0
	24 7 5 10.5	24 5 47 52.3	24 57 35.0	24 33 30.8
	27 5 9.7	27 47 51.0		
			28 57 35.6	
Mean	7 5 10.17	5 47 52.03	4 57 35.30	7 33 30.40
Aberration	- 9.37	- 4.24	- 1.60	- 3.52
Nutation	- 8.26	- 7.52	- 6.75	+ 4.20
Precession	- 2.56	- 1.09	- 0.32	- 1.36
Refraction	+ 7.08	+ 5.80	+ 4.95	+ 7.55
Mean Zen. Dist. 11 Oct. 1766	7 4 57.06	5 47 44.98	4 57 31.58	7 33 37.27
Ditto Plane East	7 4 50.62	5 47 36.21	4 57 24.64	7 33 44.52
True mean Zen. Dist. Oct. the 11th 1766	7 4 53.84	5 47 40.60	4 57 28.11	7 33 40.90
True Zen. Dist. Observed at Brandywine in Jan. & Feb. reduced to the 1st. Jan., 1764	7 4 22.2	5 47 32.3	4 57 26.3	7 33 23.1
Precession to Oct. 11, 1766	+34.61	+14.56	+ 4.28	+18.97
Reduced to Oct. 11, 1766	7 4 56.81	5 47 46.86	4 57 30.58	7 33 42.07

	Alpha Cygni	Capella
True Zen. Dist. Observed in Mr. Bryan's field reduced to 1st. Jan. 1764	4 43 25.95	6 00 26.60
Precession to 11th Oct. 1766	+34.59	+14.56
True Zen. Dist. 11th Oct. 1766	4 44 00.54	6 00 41.16
Ditto Observed at the Middle Point	5 59 52.92	7 16 29.20
Celestial Arch between the Observatory in Mr. Bryan's field and the Middle Point	1 15 52.38	1 15 48.04

264

(Undated) After this leaf comes in the two sheets A and B - here leave one
or one leaf blank.

(Charles Mason)   265

(Undated) 63° 5' 40".6 Distance to Pole 1 Jan. 1750
  - 5' 19".8 = Precession to October 11, 1766
 63° 0' 20".8
  -10".0 = Aberration and Nutation
 63° 0' 10".8 = Apparent Declination of Star
 26° 59' 49".2 Alpha Ursae Majoris (Polar Distance) Pole Apparent

For the Angle at the Middle Point (of our 1st Line with the Meridian) by Celestial Measurements.

51° 32' 26"   24° 32' 37"
26° 59' 49"

 75° 10' 51".2
  - 4' 6".1
 75° 6' 45".1 Beta Ursae Minoris (Declination)
Aberration : Nutation : 0
 14° 53' 15" Beta Ursae Minoris to the Pole

Sum Sides 78° 32' 15"   12° 16' 18" = one-
One-half Sum 39° 16' 08"   half Difference

	(log)
As Sine 39° 16' 8" - 1/2 Sum 1st (Line) =	9.8013767
: Sine one-half Difference 12° 16' 18"	9.3274554
Co Tang one-half P = 85° 58' 22"	8.8475990
	10.1750544
To Tang: one-half Difference Angles-1° 21' 16"	8.3736777
As Cos one-half Sum Sides 39° 16' 8"	9.8888443
: Cosine one-half Difference 12° 16' 18"	9.9899616
:: Co Tang one-half Angle P 85° 58' 22"	8.8475990
	18.8375606
: Tangent one-half Sum angles 5° 4' 41"	8.9487163

one-half Difference angles - 1° 21' 16"
  Hence 3° 43' 25" = Angle Z = the Angle our first Line
makes with the Meridian by Alpha Ursae Majoris
 51° 32' 26" Difference 36° 39' 11"
 14° 53' 15"   18° 19' 35" = One-half Difference
 66° 25' 41"
One-half 33° 12' 50"

166

	(log)		(log)

Sine   33° 12' 50" = 9.7385951   As Cosine one-half Sum Sides 33° 12' 50" = 9.9225342

: Sine   18° 19' 35" = 9.4975235   : Cosine one-half difference 18° 19' 35" = 9.9773947

Co-Tangent one-half angle   83° 19' 11" = 9.0686461   :: Co-Tang one-half P   83° 19' 11" = 9.0686461

     18.5661696   9.0460408

Tangent one-half Difference angle 3° 50' 47"   8.8275745   : Tangent one-half Sum Angles 7° 34' 12"   9.1235066

                           -3° 50' 47"

                           3° 43' 25" = Angle Z or

Angle at the Zenith = the Angle our first Line
makes with the Meridian according to Beta
Ursae Minoris.   Figures a and b   266

57° 42' 57".0 a' Pole 1st Jan. 1750 of Beta Ursae Majoris

  - 5' 19".1 = Precession to October 11, 1766

57° 37' 37".9   Mean distance a' Pole on Ditto

              = Aberration and Nutation

              = Apparent Polar Distance 11th October 1766

For the Angle our 1st Line makes with the Meridian by Terrestrial Measure
Here M, the Middle Point, MN = 80 Chains 00 Links measured
PM . the Line . PN = 5 chains 14 feet and 0.3 of an inch = 5 Chains 212.5 Links, then
as NM, the Meridian = 80 Chains 00 Links (logarithm) = 1.9030900

         : Rad   = 10.

         :: PN 5.2125 Chains   0.7170461

         Tangent angle M 3° 43' 40".5   8.8139561

Angle according to Alpha Ursae Majoris   3° 43' 25" }   Celestial Measures

Ditto by Beta Ursae Minoris   3° 43' 25" }

                      3° 43' 30" =   Angle our 1st Line makes with
                                 the Meridian at the Middle Point.

Latitude of the Observatory in Brandywine   39° 56' 19"

Mean of the Archs by the different stars leaving out Capella   1° 28' 45"

Latitude of the Middle Point   37° 27' 34"   Figure

Distance of the Pole from the Middle Point   52° 32' 26"   267

The Right Ascension of the Mid-Heaven of Alpha Ursae Majoris when Passing 1 Line (probably Meridian)
22h 16m 53.8s   by obs. : on 12th October 1766 By daily Motion of the Clock

     16m 55.1s   Ditto on 13th

     16m 54.7s   Ditto on 16th using the Motion of the Clock by Alpha Cygni and Beta Andromedae

22h 16m 54.5s   = Mean =   334° 13' 38"

Right Ascension of Alpha Ursae Majoris   162° 16' 54"

Angle at the Pole   171° 56' 44"

Right Ascension of the Mid-Heaven when Beta Ursae Minoris passed the Line.

  1h 58m 7.8s (by observation on the 14th day using the Motion of the Clock by Alpha Cygni
           and Beta Andromedae and 1h 58m 9.0s if the daily Motion of the Clock is
           altered by Alpha Cygni.
           by Ditto on 15th using the Clocks daily Motion = 55 seconds this 24 hours.

     58m 7.1s by Ditto on 16th using the Clocks Motion by Alpha Cygni and Beta Andromedae

1h 58m 7.5s = the Mean =   29° 31' 52"

Right Ascension of Beta Ursae Minoris   222° 53' 30"

Angle at the Pole   166° 38' 22"

Right Ascension of the Mid-Heaven when Beta Ursae Majoris passed the Line.   268

(Undated) 86° 32' = Angle CTO = the angle measured between CT and Radius from Newcastle and
TO the Meridian
93° 28' = Angle OTA, then angle ATP = TAL = 3° 28' for P in the Parallel of T, and A in the
Parallel of L. A the End of our 1st Line.
E the line extended to the Parallel of T.

(logs)

As Rad   10.
: Sine 3° 28'   8.7815244
:: 22.51 Chains   3.3523755
AP = TL 136.1 links   2.1338999
= what the end A of our 1st Line is South of the Tangent Point T.
= 81 miles 78 chains 31 links = 6558.31 chains = AM measured

(log)

Rad   10.000
:6558.31 chains AM =   5.8167920
:: Cos 3° 43' 30" Angle M =   9.9990815
: 6544.46 chains =   NM =   5.8158735

         Miles Chains Links
LT =   0   1   36
TO =   5   2   43
bB =   14   56   17 = the dist. between the Observatory in Brandywine and Mr. Bryan's.
Ob =   0   7   91 = Parallel Oo south of b.
          19   67   87

1587.87 Chains = Distance on a Meridian measured.
6544.46 Chains = the Tangent Line reduced to the Meridian by the Rumb or Plain Trig.
8132.33   = Whole corresponding to 1° 28' 44".99 = Difference of the Arch
= 101 miles 52 chains 33 links

1° 28' 47".21 Alpha Lyrae   ⎞
   28' 44".91 Gamma Andromedae   ⎟ Celestial Arches by the different stars, between
       44".40 Beta Persei   ⎬ the Observatory at Brandywine and the Middle Point.
       43".98 Delta Persei   ⎟
       45".09 Beta Aurigae   ⎟
       44".34 Castor   ⎠
1° 28' 44".99 = 5324".99

5324.99 seconds : 8132.33 links :: 3600 seconds : 5497.92 links
5497.92 links = 68 miles 57 chains 92 links = 1°
by reducing the line MA to a Meridian by plane Trigonometry: but what difference will   Figure
arise by Spherics in the Meridian MN says as   (log)   269
As 5497.92 chains = Length of Degree   =   5.7401984
: 3600" (Seconds in 1°)   =   3.5563025
:: 6558.31 chains = AM   =   5.8167920
                                             9.3730945
                          :4294".34 =   3.6328961
1° 11' 34".34 = AM in Degrees, Minutes, etc.
And   (log)
As 5497.92   5.7401984
: 3600"   3.5563025
= 6544.46 MN   5.8158735
                          9.3721760
4285".26   3.6319776
= 1° 11' 25".26 = MN in degrees, minutes, etc. by the Rund (probably Rhumb) or plane Trigonometry
Now Let Z the Zenith at the Middle Point
         T the Zenith at the end of the Tangent line
         P the Pole
Then ZP = 51° 32' 26" = Distance Pole at the Middle Point
and PT will be distance to Pole at the End Line, thus found
                                                (log)
Cosine   3° 43' 30"   = TZP   9.9990815
Tangent   1° 11' 34".34   8.3185337
: Tangent 1st Arch 1° 11' 25".2   8.3176152
          Side   51° 32' 26"
Second Arch   50° 21' 0".8   Cosine   9.8048841
                                   Cosine 1° 11' 34".34 9.9999059
                                                        19.8047900
Cosine 1st Arch   1° 11' 25".2   9.9999063
Cosine TP   50° 21' 1".0   9.8048837
       ZP =   51° 32' 26".0
Difference =   1° 11' 25".0   The difference between the distance of the Pole at   Figure
N by plane Trig.   1° 11' 25".26 the point M and the Point N, consequently MN.   270
                          0".26   that MN is too great in the first reduction by the rumb or plane.

168

(Undated)　　　Plane Trigonometry: and for the value of this 0.''26 as

As 1° or 3600.'' : 549792 links : : 0.''26 : 39.71 links.　Then 8132.33　　Chains

$$\begin{array}{r} -\quad 0.397 \\ \hline 8131.933 \end{array}$$ = the whole
length of the Line (in a Meridian)
corresponding to 1° 28' 44.''99, hence
the length of
a Degree as
　5324.''99 : 8131.93 Chains : : 3600''
　(= 1°) : 68 miles 57.65 Chains = 1°
Accounting for the error of
one Chain in the Measurement
of AM, found by a second Measurement
May 3, 1768, the Length of
a Degree is by the whole
Line = 68 miles 58 Chains 33 Links

　　　　　　　　N. B.　These results are from
　　　　　　　　Chain measure.　　　　　　　　　　　　　271

6544 Chains	46	Links = Nm by plane Trigonometry
	-39.7	Links
6544 Chains	06	Links = Nm by Spherics
1	36	= TL'
402	43	= TO'
7	91	= ob
6955 Chains	76	Links

1°　15'　50.''76
　　　15'　48.''43
　　　　　47.''63　　　Arches by Different stars
　　　　　52.''38
　　　　　48.''04
1°　15'　49.''45　　　Mean = 4549.''45

as 4549.''45 : 6955.76 : : 3600'' = 1°

5504 Chains 12 links = 68 miles 64 chains 12 links

This by the Middle Point and the Point (b) in
Mr. Bryan's field.

Accounting for the error of one chain found May 3rd, 1768 the
Length of a Degree is 68 miles 64 chains 91 links.　　　　　272

　　A Degree under the Equator

0°	121224	Yards Measured
10°	121444	
20°	121666	
30°	121884	
40°	122104	
50°	122324	
60°	122544	
66.5°	122687	Measured 69.7085 Miles
70°	122764	
80°	122984	
90°	123204	

Length of a Degree = 68 miles 57 chains 65 links = 68.7206 miles

$$\begin{array}{ll} & \text{(log)} \\ 68.7206 & 1.8370870 \\ \text{Cosine Latitude } 39°\ 43'\ 18'' = & \underline{9.8860155} \\ & 1.7231025 \end{array}$$

1° Longitude; 52.8570 miles = 52 miles 68 chains 56 links

$$\begin{array}{llll} 5° = & 264 \text{ miles} & 22 \text{ chains} & 80 \text{ links} \\ & \underline{-176} & \underline{75} & \underline{76} \qquad \text{run} \\ \text{to run} & 87 \text{ miles} & 27 \text{ chains} & 04 \text{ links according to the Sphere} \end{array}$$

Chains　　　　0.0857
　　　　　　　　　　80
　　　　　　　　68.560

165	miles	54 chains	88 links
+ 11		20	88
176	miles	75 chains	76 links

Note: The greatest curvature PC in 5° of Longitude　　　　　　　　　　Figure
　　　　is about 1' 30'' = 1 Inch on a Scale of one-half inch to a mile.　　　273

Dr. Bevis allows at the latitude
of 15 miles South of Philadelphia
33.989 yards to a second
(This) makes 122328 yards to a degree
= 69 miles and 858 yards.

	Parallel	39° 43' 18''
Lat.	Philadelphia	39° 56' 29''
	Brandywine	39° 56' 19''

Arch between Ditto and ⎫　　1° 28' 45''
the Middle Point　　　　⎬　　　　　　　　　　　　　　　　274
　　　　　　　　　　　　⎭

Memoranda. The following is the difference of
the Measurements between our 1st Line (from the Middle Point
to the Tangent) and the 3rd Line (Measured by the same Hands) at
different Points in the Line.

Miles from the Middle Point	Our Mile Posts fall short, that is to the South, of the Mile Posts in the third Line	
0	0	yards
2	0.5	
7	6 +	
10	7.5	
17	16	
26	25	
30	10	
32	6	
35	3	
39	2.5	
41	10	
45	33	
49	38	
50	48	
55	58	
60	63	
65	75	
70	80	
75	82 +	
80	80	
At the Tangent Point	82 -	

Yards that our Mile Posts
are South of those in the
third Line.

Note: In October, 1766, we measured from the 39 mile
Post to the 40th and from the 40th to 41 in our Line; and
found them right. This we did on the Chain Carriers
informing us that they doubted some error was made
about the 40th Mile Post. But it appears by the
Measurement made in 1768 that the error was one
Chain (too much) between the 42nd and 43rd Mile Posts.

275

1767
March
26   At Annapolis where His Excellency Horatio
Sharpe, Esquire, acquainted us the meeting last proposed
was postponed to the 28th of April next.
31   At Brandywine.

April
7   Left Brandywine.
8   At Philadelphia.
9   The Gentlemen Commissioners (for Pennsylvania) acquainted us,
they had not received any positive answer from
General Johnson, whether the Indians will permit us
to continue the West Line or not.
17   At Brandywine.
25   Left Ditto and went to Philadelphia. The Gentlemen Commissioners informed us the
meeting intended on the 28th instant was postponed to the 20th of May. The agreement
with the Indians not yet completed.
28   Left Philadelphia.
29   At Brandywine.

May
20   As yet there is no account arrived of the Success of
General Johnson; for which reason the meeting was postponed.

1767
May
24 Sun.   Received the Following Letter from Mr. Maskelyne (with
           an Ephemeris for 1767) on which I sent the Clock, belonging
           to the Royal Society by four men to be carried to Wilmington
           from thence by water (one of the men with it) to Philadelphia.

28   The Clock safely landed at Philadelphia.

June
2   Wrote to Mr. Maskelyne and Dr. Morton, with an account of the Clock's going, etc., etc.
           An Express from Sir William Johnson acquainted the Commissioners he had made an agreement
           with the Indians for to let us continue the West Line.
4   At 2h 30m to 3h 00m Apparent Time, Farenheit's Thermometer : 91°. Placed on the North side
           of a House in the open Air where it was placed last Winter. This years first hot day.
5   At 11h 30m in the forenoon and noon, 95°; at 1h 00m P.M., 94°; at 3h, 95°.
6   At 11h 00m in the forenoon 95° and at 3:00 P.M. 95°.   276
7   At sunrise, Thermometer 67°, At 11h AT = 93°. At 3h, P.M. 93° (AT = Apparent Time)
8   At 6h 30m AT 80° At 11h AT 85° At 4h P. M. 91° At 7h P.M. : 80°
9   At 2h P.M. 80°. The Air much altered; being very cool and pleasant.
10   At 4h 30m P.M. 90°. At 7 P.M. 80°.
11   At Philadelphia.
12   Ditto. Wrote to the Honorable Proprietors of Maryland and Pennsylvania
           acquainting them we were preparing for the Westward.
14 Sun.   At 2:00 P.M. Thermometer at 95°.
15   Sent 7 Men with the Telescope of the Sector
           to Fort Cumberland. The rest of the Instruments etc. by a Waggon
           to Mr. Miller in the Valley.
           Left Brandywine and proceeded for New-Town on
           Chester River in Maryland to attend the Gentlemen Commissioners.   277

           1767 June at 2:00 P.M.
           Sunday 21   95°   The height of the Fahrenheit Thermometer hung in
           Monday   94   the Shade on the North Side of a House standing on
           Tuesday   96   a Hill, about three Miles Eastward of Mr. Harland's.
           Wednesday   86   This is the same Thermometer as is taken account of
           Thursday   87   for four months past by myself. The following
           Friday   89   is by Mr. Joel Bayley.
           Saturday   91
           Sunday 28   94
           Monday   95
           Tuesday   98.5° At 4h P.M. at 102°

July 1767 at 2h P.M.		August at 2h P.M.		September at 2h P.M.		October at 2h P.M.	
1st Wednesday	88°	1st Saturday	85°	1st Tuesday	76°	1st Thursday	61°
Thursday	85	Sunday	90	Wednesday	79	Friday	65
Friday	77	Monday	91	Thursday	82	Saturday	
Saturday	79	Tuesday	93.5	Friday	78	Sunday	
Sunday	80	Wednesday	93.5	Saturday	76	Monday	
Monday	83	Thursday	91.5	Sunday	78	Tuesday	
Tuesday	86	Friday	97	Monday	79	Wednesday	75
Wednesday	82	Saturday	92	Tuesday	75	Thursday	76
Thursday	84	Sunday	98	Wednesday	74	Friday	
Friday	91	Monday	81	Thursday	76	Saturday	
Saturday	90	Tuesday	85	Friday	68	Sunday	
Sunday	92	Wednesday	90	Saturday	73	Monday	
Monday	89	Thursday	94	Sunday	78	Tuesday	
Tuesday	86	Friday	80	Monday	56	Wednesday	
Wednesday	90	Saturday	82.5	Tuesday	64	Thursday	
Thursday	93	Sunday	89	Wednesday	74	Friday	
Friday	90	Monday	81	Thursday	76	Saturday	
Saturday	88.5	Tuesday	80	Friday	67	Sunday	
Sunday	79	Wednesday	79	Saturday	70		
Monday	74	Thursday	81	Sunday	77		
Tuesday	66	Friday	85	Monday	76		
Wednesday	80	Saturday	81	Tuesday	78		
Thursday	85	Sunday	82	Wednesday	81		
Friday	92	Monday	82	Thursday	64		
Saturday	87	Tuesday	86.5	Friday	65		
Sunday	86	Wednesday	88.5	Saturday	60		
Monday	88	Thursday	89.5	Sunday	68		
Tuesday	89	Friday	89	Monday	72		
Wednesday	90	Saturday	82	Tuesday	69		
Thursday	91	Sunday	80	Wednesday	66		
Friday	93	Monday	76				

(Missing readings
are indistinct,
edge of page
frayed)

278

Greenwich, Feb. 24, 1767

Messrs. Mason and Dixon,

      Herewith I send you, agreeable to your desire, the Nautical Almanac of 1767: also a table for facilitating the computations of the Moon's distance from the Sun. I am not a little surprised at never receiving a line from you in answer to my two letters of October and November 1765 (in which I gave you an account that the Council of Royal Society had agreed to employ you to measure a degree of latitude in Pensilvania, and sent you my instructions on that head) nor any acknowledgement of your having received the instruments I sent you out on account of the Royal Society; tho Mr. Mason acquainted me you had received my letters and would write to me as soon as you received the instruments which surely must have been long ago. The Council of the Royal Society have ordered that you should send the clock home immediately as we hear it has received great damage and must be put in order directly for the ensuing transit of Venus over the Sun. The method of finding the longitude by observations of the moon is approved of greatly by the public and is coming into vogue; and will, I hope, be general in a few years. I would send you Mayer's Tables, but they are not yet completed. I hope to have them ready for publication in a short time, after which, I may send you a copy if I know they will reach you. You have probably heard that Mr. Bird has received 500 pounds sterling from the board of longitude for discovering his methods of constructing and dividing instruments, and making plates of the principal instruments at Greenwich, and taking apprentice, and instructing workmen in his art. Dolland's telescopes answer surprisingly; I have one of only 3 1/2 feet long with 3 object glasses at the Observatory which magnifies 140 times and is superior to a two foot reflector, equal to a ten foot of Dolland's with 2 object glasses, & little, if at all, inferior to the 6 foot Newtonian of the Observatory. These will be the best telescopes for carrying abroad to observe Jupiter's satellites. I desire to hear from you directly and to know what you are doing, or have done about the measure of the degree. Be pleased also to send an account of your having received the instruments & what, I am

279

280

Your sincere friend & humble Servant

N. Maskelyne

281

(An envelope addressed)

To Messrs. Mason and Dixon
Surveyors to the Honorable William
     Penn
In Pensilvania

Memoranda
1767

At the top of Savage Mountain very good free-stone. Opposite the 174th and 175th Mile Post about half a mile to the Southward, there is a remarkable Quantity of the large tall Spruce Trees.

On the Little Yochio Geni, a piece of rich land about a Mile in length and a Quarter of a mile in breadth (to the South of the Line) in which a great variety of Plants. Haws of a very large size, Hops, wild Cherry Trees etc. etc. - it appears like - a Garden desolate.

From the top of Savage Mountain to this, is a wild waste, composed of laurel swamps, dark vales of Pine through which I believe the Sun's rays never penetrated.

A pretty good tract of Land on the North side of the Line near the Little Yochio Geni.

On the big Yochio Geni are very good tracts of Land and the Hills very rich. About three Miles South of the Line, I was informed there is a tract of 500 Acres upland and 200 of rich Bottom near it on the Yochio, now void. There are seven families settled on the said River within 3 Miles of the Line. The Bottom of the Big Yochio, is of a Black, hard, round stone.

At 197 Miles 53 chains crossed a Glade (or meadow) about 10 chains wide and length to the North seen 1/2 a Mile & to the South a Mile, but where it begins or ends I know not.

At Entered - }
   Left - } a Glade

At our Station where the Sector was set up on the 17th of August we were paid a visit by 13 Delawares; one of them a Nephew of Captain Black-Jacobs, who was killed by General Armstrong at the Kittony Town in 17__. This Nephew of Black-Jacobs was the tallest man I ever saw.

From the Station we passed over very desert, woodland Barren soil with very sudden deep bottoms, immediately rising again nearly perpendicular. The tops of the Ridges chiefly chestnut, even to the top of Laurel Hill.

No fish to be found in neither of the Yochio Genies nor in the Sandy Creeks, Occasioned I believe by the great falls the waters had at leaving the Mountains, up which the fish cannot pass.

Laurel Hill (or rather Mountains), is a Wild of Wildes; the Laurel overgrown, the Rocks gaping to swallow up, over whose deep mouths you may step. The whole a deep melancholy appearance out of nature. But from the Summit of the Westernmost Ridge, viz. from the Point 214 miles 12 chains there is the most delightful pleasing View of the Western Plains the Eye can behold. From hence the end of our Line may be seen, and about 10 Miles farther, which reaches a Ridge or Ridges, that divides the Waters running into the Monaungahela from those running into the Ohio.

This Ridge terminates the Sight and makes a beautiful Horizon that may be seen more than 100 miles from North to South.

In the Rivers Cheat and the Monaungahela, we found plenty of fish of various sorts, and very large; particularly cat fish. ---- caught a Lizard near a foot in Length. Coal is found very plenty here, and beyond the River in our Line.

About two miles west of Monaungahlea we were paid a visit by Catfish, his Nephew, and Squaw (or wife) : They were very well dressed nearly like Europeans; and he (Catfish) being a Chief of the Delaware Nation, our Chief held a Council and made a Speech (and presented him with some strings of Wampom) to him; in which they acquainted them of our business there: He seemed to be very well satisfied, and promised to send the strings of Wampom to his Town, and to come again in 15 days; but he never returned.

Six Miles beyond the River, Eight Warriors of the Seneca Nation fell in with us, in their way to the Southward going against the Cherokees. These people go 700 Miles through these Deserts to War. They are one of the Six Nations, which made the Indians with us, very glad to see them. They were equipped with Blankets and Kettles, Tomahawks Guns and Bows and Arrows; they staid two days with us, got a small supply of Powder and paint; when their Captain ordered to march.

At our last station, among many others came Prince Prisqueetom, Brother to the King of the Delawares; he spoke very good English; (and though his face is deeply furrowed with time, being 86) told me, his Brother and himself had a great mind to go and see the great King over the Waters; and make a perpetual Peace with him; but was afraid he should not be sent back to his own Country.

The land westward of the Monaungahela is very rich and fertil, Rich-Weed and Pea vine, so thick you can scarcely get through it: which is the richest pasture for Cattle I ever saw.

The old Prince above mentioned gave a very good description of the Ohio and Mississippi, all agreeing with others that it runs through a plain level Country, the land very good: Meadows by nature of Miles square (having only a few Trees in them.) whose verdant plains never heard the Milk Maid singing blithe and gay. Though, who can tell, what he has done that made them; a Thousand annual Suns to him how short.

285

The following is a description of the Ohio and Mississippi, as described to me by Mr. Hugh Crawford, our Interpreter, who has traversed these parts for 28 years, either as an Indian Trader or Commander in his Majesty's Service in the late Wars.

Beginning at the Mouth of the Mississippi. The Island of New Orleans lies about 100 Miles from the Bar of the said River.

At about 100 Miles above Orleans, on the West side comes in a River nearly as large as the Mississippi. This River heads in the Mountains of Mexico. At the head of the said River, the Spanyards have a fortification - 300 Miles above Orleans is Natchees. Here the French have a Fort. This is on the East Side of the River, and one of the most beautiful places for a Settlement nature can produce, the lands exceeding rich: the Seasons one continued Spring.

Ships of two or 300 Tons may come up the River as far as this (Natchees), and sloops of 30 Tons up to the Forks of the Ohio. One place only he doubts is a little dubious, about 200 Miles below the Forks, where there is 20 or thirty small Islands, but he Judges the Navigation is good on the West Side of the Islands, but had not time to prove it.

The River Mississippi is in general about half a Mile in breadth, and by the French account 1360 Miles in Length from the Forks of the Ohio to the Mouth (in the bay of Florida) .... this length he supposes to be very near.

There are many fine River falls into the Mississippi between the Natchees and the Forks of the Ohio from both Sides, which are but very little known therefore shall leave them; but must observe the whole is a plain rich land.

The Ohio at the Forks is very near as large as the Mississippi. From the Forks on a due North Course 140 Miles up the Mississippi, lies the Country called the Illinoies; first settled by the French, who were encouraged by the French King to marry with the Indians. Each couple receiving a premium of 50 pounds provided the Native embraced the Catholic faith. By this means it soon became a fine settlement, and here the French erected a Fort; called it Fort Sharter but the Fort and Country being on the East Side of the Mississippi it fell into the Hands of the English by the Treaty of Peace in 176_ and his Britanic Majesty has now a Garison in the said Fort - Sharter.

286

The Mississippi North of the Illinois is but little known, its banks are settled by the Indians, who have had very little (and some not any) correspondence with the Europeans.

Therefore returning again to the Forks of the Ohio, and taking its course up, we find many Rivers, on both sides emptying into it, all of which my informer has been up and down for many Miles.

The land in the forks of the Mississippi is very good. Here it is much to be wished there was a Settlement. The climate and the Soil inviting every Stranger's Stay. About 50 Miles up the Ohio the French erected a Fort called Desumption, from hence by land to the Illinois about 70 Miles.

On the East side of the Ohio from its mouth up to Pitsburg (called by the French Fort du Quesne) comes in the Rivers Cherokee, Broad River, Kentucke, Great Salt Lick, Totteroy, Great Kanhawa. These all head in the Allegany Chain of Mountains.

The Mouth of the Cherokee River is about 60 Miles above the Forks. 15 Miles above this comes in Broad River. The length of the Cherokee River (is) about 400 Miles running through level country. Broad River for 200 Miles in length may be walked over in the summer, being not above two feet deep - smooth level bottom, and breadth in general one mile and a half!

Above the Great Kanhawa is little Kanhawa, near the head of which is the End of the West Line where we left off. Above the little Kanhawa is Fishing Creek and the two Weeling Creeks, which is all of note to Pitsburg.

On the West side of the Ohio comes in the Rivers (beginning at the forks), Wabash, Mineami (Rocky River), Siota, Kockhocking, Muskingum; and Beaver Creek near to Pitsburg. These all Head in Lowlands near Lake Erie, interlocking with the heads of short creeks, which runs Northward into the said Lake.

The Mouth of the Wabash River is about 150 miles above the forks. It runs through a beautiful Country, if a Desart of rich level land may be called so, where the Meadow bounds are scarcely within the limits of the Eye. Mineami (or Rocky River) the Great, (for there is a lesser between this and Siota) is very rapid, and the West branch heads very near a River of the same name that runs in to the South West end of Lake Erie.

Siota is very gentle, its Banks and the Ohio about its Mouth; is the Seat of the Shawanes and Delaware Indians, who live here by the leave of the Six Nations.

Muskingum, all gentle to the Head, whence to the head of Cayaga River is but about one mile over which the Indians often carry their Canoes, and down Cayaga in to Lake Erie. Upon these Rivers lives the Mingoes, Tuscarawas, etc. The Tuscarawas Ancient seat was in Virginia, where they have now some of their friends living. Their King with a few attendants I saw at King-William's Court House in Virginia; in March 1766, who were going to pay a visit to their Brothers.

The head of the Allegany River is about 200 Miles NE from Pitsburg and runs down on the West Side of the Allegany Mountains, through a plain, inferior for the richness of its soil to none; at Pitsburg it is joined by the Manaungahela and is afterwards called the Ohio.

From Pitsburg to the Forks where the Ohio falls into the Mississippi is about ___ Miles. From the End of our line to the Ohio on a West Course is about forty miles, on a Northwest Course about 30 Miles. The West Line that divides the Provinces of Maryland and Pennsylvania if Extended would fall on the Ohio about the mouth of Fishing Creek. From here a West Course would pass through the Southern part of the Illinois. The distance about 7 or 800 Miles. A country says my informer, through which you may travel 100 Miles, and not find one Hill, or one Acre of barren Land.

In this large tract of Land all lies waste except just on the banks of the Rivers, where the Natives in general resort.

(See date below)

Gentlemen:

You are to repair immediately to the Place on the West Line where you left off last fall, and continue that Line in the Manner heretofore directed, to the End of Five Degrees of Longitude from the River Delaware, in the Parallel of the said West Line; after which you are as you return to have a Visto opened between the several Posts that may be fixed in the said due West Line so that the said Line may be described and distinguished by one continued Visto, according to your former Instructions; Or, if you find that time can be saved by employing your Workmen in opening the said Visto, while you are taking Observations in order to correct your Deviations in proceeding with the said West Line, you are desired so to do.

While you are opening the Visto which is to describe the West Line or Parallel of Latitude, you are to set up a Post on the Summit of every Ridge over which the said West Line shall pass in the Direction of the said Line: You are likewise to heap Stones around the said Posts (where Stones may be very near and easily raised) so as that the same may be visible from Ridge to Ridge for the better ascertaining the Place where the West Line passes every Ridge.

You are also to send proper Persons to Baltimore Town in Maryland where there are one hundred and thirty nine Boundary Stones that they may convey the said stones to the proper Places in the West Line, which Stones you are to set up in the said Line as you return, in the same Manner as the other Boundary Stones have been fixed. But if it should happen that the Places, where any of the said Boundary Stones ought to be fixed are on the Tops of high Mountains to which the said Stones cannot be carried, you are in such Places to erect and heap up together large Quantities or Piles of Stones to ascertain, mark and perpetuate the said Spots or Places taking particular Notice thereof in your Minute Books and report the same to the Commissioners at their next Meeting.

290

As soon as you have extended the Line to the End of Five Degrees of Longitude you are to give immediate Advice thereof to the Commissioners that they may give Notice to each other and appoint another Meeting.

A Number of the Indians have been deputed by the Six Nations (whose Consent hath been obtained to our extending the West Line to the Western Limits of the Province of Pennsylvania) to be present at, and attend you in running the said Line, and Orders have been given for them to meet you at York town in Pennsylvania: As the public Peace and your own Security may greatly depend on the good Usage and kind Treatment of these Deputies, we commit them to your particular Care, and recommend it to you in the most earnest Manner not only to use them well yourselves but to be careful that they receive no Abuse or ill treatment from the Men you may employ in carrying on the said Work, and to do your utmost to protect them from the Insults of all other persons whatsoever.

Chester Town   18th June 1767

    Horatio Sharpe   Benjamin Chew
    John Barclay   Edward Shippen, Jr.
    Dan of St. Thomas Jenifer   Thomas Willing
    J. Beale Bordley

To Messrs Charles Mason
    & Jeremiah Dixon

291

Chester Town   18th June 1767

The Commissioners recommend to Messrs Mason and Dixon That the spirituous Liquors to be given to the Indians attending them, be in small quantities mixed with water and delivered to them not more than three times every day.

    Horatio Sharpe   Benjamin Chew
    John Barclay   Edward Shippen, Jr.
    Dan of St. Thomas Jenifer   Thomas Willing
    J. Beale Bordley

292

The Proprietors' Journal for 1767, as follows, nearly

1767
March
  22 Sun.   Left Brandywine and proceeded to Newtown on Chester River to attend the
            Gentlemen Commissioners on the 24th Instant according to their appointment in November last.
  25   At Chester Town. The Commissioners not being come, we set out for Annapolis.
  26   At Annapolis where we were informed by his Excellency
            Horatio Sharpe, Esquire: that the meeting intended the 24th was postponed
            to the 28th of April next, on account of the Commissioners not receiving any certain
            intelligence of Sir William Johnson's having agreed with the Natives for us to
            Continue the West Line.
June
  3   Were informed that an agreement was concluded with the
            Six Nations for us to proceed with the West Line, and that the Gentlemen Commissioners were to
            meet at Chester Town the 16th Instant.
  12   Wrote to the Honorable Proprietors of Maryland and Pennsylvania.
  15   Sent seven Men with the Telescope and the Sector to the Allegany Mountain where we left
            off last Summer
  17   Attended the Gentlemen Commissioners at Chester Town.
  18   Attended Ditto and received our Instructions to proceed with the West
            Line to the End of 5 degrees of Longitude from the River Delaware.

1767
July

7   The Waggons arrived at Fort Cumberland with the Instruments, Tents, etc.
Lodged with Colonel Crisep near the Forks of Potowmack; he has here a most beautiful
Estate. This is the same Gentleman mentioned in Journal of the 17th of January 1765.

8   At the Allegany Mountain; where we left off last Summer.

19   Placed a mark Eastward in a direction from the Post we left off at in the true
Parallel; to be again in the true Parallel at 10' West.

(Undated)   Thus

Let $\odot$ (be) the Post we left
off at. p another point
in the true Parallel East of $\odot$
Then the Angle D $\odot$ C = 8' 18" for
Angle N $\odot$ P = 89° 55' 51" when the Chords N $\odot$ and $\odot$ Q = 10 minutes as usual

$$\frac{4}{359° \ 43' \ 24''} = \text{four times the angle}$$

Complement =   16' 36" = the two angles A $\odot$ B and D $\odot$ C
One half   =   8' 18" = angle D $\odot$ C and A $\odot$ B, which with the measured distance
= $\odot$ p = $\odot$ C = 1 mile 78 chains, we have DC thus;
as 40 chains : 9.6575 links :: 158 chains (= 1 mile 78 chains) : 38.14 links = DC
38.14 links = DC
17.00 links = Dp = distance of the chord from the circle at the distance of 1 mile 78 chains from $\odot$
21.14   = pC = The distance to be laid off from p to C to give the chord $\odot$ N

Note: The Post at $\odot$ left off at in the true Parallel   = 165 miles 55- chains
Mark or Station at C at the top of the little Allegany = 163 miles 57   chains
Radius =   1 mile 78 chains

July

11   Widening the Visto to the Eastward to see the Mark in the said Direction.

12 Sunday

13   Began in the true Parallel and continued the Line Westward
in the above mentioned Direction.

14   Continued the Line.
At 168 miles 78 chains the Top of Savage Mountain or
the great dividing Ridge of the Allegany Mountains.

15   Continued the Line.
At 169 miles 60 chains crossed a small run or branch of the
little Yochio Geni. The Head of Savage River to the
South about one Mile.

16   Continued the Line. This day we were joined with
14 Indians, viz. Mohawks and Onondagas sent by the Six Nations
to conduct us through their country, namely three Onondagas
and eleven Mohawks. (With them came Mr. Hugh Crawford, Interpreter.)

Figure
294

17   Continued the Line.

18   Continued the Line.
At 171 miles 5 chains crossed Ditto run or a second Branch of the Little Yochio.
At 171 miles 63 chains crossed this branch the last time. In the whole about 6 or 7 times.

19 Sunday

20   Continued the Line.

21   Continued the Line.
At 173 miles 1 chain crossed a small run running Northward.

22   Continued the Line.

23   Continued the Line.

24   Continued the Line.
At 176 miles 15 chains crossed a large branch of the Little Yochio.

25   Continued the Line.
At 177 Miles 4 Chains 45 Links changed the direction to be in the
true Parallel at 10' West: There we measured a Radius
of 58 Chains, and as we began in the true Parallel the angle is 8' 18"
as usual which 40 chains gives 9.6575 Links, then
as 40 : 9.655 :: 58:14 Links which we laid off to the Northward
for   177 miles   4 chains 45 links = change
Station   177   62   45
               58   00   = Radius
At 177 Miles 39 Chains crossed the Little Meadow rùn, running in to the Little Yochio Geni.

26 Sunday

27   Continued the Line. At 178 Miles the Little Meadow South, distant about 2.5 Miles.

1767
July

28   Continued the Line.
At 179 miles 44 chains   Crossed the Little Yochio Geni.

29   Continued the Line.

30   Continued the Line.
At 182 miles 38 chains crossed a small Branch, running into the
Little Yochio.

31   Continued the Line.

August

1   Continued the Line.
At 184 Miles 13 chains. The top of little Laurel Hill.

2 Sunday

3   Continued the Line.
At 185 miles 7 chains crossed a small run.

4   Continued the Line.

5   Continued the Line.
At ⎰186 miles 2 chains⎱
At ⎨186 miles 38 chains⎬ Crossed small runs.
    ⎰187 miles 20 chains⎱

6   Continued the Line.
At   188 Miles 41 Chains 65 Links   Changed our direction to be in the true
Parallel at 10' West. Thus

next Station 188   69   50
Radius =   0   27   85   And as we began in the true Parallel
the angle is 8' 18" as usual which at 40 chains radius gives
9.6575 Links, then as 40 : 9.6575 :: 27.85 : 6.7 Links, this we laid
off to the North at 188 Miles 69 Chains 50 Links and continued the Line as follows.   296

7   Continued the Line in the direction changed.
At 189 Miles 57 Chains. The top of Winding Hill.
    189 Miles 69 Chains crossed General Bradock's Road leading
from Fort Cumberland to Fort Pit.
    190 Miles 1 Chain crossed Ditto a second time.

8   Continued the Line.
At 190 miles 34 chains crossed the above road a third time.
    191 miles 69 chains crossed a small run.

9 Sunday

10   Continued the Line.

11   Continued the Line.
At 194 Miles 25 Chains 25 Links the East Bank of the big Yochio Geni.
    194 Miles 28 Chains 00 Links the Middle of a small Island, about 200 yards wide.
    194 Miles 31 Chains 65 Links the West Bank of the river. The water
about a foot deep.

12   Continued the Line.
At 196 Miles 31 Chains crossed a small run.

13   Continued the Line.
At 197 Miles 53 Chains crossed a small run passing through a Glade.
    198 Miles 5 Chains crossed a small run.

14   Continued the Line.
At 198 Miles 69 Chains the top of the ridge that divides the
        waters of the Yochio Geni from the waters
        of Sandy Creek, which runs into
        Cheat River.

15   Continued the Line.
At 199 Miles 33 Chains crossed a small run, running into Sandy Creek.

16 Sun. Sent for the Sector, etc. From Mr. Spears's at the
crossing of the Yochio Geni on Braddock's Road.   297

179

1767
August
17

Set up the Sector in the direction of our Line
at the distance of 199 Miles 63 Chains 68 Links from the Post
marked West in Mr. Bryan's field and made the
following Observations.

Plane EAST

	Star Name	Nearest Point on the Sector		Revolutions and Seconds on the Micrometer		Difference		Apparent Zenith Distance		
		o	'	R	"	'	"	o	'	"
17	Capella	6	0+	7	36	0	27	6	0	27.0
				7	9					
18	Alpha Lyrae	1	10-	7	4	1	27.5	1	8	32.5
				5	20.5					
	Delta Cygni	4	50+	3	51+	1	2.6	4	51	2.6
				2	41-					
	Gamma Cygni	0	10+	9	18-	1	58.3	0	11	58.3
				11	32					
	Gamma Cygni	0	15-	9	18-	3	4.2	0	11	55.8
				5	41.5					
	Alpha Cygni	4	45-	7	39	0	52.0	4	44	8.0
				8	39					
	Capella	6	0+	10	40.5	0	24.8	6	0	24.8
				10	16-					
19	Alpha Lyrae	1	10-	6	17.5	1	27.2	1	8	32.8
				4	34+					
	Delta Cygni	4	50+	4	18	1	4.7	4	51	4.7
				3	5+					
	Gamma Cygni	4	45-	4	19.5	(Not reduced)				
				5	12.5					
	Capella	6	0+	9	4-	0	26.2	6	0	26.2
				8	29.5					
20	Alpha Lyrae	1	10-	9	32	1	28.0	1	8	32.0
				7	48					
	Delta Cygni	4	50+	6	46+	1	2.3	4	51	2.3
				5	36					
	Gamma Cygni	0	10+	8	30.5	1	56.5	0	11	56.5
				10	43					
	Alpha Cygni	4	45-	9	19.5	0	52.0	4	44	8.0
				10	19.5					

298

20

After we had made the last Observation we
turned the Instrument

Plane WEST

	Star Name	Nearest Point on the Sector		Revolutions and Seconds on the Micrometer		Difference		Apparent Zenith Distance		
	Capella	6	0	8	39+	0	35.4	6	0	35.4
				9	23-					
21	Alpha Lyrae	1	10-	8	33-	1	31.6	1	8	28.4
				10	20+					
	Delta Cygni	4	50+	10	35+	1	10.7	4	51	10.7
				12	2					
	Gamma Cygni	0	10+	11	27	1	53.0	0	11	53.0
				9	18					
	Alpha Cygni	4	45-	9	39.5	0	47.5	4	44	12.5
				8	44					
22	Alpha Lyrae	1	10-	5	42.5	1	34.0	1	8	26.0
				7	32.5					
	Delta Cygni	4	50+	7	37+	1	11.0	4	5	
				9	4+					
	Gamma Cygni	0	10+	9	13.5	1	52.8	0	11	52.8
				7	5-					
	Alpha Cygni	4	45-	5	41-	0	45.7	4	44	14.3
				4	47					

23 Sun.   Cloudy.
24   Computing our Observations etc. as follows.

299

180

1767 August		Alpha Lyrae			Delta Cygni			Gamma Cygni			Alpha Cygni			Capella		
		o	'	"	o	'	"	o	'	"	o	'	"	o	'	"
								Plane EAST								
17														6	0	27.0
18		1	8	32.5	4	51	2.6	0	11	58.3	4	44	8.0	6	0	24.8
19				32.8										6	0	26.2
20				32.0		51	2.3		11	56.5		44	8.0			
Mean 19d		1	8	32.43	4	51	2.45	0	11	57.40	4	44	8.0	6	0	26.0
Aberration				+13.86			-11.46			+ 9.47			- 8.45			+ 7.97
Deviation				- 3.75			+ 1.63			- 0.40			- 0.23			- 6.05
Precession				+ 9.14			-30.03			+40.30			-45.14			-19.19
Refraction				+ 1.20			+ 5.60			+ 0.20			+ 5.50			+ 7.00
Mean Zen. (Dist.) 1st Jan. 1764		1	8	52.88	4	50	28.19	0	12	46.97	4	43	19.68	6	0	15.73
								Plane WEST								
20														6	0	35.4
21		1	8	28.4	4	51	10.7	0	11	53.0	4	44	12.5			
22			8	26.0	4	51	11.0	0	11	52.8	4	44	14.3			
(Mean)		1	8	27.20	4	51	10.85	0	11	52.90	4	44	13.40	6	0	35.4
Aberration				+14.35			-11.92			+10.08			- 9.11			+ 7.95
Deviation				- 3..75			+ 1.63			- 0.40			- 0.23			- 6.05
Precession				+ 9.14			-30.03			+40.30			-45.14			-19.19
Refraction				+ 1.20			+ 5.60			+ 0.20			+ 5.50			+ 7.00
		1	8	48.14	4	50	36.13	0	12	43.08	4	43	24.42	6	0	25.11
				52.88			28.19			46.97			19.68			15.73
True Zen. Dist.		1	8	50.51	4	50	32.16	0	12	45.02	4	43	22.05	6	0	20.42
Ditto at Post Marked West		1	8	41.80	4	50	40.40	0	12	33.00	4	43	31.20	6	0	31.80
Offset		South		8.71	South		8.24	South		12.02	South		9.15	South		11.38
				8.24												
				12.02												
				9.15												
				11.38												
(Mean)				9.9												

(Mean) 9.9 = 15 chains 00 links to be laid off to the Southward.   300

Miles from the Post Marked West in Mr. Bryan's Field	Offsets from the Circle		Offsets from the Triangle		True Offsets	
	Chains	Links	Chains	Links	Chains	
165.68	0	00	0	00	0.00	Sector
166	0	02	0	14	0.16	
167	0	11	0	57	0.68	
168	0	18	1	00	1.18	
169	0	23	1	46	1.69	
170	0	25	1	90	2.15	
171	0	27	2	34	2.61	
172	0	27	2	76	3.03	
173	0	26	3	22	3.48	
174	0	23	3	65	3.88	
175	0	18	4	08	4.26	
176	0	12	4	52	4.64	
177	0	03	4	97	5.00	
178	0	0	5	48	5.48	
179	0	08	5	92	6.00	
180	0	15	6	34	6.49	
181	0	23	6	73	6.96	
182	0	25	7	16	7.41	
183	0	27	7	61	7.88	
184	0	27	8	05	8.32	
185	0	26	8	49	8.75	
186	0	23	8	93	9.16	
187	0	18	9	37	9.55	
188	0	06	9	81	9.87	
changed 188 miles 41 ch. 65 links	0					
189	0	05	10	25	10.30	
190	0	14	10	69	10.83	
191	0	21	11	13	11.34	
192	0	25	11	58	11.83	
193	0	27	12	02	12.29	
194	0	27	12	46	12.73	
195	0	26	12	90	13.16	
196	0	24	13	34	13.58	At this Station (199.78) Mr.
197	0	20	13	78	13.98	John Green, one of the Chiefs of
198	0	14	14	22	14.36	the Mohawk Nation, and his
199	0	06	14	65	14.71	Nephew left us, in order to re-
199 miles 63 ch. 68 links	0	0	15	00	15.00	turn to their own Country.

198 miles 69 ch. 00 links (Last Station)   301

Undated   Here ABCD, the true Parallel. A the point we left off at, at the foot of
Savage Mountain in 1766; where we began in 1767. The points E and F, similar to B and C
the points of changing the direction to the Northward, each an angle of 8' 18".
AEFG the Line run instead of the true chords Abcd.
G the point where the Sector was set up on the 17th of August, where by the Observations,
GD (or Gd) = 15 chains 00 links = the greatest offset. Hence the Offsets to the Chords
Abcd are in proportion to the distance from the point A, as according to the Triangular Column B,
to which add the offsets of the Circle from the Chords gives the true offsets south as by the   Figure
Column C. (See page 301).   302

25   Began to open a Visto Eastward in the true Parallel
and appointed Hands to continue it to where we
began at Savage Mountain.

26   Began in the true Parallel to continue the
Line Westward. Found the direction as
on the 19th of July thus. The Radius to the Eastward
was = 70 chains 76 links. Then as 40 chains : 9.6 links :: 70.76 chains : 16.98 links

                  The Chord from the Circle   <u>10.98</u> links

                             Rest   6.00 links

This (6 links) we laid off to the Southward from the
Point in the Parallel 70 chains 76 links to the Eastward of the Instrument;
and proceeded in this direction as follows.

27   Continued the Line.
At 200 Miles 17 Chains Entered a Glade or Meadow.

200	21	Crossed a Run, Running North.
200	30	Left the above Glade.
201	10	Entered the same Glade a second time.
201	21	Crossed a Run running North.
201	29	Left the Glade. This Glade

is very large both to the North and South of the Line.

28   Continued the Line.

29   Continued the Line.

30 Sun.   Continued the Line.

31   Continued the Line.
At 204 Miles 11 Chains⎫
     205 Miles 60 Chains⎭   crossed small Runs, running South.
At 204 Mile Post the Big Meadows by information
are North, distant about 5 Miles.

303

September

1   Continued the Line.
At 206 miles 56 chains   Crossed little Sandy Creek, about
20 yards in breadth.

2   Continued the Line.
At 208 miles 59 chains   Crossed big Sandy Creek -- about 30
yards wide. Both these creeks
run Southward.

3   Continued the Line.
Between 209 miles 63 chains and 210 miles 13 chains crossed a
Small run 5 times; the last time running Southward: At
the last time of crossing this Run viz. at 210 miles 13 chains we
Entered the foot of Laurel Hill.

4   Continued the Line.
At 211 miles 13 chains 28 links. Changed our direction to be again in the
true Parallel at 10 minutes West. Thus at 32 chains 00 links Eastward of the
point (for we could not see the point itself, it being in a deep bottom) we laid off
7.7 links to the Southward which corresponds to the usual angle of 8' 18"
at the distance of 40 chains and here placed a Mark. And at 212 miles
28 chains 92 links which gives a Radius of 1 mile 15 chains 64 links
we laid off 22.95 links to the North (which corresponds to the angle 8' 18")
and from this point and the last mentioned Mark we continued the Line as follows.
At 211 miles 30 chains Crossed a small run running South.

5   Continued the Line.

6 Sunday

7   Continued the Line.
At 212 miles 61 chains Crossed a Small run, running South.
   212 miles 77 chains The Head of a large Spring.

8   Continued the Line.
At 214 miles 12 chains. The top of the highest ridge of
Laurel Hill in the Line.

304

1767
September
9   Continued the Line.
    At 116 miles 32 chains Crossed McCulloch's Creek running Northerly.
10   Continued the Line.
    At 217 miles 13 chains Crossed the above Creek a second time.
    this is at the foot of Laurel Hill on the West Side.
    At 217 miles 51 chains Crossed the above Creek a third time.
11   Continued the Line.
    At 218 miles 31 chains Crossed the above mentioned Creek a 4th time, running Southward.
12   Continued the Line.
    At 219 miles 22 chains 25 links The East Bank of the River
    Cheat and at 219 miles 34 chains 50 links The West Bank of the
    said River.   We crossed the River
    obliquely, but at Right Angles it is about Ten
  Chains in breadth, having very level smooth bottom.
    The water at present very low and is contained
    in some places where it pretty freely runs; in about
    20 yards wide and about two feet deep.
    Here two of the Mohawks made an objection against
    our passing the River, but a Council being called, the Chiefs
    determined we should pass.
13 Sunday
14   Continued the Line.
15   Continued the Line.
16   Continued the Line.
    At 221 miles 00 chains and at 222 miles 09 chains crossed small runs now nearly dry.   305
17 ⎫   Brought the Sector from our last Station.
18 ⎭
19   Set up the Sector in the Direction of our
    Line at the distance of 222 miles 24 chains 12 links from the
    Post marked West in Mr. Bryan's field and made
    the following Observations.
    N.B. This Point is the top of a very high steep Bank; at the foot of
    which is the River Monaungahela.

Plane EAST

	Star Name	Nearest Point on the Sector		Revolutions and Seconds on the Micrometer		Difference		Apparent Zenith Distance		
		o	'	R	"	'	"	o	'	"
19	Delta Cygni	0	10+	5	48.5	1	37.5	0	11	37.5
				7	42					
	Capella	6	0+	7	23+	0	42.0	6	0	42.0
				6	33+					
20 Sun.	Alpha Lyrae	1	10-	7	17.5	1	46.0	1	8	14.0
				5	15.5					
	Delta Cygni	4	50+	5	49	1	21.5	4	51	21.5
				4	19.5					
	Gamma Cygni	0	10+	5	22+	1	36.2	0	11	36.2
				7	14.5					
	Alpha Cygni	4	45-	8	30.5	0	29.2	4	44	30.8
				9	8-					
	Capella	6	0+	7	10	0	41.0	6	00	41.0
				6	21					
21	Alpha Lyrae	1	10-	12	23	1	47.0	1	8	13.0
				10	20					
	Delta Cygni	4	50+	10	30+	1	23.3	4	51	23.3
				8	51					
	Gamma Cygni	0	10+	5	38-	1	36.6	0	11	36.6
				7	30+					
	Alpha Cygni	4	45-	8	37-	0	27.8	4	44	32.2
				9	12.5					

After these Observations we immediately turned the Sector Plane WEST

	Star Name	Nearest Point on the Sector		Revolutions and Seconds on the Micrometer		Difference		Apparent Zenith Distance		
	Capella	6	0+	5	49+	0	49.0	6	00	49.0
				6	46+					306

	Star Name	Nearest Point on the Sector		Revolutions and Seconds on the Micrometer		Difference		Apparent Zenith Distance		
		o	'	R	"	'	"	o	'	"
22	Alpha Lyrae	1	10	7 / 9	10.5 / 19.5	1	53.0	1	8	7.0
	Delta Cygni	4	50+	8 / 10	51 / 35	1	28.0	4	51	28.0
	Gamma Cygni	0	10+	10 / 9	47+ / 7	1	32.3	0	11	32.3
	Alpha Cygni	4	45-	7 / 7	30+ / 5	0	25.3	4	44	34.7
	Capella	6	0+	2 / 3	45+ / 42.5	0	49.2	6	0	49.2
23	Alpha Lyrae	1	10-	3 / 5	19- / 24	0	49.3	1	8	10.7
	Capella	6	0	5 / 6	40.5 / 38	0	49.5	6	0	49.5
24	Cloudy									
25	Alpha Lyrae	1	10-	5 / 7	9 / 17	1	52.0	1	8	8.0
	Delta Cygni	4	50+	7 / 8	13.5 / 51	1	29.5	4	51	29.5
	Gamma Cygni	0	10+	8 / 6	23.5 / 36	1	31.5	0	11	31.5
	Alpha Cygni	4	45-	5 / 5	28.5 / 0.5	0	28.0	4	44	32.0
26	Alpha Lyrae	1	10-	7 / 10	50- / 4-	1	50.0	1	8	10.0
	Delta Cygni	4	50+	10 / 11	7 / 44	1	29.0	4	51	29.0
	Gamma Cygni	0	10+	7 / 5	22+ / 34.5	1	31.8	0	11	31.8
	Alpha Cygni	4	45-	4 / 4	34.5 / 10-	0	24.8	4	44	35.2

27 Sun. Computing our Observations as follows.

Plane EAST

	Alpha Lyrae			Delta Cygni			Gamma Cygni			Alpha Cygni			Capella		
	o	'	"	o	'	"	o	'	"	o	'	"	o	'	"
	19						19 0	11	37.5				19 6	0	42.0
20 Sun.	20 1	8	14	20 4	51	21.5	20 0	11	36.2	20 4	44	30.8	20 6	0	41.0
	21 1	8	13.0	21 4	51	23.3	21	11	36.6	21 4	44	32.2			
Mean	1	8	13.50	4	51	22.40	0	11	36.77	4	44	31.50	6	0	41.50
Aberration			+17.48			-17.20			+15.63			-15.51			+ 7.18
Deviation			- 3.51			+ 1.40			- 0.21			- 0.46			- 5.82
Precession			+ 9.38			-30.90			+41.35			-46.30			-19.67
Refraction			+ 1.20			+ 5.60			+ 0.20			+ 5.50			+ 7.00
Mean Zen. Dist.	1	8	38.05	4	50	41.30	0	12	33.74	4	43	34.73	6	0	30.19
Plane East															

1767
September

Plane WEST

	Alpha Lyrae			Delta Cygni			Gamma Cygni			Alpha Cygni			Capella		
	o	'	"	o	'	"	o	'	"	o	'	"	o	'	"
21													6	0	49.0
22	1	8	7.0	4	51	28.0	0	11	32.3	4	44	34.7		0	49.2
23		8	10.7											0	49.5
25		8	8.0		51	29.5		11	31.5		44	32.0			
26		8	10.0		51	29.0		11	31.8		44	35.2			
Mean	1	8	8.92	4	51	28.83	0	11	31.87	4	44	33.97	6	0	49.23
Aberration			+17.57			-17.65			+16.16			-16.07			+ 7.02
Deviation			- 3.51			+ 1.40			- 0.21			- 0.46			- 5.82
Precession			+ 9.40			-30.96			+41.42			-46.40			-19.72
Refraction			+ 1.20			+ 5.60			+ 0.20			+ 5.50			+ 7.00
Mean Zen. Dist. Plane West	1	8	33.58	4	50	47.22	0	12	29.44	4	43	36.54	6	0	37.71
Ditto Plane East	1	8	38.05	4	50	41.30	0	12	33.74	4	43	34.73	6	0	30.19
Mean Zen. Dist 1st Jan. 1764	1	8	35.82	4	50	44.26	0	12	31.59	4	43	35.63	6	0	33.95
Ditto at the Post Marked West	1	8	41.80		50	40.40		12	33.00			31.20			31.80
Difference too much			5.ʺ98			3.ʺ86			1.ʺ41			4.ʺ43			2.ʺ15
			South			North			North			North			North

```
                                 North
                                 5.ʺ98
                                 3.86
                                 1.41
                                 4.43
                                 2.15
            Mean = 17.ʺ83 ÷ 5 = 3.ʺ57 = 5 ch. 41 links that we are
                            to the South of the true Parallel.                    308
```

(Undated)

Offsets to be laid off to the Northward

Miles from the Post marked West	Offsets of the Circle to the Chord Links	Triangle B		True Offsets C		
		Chains	Links	Chains	Links	
199.796	0	0	0	0	0	
200	3	0	6-	0	3	
201	13	0	3	0	17	
202	20	0	54	0	34	
203	24	0	78	0	54	
204	26	1	2	0	76	
205	27	1	26	0	99	
206	27	1	50	1	23	
207	27	1	74	1	47	
208	25	1	98	1	73	
209	20	2	22	2	02	
210	13	2	46	2	33	
211	3	2	70	2	67	
211 miles 13 ch. 28 links	0	-	--	-	--	Change
212	7	2	94	2	87	
213	15	3	18	3	03	
214	21	3	42	3	21	
215	24	3	66	3	42	
216	26	3	90	3	64	
217	27	4	14	3	87	
218	27	4	38	4	11	
219	25	4	62	4	37	
220	21	4	86	4	65	
221	15	5	10	4	95	
222	5	5	34	5	29	
222.301	0	5	41	5	41	Sector

309

Here AcD the true Parallel. A a point in the true Parallel where
we began the 26th of August. ABC the Line run instead of the Chords
Ab and bD. C the point the Sector was set up at on the 19th of
September; where according to Observations DC = 5 chains 41 links = the greatest offset.
Hence the offsets from ABC to the Chords Ab, bD (the change at b of 8' 18"
being made at its proper place viz. at 11.37 miles from A) are in proportion to the
distances from A, as by Column B from which subtract the offsets from
the Chord to the Circle, gives the true offsets North, as by Column C.

Figure
310

1767
September
  28   Began to open a Visto to the Eastward in the
           true Parallel to gain a Direction Westward.
  29   Twenty-six of our Men left us; they would not
           pass the River for fear of the Shawanes and Delaware
           Indians. But we prevailed upon 15 ax men to proceed
           with us, and with them we continued the Line Westward
           in a direction found as on July 10th and the 26th of August
           thus.
  30   Continued the Line.
           At 222 miles 34 chains 50 links the East Bank of the River Monaungahela.
              222 miles 40 chains 25 links the West Bank of Ditto.
           The Line crosses this River a little to the Southward of
           a Right Angle to the River. The Breadth at Right Angles about 5 chains, the
           Running water very low, and might be contained in the space
           of about five Yards wide and Six Inches deep.
           At 222 miles 74 chains crossed a Small run, running South.

October
  1   Continued the Line.
  2   Continued the Line. Sent a Man to set Stones on the Line, etc.
           and to send us hands from Fort Cumberland.
           At 224 miles   5 chains Crossed the above run.
              224 miles 25 chains Crossed Ditto a 3rd time.
  3   Continued the Line.
  4 Sunday
  5   Continued the Line.
  6   Continued the Line.
           At   {227 miles   2 chains}Crossed small runs, running South.
               {227 miles 77 chains}

311

  7   Continued the Line. We have now our
           usual complement of Hands.
  8   Continued the Line.
           At 230 miles 22 chains   Crossed a small run, running Northerly.
           At 230 miles 36 chains   Crossed a small run, running Ditto.
  9   Continued the Line to a High ridge. At 231 miles 20 chains Crossed a War Path.
           At 231 miles 71 chains Dunchard Creek. This Creek takes its
           name from a small town settled by the Dunchards
           near the Mouth of this Creek on the Monaungahela; about 7 or 8
           Miles North of where we crossed the said River.   The
           Town was burnt, and most of the Inhabitants killed by the Indians in 1755.
           At 232 miles 43 chains crossed Dunchard's Creek a second time.
           At 232 miles 74 chains crossed Ditto a third time.
           This day the Chief of the Indians which joined us on the 16th of July informed us
           that the above mentioned War Path was the extent
           of his commission from the Chiefs of the Six Nations
           that he should go with us, with the Line; and that he would not
           proceed one step farther Westward.

312

  10   The Indians with us still persisting that they
           will not go any farther Westward with the Line; we
           sent for the Sector which was left at our Store
           House at the Forks of Cheat and Monaungahela.
  11 Sun. Set up the Sector in the Direction of our Line
           at the distance of 233 Miles 13 Chains and 68 Links
           from the Post marked West in Mr. Bryan's Field, and
           made the following Observations.

	Star Name	Nearest Point on the Sector		Plane EAST Revolutions and and Seconds on the Micrometer		Difference		Apparent Zenith Distance		
		o	'	R	"	'	"	o	'	"
11	Capella	6	0+	6	15	0	44.5	6	0	44.5
				5	22.5					
12	Alpha Lyrae	1	10-	8	17	1	45.5	1	8	14.5
				6	15.5					
	Delta Cygni	4	50+	5	50.5	1	23.0	4	51	23.0
				4	19.5					
	Gamma Cygni	0	10+	6	2	1	34.3	0	11	34.3
				7	44+					
	Alpha Cygni	4	45-	9	48+	0	26.0	4	44	34.0
				10	22+					
	Capella	6	0+	1	13-	0	41.4	6	0	41.4
				0	23+					

Sent the Ax Men to open
a Visto in the true Parallel
East of Monaungahela while
we are making our Observations.

	Star Name	Nearest Point on the Sector		Plane EAST Revolutions and and Seconds on the Micrometer		Difference		Apparent Zenith Distance		
13	Alpha Lyrae	1	10-	8	51+	1	45.8	1	8	14.2
				6	49.5					
	Delta Cygni	4	50+	6	30-	1	24.7	4	51	24.7
				4	49					
	Gamma Cygni	0	10+	6	8.5	1	35.2	0	11	35.2
				8	0					
	Alpha Cygni	4	45-	10	43	0	26.0	4	44	34.0
				11	17					

Turned the Sector Plane WEST   313

	Star Name	Nearest Point on the Sector		Revolutions and Seconds on the Micrometer		Difference		Apparent Zenith Distance		
14	Cloudy									
15	Alpha Lyrae	1	10-	6	2.5	1	49.2	1	8	10.8
				8	8-					
	Gamma Cygni	0	10+	4	48	1	31.5	0	11	31.5
				3	8.5					
	Alpha Cygni	4	45-	3	44	0	26.3	4	44	33.7
				3	18-					
	Capella	6	0+	14	38	0	49.5	6	0	49.5
				15	35.5					
16	Alpha Lyrae	1	10-	7	6-	1	47.0	1	8	13.0
				9	9-					
	Delta Cygni	4	50+	9	8.5	1	27.8	4	51	27.8
				10	44+					
	Gamma Cygni	0	10+	9	15.5	1	32.0	0	11	32.0
				7	27.5					
	Alpha Cygni	4	45-	5	31-	6	26.0	4	44	34.0
				5	5-					
	Capella	6	0+	3	38-	0	49.8	6	0	49.8
				4	35.5					
17	Alpha Lyrae	1	10-	5	40-	1	49.6	1	8	10.4
				7	45+					
	Delta Cygni	4	50+	7	35	1	27.0	4	51	27.0
				9	18					
	Gamma Cygni	0	10+	8	22.5	1	31.0	0	11	31.0
				6	35.5					
	Alpha Cygni	4	45-	6	15-	0	24.7	4	44	35.3
				5	42					

18 Sun. Computing our Observations as follows
Sent for the Ax Men from the East Side of the River Monaungahela.   314

Plane EAST

	Alpha Lyrae (° ′ ″)		Delta Cygni (° ′ ″)
12	1 8 14.5	12	4 51 23.0
13	1 8 14.2	13	4 51 24.7
Mean	1 8 14.35		4 51 23.85
Aberration	+17.02		-18.39
Deviation	- 3.31		+ 1.16
Precession	+ 9.53		-31.40
Refraction	+ 1.20		+ 5.60
Mean Zen. Dist. Plane East	1 8 38.79		4 50 40.82

Plane WEST

	Alpha Lyrae		Delta Cygni
15	1 8 10.8		
16	1 8 13.0	16	4 51 27.8
17	10.4	17	27.0
Mean	1 8 11.40		4 51 27.40
Aberration	+16.84		-18.32
Deviation	- 3.31		+ 1.16
Precession	+ 9.50		-31.50
Refraction	+ 1.20		+ 5.60
Mean Zen. Dist. Plane West	1 8 35.69		4 50 44.34
Ditto Plane East	1 8 38.79		40.82
Mean Zen. Dist. 1 Jan. 1764	1 8 37.24		4 50 42.58
Ditto at the Post Marked West	41.80		40.40
	South 4.″56		South 2.″18

2.″18
0.″28
2.″08 (Refer to page 316)
1.″15

11.″15 ÷ 5 = 2.″23 (mean) = 223 feet = 3 chains 38 links   315
to be laid off to the Northward.

Plane EAST

	Gamma Cygni (° ′ ″)		Alpha Cygni (° ′ ″)		Capella (° ′ ″)
				11	6 0 44.5
12	0 11 34.3	12	4 44 34.0	12	0 41.4
13	0 11 35.2	13	4 44 34.0		
Mean	0 11 34.75		4 44 34.0		6 0 42.95
Aberration	+17.30		-17.70		+ 5.49
Deviation	- 0.00		- 0.61		- 5.61
Precession	+42.00		-47.05		-19.98
Refraction	+ 0.20		+ 5.50		+ 7.00
Mean Zen. Dist. Plane East	0 12 34.25		4 43 34.14		6 0 29.85

Plane WEST

	Gamma Cygni		Alpha Cygni		Capella
15	0 11 31.5	15	4 44 33.7	15	6 0 49.5
16	0 11 32.0	16	4 44 34.0	16	6 0 49.8
17	31.0	17	35.3		
Mean	0 11 31.50		4 44 34.33		6 0 49.65
Aberration	+17.40		-17.80		+ 5.06
Deviation	0.00		- 0.61		- 5.61
Precession	+42.10		-47.20		-20.04
Refraction	+ 0.20		+ 5.50		+ 7.00
Mean Zen. Dist. Plane West	0 12 31.20		4 43 34.22		6 0 36.06
Ditto Plane East	34.25		34.14		29.85
Mean Zen. Dist. 1 Jan. 1764	0 12 32.72		4 43 34.18		6 0 32.95
Ditto at the Post Marked West	33.00		31.20,		31.80
	South 0.″28		South 2.″98		South 1.″15 316

Hence the Offsets at every Mile Post to our last Station
at the Monaungahela as follows.

Miles from the Post Marked West in Mr. Bryan's Field	Offsets to the Circle	Offsets in the Triangle B		True Offsets (North) C	
	Links	Chains	Links	Chains	Links
222.301	0	0	0	0	0
223	7	0	22	0	15
224	15	0	53	0	38
225	21	0	84	0	63
226	25	1	15	0	90
227	27	1	46	1	19
228	27	1	77	1	50
229	27	2	08	1	81
230	25	2	39	2	14
231	22	2	70	2	48
232	16	3	01	2	85
233	9	3	33	3	24
233.171	0	3	38	3	38

Here AbC the true Parallel. A the
Point begun at on the 29th of Sept.
B where the Sector was set up, on
the 11th of October where by the
Observations, BC = 3 chains 38 Links.
Hence the Offsets to the Chord ApC,
Column B, from which Subtract the
Offsets of the Chord to the Circle,
gives the true Offsets North (from
the Line run AB) as by Column C.

Note: The Sector stood on the top of a very lofty Ridge, but
when the Offset was made of 3 Chains 38 Links it fell a little
Eastward of the top of the Hills; we therefore extended the true
Parallel 3 Chains 80 Links Westward which fell on the top of the said
Ridge; there viz. at 233 Miles 17 Chains 48 Links from the Post marked West
in Mr. Bryan's Field, we set up a Post marked W on the West Side and heaped
around it Earth and Stone three yards and a half diameter at the Bottom and
five feet High. The figure nearly conical.

Figure
317

1767
October

19	The Ax Men Returned from the Monaungahela.
20	Began to open a Visto in the True Parallel Eastward.
21	Continued the said Visto Eastward.
22	Continued Ditto.
23	Continued Ditto. This day we were joined by the Hands we sent to open a Visto Eastward on the 25th of August.
24	Continued the Line to the 225 Mile Post.
25 Sun.	Received a Letter from the Honorable Thomas Penn, Esquire.
26	Continued the Line to the River Monongahela.
27	Continued the Line.
28	Continued Ditto.
29	Rain.
30	Continued Ditto.
31	Continued the Line to the 209th Mile Post.
	Note: About 7 miles of the Weeks work was cut by the Hands sent back on the 12th Instant.

November

1 Sunday	
2	Rain.
3	Continued the Line.
4	Continued the Line.
5	Continued the Line to the Post Standing at 199 Miles 63 Chains 68 Links which finished: There being now one continued Visto opened in the true Parallel from the Intersection of the North Line from the Tangent Point with the Parallel to the Ridge we left off at on the 9th of October last. Mr. Hugh Crawford with the Indians and all Hands (except 13 kept to Erect Marks in the Line etc.) Left us in order to proceed Home.
6	Continued making marks in the Line as before.
7	Continued Ditto to the 195th Mile Post.

318

1767
November
   8 Sunday
   9   Continued Making Marks.
  10   Continued Ditto.
  11   Continued Ditto.
  12   Continued Ditto. Snow.
  13   Continued Ditto. Snow about 2 Inches deep.
  14   Continued Ditto the 177th Mile Post.
  15 Sunday
  16   Continued Ditto.
  17   Continued Ditto.
  18   Continued Ditto. Snow and moved to the foot of Savage
           Mountain on the West Side.   319
  19   Continued Ditto. Snow 12 or 14 Inches deep.   Made a pile
           of Stones on the Top of Savage or the great dividing
           Ridge of the Allegany Mountains.
           At 169 miles 26 chains being in the West side of Savage Mountain
           a small Run which is said to run Northward and then through
           a gap in Savage Mountain in to Wills Creek.
  20   The weather being so bad our Hands would not
           proceed on their work. We then proceeded to Mr. Kellams (in
           the Road from Fort Pit to Fort Cumberland) at the Gap in Savage Mountain.
  21   Seven of our hands left us.
  22 Sun.   Proceeded to Mr. Tumblestone's in Wills Creek Valley.
           Employed more hands.
  23   Set a Pile of Earth etc. on the Top of Little Allegany Mountain.
  24   Set a Pile on the Top of Wills Creek and the Nobbley Mountain.
  25   Set a Pile on the Tops of Eivits and Flintstone Mountains.
  26   Set Ditto on the Tops of the Big Warrior and Little Warrior Mountains.
  27   Set Ditto on the Ragged Mountain.
  28   Set a Pile at 143 miles 14 chains. Proceeded to
           the Top of Town Hill.   320
           Where we found hands at work which had just finished
           a Pile employed by R. Farlow whom we dispatched on
           the second of October to set stones in the Lines, Piles, etc.
  29 Sun.   At Town Hill, Discharged Six Hands.
  30   Piles being set by R. Farlow at 137 miles 11 chains and the
           Top of Sidelong Hill; and the Stones at the proper
           places* to the 135th Mile Post from the Post marked West
           which reached to Sidelong Hill (inclusive) we proceeded
           to Mr. Matson's in the Conollaways.
           Sent Mr. Jonathan Cope (chain carrier) along the
           Line over the North Mountain to see that the Stones are
           at their Proper Places.

           *excepting the 80th Mile Post which is 125 Yards East
           of its true Place: The true place of the Mile Post falling
           in Marsh Creek was the reason of its being placed East.

           The 120th Mile Stone stands five yards East
           of its true Place; it could not be set at its proper place
           for a great Stone.
           The above Mentioned Mile Posts, viz. 135th, the 80th and 120th
           are the 132nd, the 77th and the 117th from the Beginning
           of the West Line.
December
   4   In Coneeocheague.
           Sent Expresses to Annapolis and Philadelphia to acquaint
           the Gentlemen Commissioners we shall be in Philadelphia the
           15th Instant.
  10   At Brandywine.
  11   Received a Letter from Benjamin Chew, Esquire, (one of the Gentlemen Commissioners)
           acquainting us that the Commissioners were to meet at
           Christiana Bridge the 23rd Instant.   321

191

Gentlemen:

       I received your favor of the 4th Instant and
have only to inform you that we wrote yesterday to the
Maryland Commissioners to meet us at Christiana Bridge
on Wednesday the 23rd Day of this Instant. We expect
them to confirm and put an end to this tedious Business
so as to leave nothing more to be done than setting
up the remainder of the Boundary Stones if it is
possible to get them to their proper Stations at an
Expense which can be borne. Wherever you may be in
the Mean Time we hope to have your Company at
the Bridge on the 23rd. I am Gentlemen,

      Your Humble Servant

Philadelphia, Dec. 10, 1767   Benjamin Chew   322

(Undated   Editorial Note:
      Here we have an envelope addressed to
        Messrs. Mason and Dixon)   323

1767
November
  19   Our Journal from the 19th of November I have described for the Commissioners
      as follows (See original document--inconclusive.)
      Continued the Erecting Marks in the Line.
      Snow 12 or 14 Inches deep. Made a Pile of Stones on the Top of
      Savage or the great dividing Ridge of the Allegany Mountain.
      Note: West of this Mountain to the End of the Line the Mile Posts
      are 5 feet in length, 12 Inches Square, and set 2 feet in the Ground
      and round them are heaped Earth or Stone 8 feet in Diameter at
      Bottom and 2. 5 feet High.
  20   The Weather being so bad our Hands would not proceed
      on their work.
  21*   Seven of our Hands left us.
22 Sun. ** The above Desertion of our Hands prevents us from
      making Heaps around the Mile Posts as before.
      Proceeded in to Wills Creek Valley.
  23   Continued Erecting Marks on the Tops of the Mountains,
      Got more Hands.
  24   Continued Ditto,
  25   Continued Ditto,
  26   Continued Ditto,
  27   Continued Ditto.
  28   Continued Ditto. Marks are now set on the Tops of all the High
                Ridges and Mountains to the Top of Sidelong Hill.
29 Sun.   Discharged most of our Hands.
      Note: The Mile Posts between the Top of Savage Mountain and the
          End of the Line have Heaps of Earth or Stone Round them
          (as observed in Minutes of 19th November) of Eight feet Diameter at
          Bottom and 2 1/2 feet High.   324

(Editorial Note: *This date appears erroneously listed by Mason as 27th Nov.
          **This date also appears to be in error and is corrected herein.)

(Undated)   At the following Points in the Line, being the Tops of
High Ridges and Mountains, are set Posts about 12 Inches Square
Marked W on the West Side, and around them Heaps of Earth
or Piles of Stone Three Yards and a half Diameter at Bottom
and five feet High: none less, but many four Yards Diameter and
Six or Seven feet High.

Miles from the Post Marked
West in Mr. Bryan's Field.

Miles	Chains	
135	29	The Top of Sidelong Hill
137	11	
140	54	The Top of Town Hill
143	14	
146	52	The Top of the Ragged Mountain
149	17	Little Warrior Mountain
151	47	The Great Ditto.
153	22	Flintstone Mountain
155	32	Evit's Mountain
157	63	Nobbley Mountain
159	71	Will's Creek Mountain
163	59	The little Allegany Mountain
168	76	The top of the Allegany Mountain
172	27	
173	75	
176	46	Top of little Meadow Mountain
178	53	
182	19	
184	17	Top of little Laurel Hill
185	45	
186	63	
187	50	
190	12	The Top of Winding Hill
193	25	
196	20	
198	63	
199	63	
202	44	
205	16	
207	45	
209	19	
210	60 }	On Laurel Hill
212	26 }	
214	12	The Top of the Highest Ridge on Ditto
217	58	
218	67	
220	51	
222	24	
223	14	
226	40	
227	57	
228	64	
229	75	
230	77	
233	17	The top of the Westernmost Ridge to which the Line is Extended.

325

Some of these Mountains not being at Right Angles to the Line 1st Run; Causes these Points to
be something different in distance from the Post marked West, from what is laid down before
the Line was corrected by Offsets.
From the Points 168 Miles 76 Chains There is an Extensive View Eastward and Westward.
        214 Miles 12 Chains The Line may be seen to Winding Hill,
And, to the End, Westward; from these Points the Curvature of the Line appears very regular.
The Stones are extended from (the 65th Mile) where they Ended last Year, to 132 Miles
from the Beginning of the West Line; They are all set in the same manner as described
in Minutes of the 20th of November 1766; and are all at their Proper places except the
77th and the 117th. The Place of the 77th falling in Marsh Creek, it is Set 125 Yards East
of its true Place. The Place of the 117th falling on a Great Stone it is Set five yards East.
The 64th Mile which was left last year, is also Set.

1767
December
    4   In Conecocheague.
             Sent Expresses to Annapolis and Philadelphia to acquaint
             the Gentlemen Commissioners that we shall be in Philadelphia
             the 15th Instant.
             Thus far the same as to the Commissioners from the 19th of November.   326
    24   Attended the Gentlemen Commissioners at Christiana Bridge.
    25   Attended Ditto.
    26   Attended Ditto: When the Gentlemen Commissioners read their
             Minutes to us, by which we understand they have no further
             `occasion   for us to run any more Lines for the Honorable Proprietors,
             (but they did not choose to give us a discharge in writing).
             Received Instructions to Draw a Map or Plan of the Lines,
             and to give it in to either the Commissioners for Pennsylvania
             or Maryland; as soon as possible.
             The Gentlemen Commissioners also asked us for the Length of
             a Degree of Longitude in the Parallel of the West Line.
    28   At Brandywine.

1768
January
    6   Left Ditto and went to Philadelphia.
    8   Gave into the Hands of the Reverend Mr. Peters (one of the
             Gentlemen Commissioners) the following: Directed to the Gentlemen Commissioners
             for Dividing the Provinces of Maryland and Pennsylvania.
             By comparing our mensuration of a Degree of the Meridian
             with that made under the Arctic Circle, supposing the Earth
             to be a Spheroid of a uniform Density: a Degree of
             Longitude in the Parallel of the West Line is 53.5549 Miles.
             But the Earth is not known to be exactly a Spheroid,
             nor whether it is everywhere of equal Density; and our
             own experiment being not yet finished: We do not give
             in this as accurate.
    13   At Brandywine.
    19   Measured the Rods sent in by the Royal Society, and found
             them too Long for the Standard (brass rod of 5 feet).
             Thermometer at Freezing.   327

This day received of Mr. Peters the following Letter from Mr. Penn. N.B. The seal was broke.

                                                                        Duplicate
Messrs. Mason and Dixon
        I have received your Letter of the 6th of January with a particular account
of your proceedings since your last, and we are very well satisfied with the
accounts you give of them. We apprehend that you cannot have put Stones
at every mile of the Line, from Cape Henlopen to the middle of
the Peninsula, or in the Tangent Line, unless you had many made in
Pennsilvania; the particular places you have noted down (where the
Parallel of Latitude has crossed) we are very well pleased with; as
we are, that you made use of your time, when not employed by us,
to run the Degree of Latitude for the Royal Society, about which my Lord
Morton often speaks to me.
        I am at a loss to know, what was the Commissioners' reason
for ordering you to run the parallel of Latitude from the place where
the Meridian Line intersects it, to the River, as I have not received from
them their minutes, and when you write next let me know them, lest
they should omit it.
        I shall expect to hear further from you, if you proceed to extend
the Line farther Westward, in the mean time remain

                         Your affectionate Friend

London, June 17, 1767   Thomas Penn   328

Messrs. Mason and Dixon

       I was very well pleased to find by your Letter of the
12th of June, that you had received an account that the Indians had given their
consent to Sir William Johnson that you might extend the division Line between
Maryland and Pennsilvania to the extent of the province of Maryland, and that
you were to receive your Instructions from the Commissioners the 16th of the same
month. We sent several months (since) one hundred and forty Stones, and am
now shipping to Maryland sixty eight, which we think will about compleat
the work, which we hope to hear you will finish this Year. I am

Your very affectionate Friend

London   August 7, 1767   Thomas Penn   329

(Undated.   'An envelope addressed as follows)

     To
   Messrs. Mason and Dixon
            in
              Philadelphia
   By Mr. Hamilton   330

1768
January
 19

Sun Eclipsed

Time by the Watch			Sun's Limbs by Reflection		Time by the Watch			
10h	19m	40s	49°	03'	1h	53m	45s	Equal Altitudes of the Sun's Lower Limb
	22	20	49	26	1	51	00	In the afternoon Observations the Sun's
	26	5	50	4	1	47	30	Lower Limb was rendered dubious
	29	20	50	36	1	44	30	something, by the Moon's Body.
	35	00	52	43				
	37	00	52	58*				
	39	40	53	21*				Altitudes of the Sun's Upper Limb
	53	00	55	18*				
	55	40	55	38*				
	59	00	54	51*				
11h	2	35	55	16*				Ditto for the Sun's Lower Limb
	8	10	55	51*				
	17	30	56	45*				

To these numbers add 2' 30" for adjustment of the Quadrant: Then
the Half is the approximate Altitudes of the Solar Limbs; as they were
all made by reflection with a Hadley's Quadrant.
The air was very Hazy during all these Observations, except
those marked * at which times the solar Limbs appeared clear.
At the Beginning of the Eclipse the Air was so thick
the time could not be determined to any certainty: At the
End the Sun was entirely hid by clouds.
At the Middle the Sun (through a Haze) appeared to be about 10 Digits
Eclipsed. At this time the usual light was
very much diminished.

27   Left Brandywine and went to Philadelphia.
28   Wrote to the Astronomer Royal, and M: Katy, Esq., S. R. S.
          To Mr. Williams, Mr. Kingston and Mr. Carrier the 30th day.
29   Delivered to the Rev. Richard Peters, Plans
          of the Lines Dividing the Provinces of Maryland
          and Pennsylvania.
          Wrote to the Honorable Proprietors of Ditto, acquainting
          them of our proceedings since the 12th of June last; and that
          we had no further Instructions to execute from the Gentlemen
          Commissioners; but were preparing to remeasure the Line   331
          for the Royal Society. Wrote to Mr. Bird.

1768
January
31 Sun.   Examined the Sector and Transit Instruments at the State House
            and found them good.

February
1   At Brandywine.
2   At Mr. Joel Bailey's who is making two levels in
            order to carry two of the Rods each, as by the figure following.
            The Rods having been a long time kept in a Dry room
            I measured them when the Thermometer stood at 54°.5
            (the brass standard of 5 foot having been kept by the Thermometer), and found
            them all = the standard except that marked B, which was at least three
            of the divisions at the End of the brass standard, too long.
            I ordered the Rods to be kept in the Open Air and Wet.
3   Thermometer at Sun rise 25°.   At 2h P. M.   38°. ⎫ Placed in the Open
4   Thermometer at Sun rise 27°.   At 3h P. M.   38°. ⎬ Air on the North Side
5   Thermometer at Sun rise 32°.   At 3h P. M.   36°. ⎭ of a House.
            The Rods having been kept wet (in snow since the 4th at Night)
            and in the Open Air since the second; and the Standard Brass in
            a room; in to which I brought the Rods and Thermometer;
            The Thermometer rose to 54°. I then measured the Rods.

                          ⎧ A four Divisions ⎫
            and found   ⎨ B six Ditto   ⎬ too long: This was done at 3h P. M.
                          ⎩ C four Ditto   ⎭
                            D four Ditto

            I kept the Thermometer and brass standard together 'till 8h P. M.
            and the room in the same state of heat (viz. Thermometer 53°, 54° and 55°)
            and measured the Rods, and found them the same as before.
6   I laid the Rods* to the Levels, which were adjusted
            to the Rods when the Thermometer stood at 55° and the rods had been dry a long time; and
            found the Rods were too long for the Levels by the Quantity above.
            The Levels had always been kept in the dry. I now
            put the Levels with the Rods out in the Open Air.
            Corrected the Rod B and made it = A = C = D.
            Hung up Plumb Lines of silver wire at the Middle and Ends of the
            Levels and found they corresponded extremely near.

            *The Rods having been put out all night in the Wet and open Air, and the Levels still in the Rain.   332

10   Examined the Levels and found they were now too long for the
            Rods. The weather has been very moderate since the 6th, never
            colder than just freezing.
18   Mr. Bailey informed me the Levels still continued too long for the Rods,
            as on the 10th Instant. The weather very moderate
            (some snow) since the 10th Instant: not colder than just freezing.
22   Mr. Bailey brought to Mr. Harland's the Levels: (each 20 feet in Length)
            for measuring the Lines.
23   Began at Ditto in the Parallel where the Sector was set up in 1764
            and in December 1767 to remeasure the Line with the Levels for
            the Royal Society; the Levels having the Rods (sent us by the Royal Society)
            first to them: The Measuring the Lines with the Rods by laying them End
            to End being impracticable.
            From the Point where the Sector stood to a mark on
            the North Side of the River Brandywine = 17 Levels.
            (At 10h A. M. measured with the Brass Standard one Rod and found it
            3 Divisions too long: Therefore the 4 Rods = 12 Divisions
            too long by supposing all the Rods equal.
            AB the Creek or River. -- measured by the Cord, 8 Levels wanting 8 Inches.
            At 3h P. M. The Rods as before. Thermometer 53°.
            From B, the South Side of the Creek, to the next mark on the North Side
            of Ditto = 6 Cords and 8 Levels = 86 Levels.
            Here also AB the Creek.
            From B on the South Side a second time to a
            mark on the North Side a third time = 7 Cords   Figures a and b
            and 9 Levels = 100 Levels.   333

196

24   Here AB the Brandywine a third time (A the South Side)

Altitude of A above B about 20 feet

by estimation; or 8° Elevation by the Quadrant:

At 9h A.M. Thermometer 54° one of the Rods two divisions longer than the Brass.

Therefore suppose the 4 Rods = 8 Divisions Longer.

At 1h 30m P.M. Thermometer = 44°, one Rod 3 Divisions too long.

Measured in all this day 25 Cords besides the Creek. 13 Levels = one Cord

as before.

At 5h P.M. Thermometer 39°. One Rod 8 Divisions too long.

This day we measured different Rods and found they are not

of equal lengths. Though they were all equal to the Standard when the Thermometer

stood at 55° (excepting B which was corrected on the 6th Instant) see Minutes of the

second Instant.

25   -------------

26

Rods

At 9h 30m A.M. $\begin{cases} A = 6 \\ B = 2 \\ C = 2 \\ D = 2 \end{cases}$ Divisions Longer than the Brass Standard   N.B. Each of these Divisions is = 1/100 part of an Inch.

Thermometer 40°

16 Cords and one Level wanting 3 feet 8 Inches reached the

Stake on the South Side of the Road leading from

At 4h 30m P.M. $\begin{cases} A = 3.5 \\ B = 2 \\ C = 2 \\ D = 3.5 \end{cases}$ Divisions Longer than the Brass Standard

Thermometer 45°

Measured in all this day 19 Cords: Figure

each Cord = 13 Levels as before.   334

27   Rain.

28 Sun.   At Mr. Jacob Dwight's.

29   At 8h 30m A.M. $\begin{cases} A = 4 \\ B = 0 \\ C = 0 \\ D = 4 \end{cases}$ Longer than the Standard

Thermometer 60°

Measured in all this day 8 Cords: Each

Cord now = 10 Levels.

Rain in the Afternoon and Snow at Night.

March

1

Divisions   Divisions

At 9h 00m A.M. $\begin{cases} A = 8 \\ B = 3 \\ C = 5 \\ D = 7 \end{cases}$ Longer   At 4h 30m P.M. $\begin{cases} A = 6 \\ B = 4 \\ C = 5 \\ D = 6 \end{cases}$ Longer

Thermometer 32°   Thermometer 42°

Since 9h A.M. measured 25 Cords

and after 4h 30m P.M. Ditto 7 Cords.

Measured in all this day 32 Cords,

each Cord = 10 Levels as yesterday.

2   At 8h 30m A.M. $\begin{cases} A = 7 \\ B = 4 \\ C = 4- \\ D = 5.5 \end{cases}$ Longer

Thermometer 32°

At 1h 00m P.M. $\begin{cases} A = 5 \\ B = 0 \\ C = 2 \\ D = 3 \end{cases}$ Longer

Thermometer 41°

Measured 20 Cords

At 5h 30m P.M. $\begin{cases} A = 5 \\ B = 0.5 \\ C = 2 \\ D = 4 \end{cases}$ Longer

Thermometer 48°

Measured 17 Cords.

In all this day 37 Cords: Each   335

10 Levels as before

3   At 8h 15m A.M.   A = 7.5
           Thermometer 40°   B = 2   Longer than
                                C = 3   the Standard
                                D = 6

Measured 13 Cords and 7 Levels which reached
to the Mark on the North Side of the Road
leading from Philadelphia to Nottingham.

        At 2h P.M.   A = 5
           Thermometer 48°   B = 1   Longer
                                C = 2.5
                                D = 4

Measured 23 Cords.

        At 5h P.M.   A = 5.5
           Thermometer 48°   B = 1   Longer
                                C = 3
                                D = 5

Since 2h P.M. measured 12 Cords.
In all this day 35 Cords: Each
10 Levels as before.

4   At 8h 30m A.M.   A = 6.5
           Thermometer 31°   B = 3.5 Longer than
                                C = 4.5 the Standard
                                D = 4.5

Measured 20 Cords.

        At 2h P.M.   A = 5.5   A = 5.5
           Thermometer 38°   B = 2.5 Longer   At 5h 30m P.M.   B = 2.5 Longer
                                C = 3   Thermometer 30° C = 4.5
                                D = 5   D = 6   Measured 15 Cords since
In all this day 35 Cords. Each 10 Levels as before.   2h P.M.

5   At 8h A.M.   A = 7   A = 4.5
           Thermometer 27°   B = 3   Longer   At 1h P.M.   B = 1   Longer
                                C = 4   Thermometer 41° C = 2.5
                                D = 4   D = 4   Since 8h A.M. we measured
Five Cords three Levels and 17 feet reached   22 Cords
the Mark near Mr. Milhouse's.

        At 5h 30m P.M.   A = 5.5
           Thermometer 29°   B = 3   Longer
                                C = 4
                                D = 4

Since 1h P.M. measured 12 Cords. In all this day 34 Cords. Each Cord = 10 Levels as before.   336

6 Sun.   At Mr. Allen's.

7   At 8h 15m A.M.   A = 6
           Thermometer 28°   B = 3.5 Longer than
                                  C = 2.5 the Standard
                                  D = 3.5

Very dry winds with Frost.

        At 2h P.M.   A = 3
           Thermometer 38°   B = 0   Longer. We have now
                                C = 3   measured 25 Cords.
                                D = 3

Measured all day 30 Cords wanting 3 Levels 12 feet. A marked Stump.

        At 5h 45m P.M.   A = 4
           Thermometer 36°   B = 1
                                C = 2   Longer
                                D = 3.5 Measured 9 Cords since 2h P.M.

In all this day 34 Cords: Each Cord as before.

8   At 8h A.M.   A = 5
           Thermometer 36°   B = 2- Longer than
                                C = 1   the Standard
                                D = 2.5

8

At 1h 30m P.M.
Thermometer 52°

$\begin{cases} \text{A} = 0.5 & \text{Longer} \\ \text{B} = 1 \\ \text{C} = 2+ \\ \text{D} = 1 \end{cases}$ Shorter than the Standard. Since 8 A.M. measured 23 Cords.

At 5h 30m P.M.
Thermometer 45°

$\begin{cases} \text{A} = 2 \\ \text{B} = 1.5 \\ \text{C} = 1 \\ \text{D} = 1.5 \end{cases}$ Longer Measured since 5h 30m 17 Cords.

In all this day 40 Cords. Each Cord 10 Levels as before.

9

At 8h 15m A.M.
Thermometer 51°

$\begin{cases} \text{A} = 5:: \\ \text{B} = 0.5 \\ \text{C} = 0.5 \\ \text{D} = 0.5 \end{cases}$ Longer

At 2h 00m P.M.
Thermometer 66°

$\begin{cases} \text{A} = 1.5 \\ \text{B} = 3.5 \\ \text{C} = 3.5 \\ \text{D} = 2.5 \end{cases}$ Shorter than the Standard Since 8h A.M. measured 27 Cords.

At 5h 30m P.M.
Thermometer 52°

$\begin{cases} \text{A} = 2 & \text{Longer} \\ \text{B} = 0 \\ \text{C} = 0.5 \\ \text{D} = 0 \end{cases}$ Shorter Since 2h 00m P.M. measured 11 Cords.

In all this day 38 Cords: Each 10 Levels.

Figure 337

10

At 8h 45m A.M.
Thermometer 58°

$\begin{cases} \text{A} = 2 & \text{Longer} \\ \text{B} = 1.5 \\ \text{C} = 1.5 \\ \text{D} = 0 \end{cases}$ Shorter than the Standard

Measured 15 Cords 3 Levels 3 Feet which reached the
Point where the Sector stood in Mr. Bryan's field.
And 18 Cords wanting 16 feet or 17 Cords
nine Levels and four feet reached to the Post
marked West in Mr. Bryan's Field.
That is Measured in all this day 17 Cords 9 Levels 4 feet which
we finished at 0h 30m P.M.

Thermometer then
at 61°

$\begin{cases} \text{A} = 1.5 & \text{Longer} \\ \text{B} = 1.5 \\ \text{C} = 2 \\ \text{D} = 1 \end{cases}$ Shorter than the Standard

11

Began at the Corner in the West Line

At 11h A.M.
Thermometer 60°

$\begin{cases} \text{A} = 0 \\ \text{B} = 3 \\ \text{C} = 1 \\ \text{D} = 0 \end{cases}$ The Rods Shorter than the Standard

Measured Five Levels and 3 feet from the Corner to the Mile
Post. Began again at the Mile Post and
Measured 11 Cords. Each Cord = 12 Levels
which we propose using all the way: 22 of
the said Cords = a Mile.
Rain in the afternoon.
Measured in all this day 11 Cords 5 Levels 3 feet.

338

12

At 9h A.M.
Thermometer 52°

$\begin{cases} \text{A} = 3.5 \\ \text{B} = 0 \\ \text{C} = 0.5 \\ \text{D} = 3 \end{cases}$ The Rods Longer than the Standard

Measured 9 Cords
At 1 P.M.
Thermometer 58°

$\begin{cases} \text{A} = 1 & \text{Longer} \\ \text{B} = 0.5 & \text{Shorter} \\ \text{C} = 0 \\ \text{D} = 0.5 & \text{Longer} \end{cases}$ Than the Standard

When we had measured a Mile by the Levels it
wanted 8.5 feet of the 1st Mile Stone.

199

1768
March
12

At 5h 30m P.M. $\begin{cases} A = 3 \\ B = 2- \\ C = 1 \\ D = 2+ \end{cases}$ Longer

Thermometer 53°

Measured 13 Cords since 1h P.M.

Measured in all this day 22 Cords = 1 Mile.
The Cords being each = 12 Levels as yesterday

13 Sun. At Newark.

14   Preparing Plumb Staff, etc., for to measure with
15   one Level only by an internal Contact.
16   Attempted to measure with one Level, and found
     it impracticable.
17   Began where we left off on the 12th Instant to measure as
     before.

At 10h A.M. $\begin{cases} A = 3.5 \\ B = 1 \\ C = 1.5 \\ D = 3 \end{cases}$ Longer than the Standard

Thermometer 34°

At 2h P.M. $\begin{cases} A = 3.5 \\ B = 2.5 \\ C = 0.5 \\ D = 2.5 \end{cases}$ Longer

Thermometer 40°

Since 10h A.M. measured 11 Cords
When we had measured 2 miles; it wanted
14 feet of the second Mile Stone.

At 5h P.M. $\begin{cases} A = 3 \\ B = 2 \\ C = 1 \\ D = 2 \end{cases}$ Longer

Thermometer 36°

Measured since 2h P.M. 12 Cords
In all this day 23 Cords, each Cord = 12 Levels as before   339

18

At 8h 30m A.M. $\begin{cases} A = 3.5 \\ B = 0.5 \\ C = 1 \\ D = 3.5 \end{cases}$ Longer than the Standard

Thermometer 36°

When we had measured by the Levels three Miles; it
wanted one Level 2 1/2 feet of the 3rd Mile Stone.

At 2h P.M. $\begin{cases} A = 3 \\ B = 1 \\ C = 1 \\ D = 0 \end{cases}$ Longer / Shorter than the Standard / Longer

Thermometer 42°

We have measured since 8h 15m A.M. 22 Cords = 1 Mile

At 5h 30m P.M. $\begin{cases} A = 2 \\ B = 1 \\ C = 2+ \\ D = 2 \end{cases}$ Longer than the Standard

Thermometer 35°

Measured since 2h P.M. 13 Cords.
In all this day 35 Cords; each 12 Levels as before.
N. B. That at 33 Cords the 4th Mile Stone was opposite :: as near as could be Judged The
stone being on the Circle * at a Distance from the Meridian
The 1st Mile Post from the Tangent Point as last measured;
was five Levels South of our 4th Mile made by the Levels, that is when we had
measured by the Levels 4 Miles it wanted 5 Levels of the 4th Mile Stone or Post.
The Chain Carriers made a Mistake in Measuring the 1st time from the Tangent
Point to the West Line; see Journal minutes of the _____.
*Circle Round Newcastle of 12 Miles Radius.

1768
March
19

At 9h A.M.
Temperature 36°
$\begin{cases} A = 4 \\ B = 1.5 \\ C = 2 \\ D = 4 \end{cases}$ Longer than the Standard

At Noon
Temperature 31°
$\begin{cases} A = 5 \\ B = 2 \\ C = 4 \\ D = 3.5 \end{cases}$ Longer than Ditto

Measured in all this day 19 Cords five Levels and 7 feet which
reached the Tangent Point.

	Cords	Levels	feet			
1st day measured	11	5	3			
2nd Ditto	22	0	0			
3rd Ditto	23	0	0			
4th Ditto	35	0	0			
5th Ditto	19	5	7			
	110	10	10	= 5 Miles	3 chains	18 Links

340

20 Sun.
21   Sent to Philadelphia for Tents, Blankets, etc.
22
23
24   Examined the Levels by Plumblines hung at the Ends of the Levels; and
found them all good except one which we had altered a little on the 16th
Instead of endeavoring to measure with one Level.
Having found it very troublesome to keep the Levels equal in Length
to the Rods, we fixed pieces of Brass on the Levels at every 5 feet, and
drew a Division on them: and began to measure the Levels themselves
instead of the Rods.
Began at the point where the 12 Mile Line from Newcastle crosses our
1st Line.
The Level marked B = 8 Divisions at the End of the Standard shorter than the Standard.
Ditto   D = 0   Thermometer 49°
Measured in all this day 11 Cords. Each Cord = 12 Levels; which length
will always be used.
25   At Newark.
26   Corrected the Level B and made it = the Standard: that is 4 times
the standard Brass Rod = one Level.
At Noon   the Level D 5 Divisions Shorter than 4 times the Standard.
Thermometer 57°
Measured 10 Cords 7 Levels 1 foot which reached the 81 Mile Post.
Began again at the Mile Post and Measured 7 Cords.
At 6h P.M. the Level $\begin{cases} B \;\; 8 \;\;\;\; Longer \\ D \;\; 1\,1/2 \;\; Shorter \end{cases}$ than the Standard
Thermometer 43°
Measured in all this day 17 Cords 7 Levels 1 foot

341

27 Sun.   At Mr. Williams's.
28   Snow.
29   At 8h A.M. the Level $\begin{cases} B \;\; 14 \; Divisions \\ D \;\;\;\; 5 \; Divisions \end{cases}$ Longer
Thermometer 40°
Compared two Thermometers and they agreed within one Division.
At the 80th Mile Post we were behind the Mile Post 14 feet and 8 Inches.
At 2h P.M. $\begin{cases} B = 11 \; Longer \\ D = \;\; 2 \; Shorter \end{cases}$ Measured since 8 A.M. 22 Cords
Thermometer 47°
At 5h 30m P.M. $\begin{cases} B = 9.5 \; Longer \\ D = 1.5 \end{cases}$ Since 2:00 P.M. measured 22 Cords
Thermometer 40°
In all this day 44 Cords = 2 Miles.
30   At 8 1/2 A.M. $\begin{cases} B = 11 \; Long \\ D = \;\; 3 \end{cases}$
Thermometer 38°
When we came to the 78th Mile; we were 2 Levels 5 feet
behind or short of the Post.
At 2h 30m P.M. $\begin{cases} B = 5 \;\;\; Longer \\ D = 2.5 \; Shorter \end{cases}$
Thermometer 61°
Measured 24 Cords since 8h 30m A.M.
At 6h 15m P.M. $\begin{cases} B = 11 \; Longer \\ D = \;\; 1 \; Shorter \end{cases}$
Thermometer 45°
Measured since 2h 30m P.M. 16 Cords.
In all this day 40 Cords.

1768
March

31   At 8h 15m $\begin{Bmatrix} B = 12 \\ D = 3 \end{Bmatrix}$ Longer
Thermometer 45°

At 2h P.M. $\begin{Bmatrix} B = 9.5 \\ D = 1 \end{Bmatrix}$ Long
Thermometer 62.5°

Measured 17 Cords.

When we came to the 76th Mile, we were three Levels
and a half behind the 1st Mile Post.

At 6h 30m P.M. $\begin{Bmatrix} B = 12 \\ D = 5 \end{Bmatrix}$ Longer
Thermometer 49°

Since 2 P.M. measured 16 Cords.

Measured in all this day 33 Cords.

Broke one of the Thermometers.

April

1   At 8h A.M. $\begin{Bmatrix} B = 13 \\ D = 6.5 \end{Bmatrix}$ Longer
Thermometer 39°

At the 75th Mile we were 4 Levels 4 Feet
behind or short of the Mile Post.

At 2h P.M. $\begin{Bmatrix} B = 13 \\ D = 6 \end{Bmatrix}$ Longer
Thermometer 52°

Since 8h A.M. measured 27 Cords.

At 6h P.M. $\begin{Bmatrix} B = 12.5 \\ D = 6.5 \end{Bmatrix}$ Longer
Thermometer 35°

Measured since 2h P.M. 17 Cords.

Measured in all this day 44 Cords.

2   At 9h A.M. $\begin{Bmatrix} B = 13 \\ D = 5 \end{Bmatrix}$ Long
Thermometer 40°

At 2h 30m P.M. $\begin{Bmatrix} B = 10 \\ D = 4 \end{Bmatrix}$ Long
Thermometer 46°

Measured 19 Cords.

At the 7th Mile we were 6 Levels 7 Feet
behind the Mile Post.

At 6h 15m P.M. $\begin{Bmatrix} B = 11 \\ D = 4 \end{Bmatrix}$ Longer
Thermometer 37°

Measured since 2h 30m P.M. 14 Cords.

Measured in all this day 33 Cords.

3 Sun.   At Mr. Turner's at Head of Bohemia.

4   At 9h 30m A.M. $\begin{Bmatrix} B = 5 \\ D = 1 \end{Bmatrix}$ Longer
Thermometer 38°   Shorter

At 3h P.M. $\begin{Bmatrix} B = 10 \\ D = 2 \end{Bmatrix}$ Longer
Thermometer 51°

Since 9h 30m A.M. measured 26 cords: and
after this when we had measured 15 Cords and
8 Levels wanting 9 Inches it reached the 70th
Mile Post.

At 6h P.M. $\begin{Bmatrix} B = 10 \\ D = 3 \end{Bmatrix}$ Longer
Thermometer = 36°

Measured since 3h P.M. 16 Cords.

Measured in all this day 42 Cords.

Snow in the Evening.

5   Snow.

6   At 8h 30m A.M. $\begin{Bmatrix} B = 10 \\ D = 4 \end{Bmatrix}$ Longer
Thermometer 37°

Measured 16 Cords to the Mark on the North Side of Bohemia River.

In Figure 1   AB =
the Line crossing the
River Bohemia obliquely.

AC or Base on the
North side of the River.

The Angle C found from
Figure 2 =

The Angle C in Fig. 2 = the Angle C in Fig. 1.

6   Measured from a Mark at B on the South side of the
River to the North side of a Fork of the River = 3 Cords.

At 3h P.M.   {B = 10}   Longer
Thermometer 51°   {D =   3}

At 6h 15m P.M.   {B = 10.5} Long.
Thermometer 38°   {D =   2.5}
Since 3h P.M. measured 17 Cords. One of these was measured with
a Cord over the Fork of the River mentioned above.
Measured in all this day 36 Cords; besides the River Bohemia.

7   Snow all day and frost at Night.

8   At 11h A.M.   {B = 16}   Long.
Thermometer 37°   {D =   7}
Measured 27 Cords and 7 feet which reached
the 67th Mile Post.
At 6h 15m P.M.   {B = 10.5} Longer
Thermometer 40°   {D =   5 }
Measured in all this day 33 Cords.

                                                Figures a and b
                                                  344

9   At 9h A.M.   {B = 12 } Longer
Thermometer 44°   {D =   4.5}
Measured the Brass Standard by a foot Sector made
of Ivory by Mr. Bennet and found it wanted 0.15 of an
Inch in 5 feet. Thermometer as above.
Measured 16 Cords one Level and 3 feet which
reached the 66th Mile Post.
At 2h P.M.   {B = 5   Longer
Thermometer 57°   {D = 5   Shorter
Tried the Standard again by the Sector and found
it the same as above.
Since 2h P.M. measured 17 Cords.
At 6h P.M.   {B = 5   Longer
Thermometer 51°   {D = 3   Shorter
Measured in all this day 33 Cords.

10 Sun.   At Warwick.

11   At 9h A.M.   {B = 3+   Longer
Thermometer 59°   {D = 5   Shorter
At 5 Cords 1 Level 18 feet - the 65th Mile Post
At 2h 30m P.M.   {B = 5}   Shorter
Thermometer 66°   {D = 11}
Measured since 9h A.M. 24 Cords: and
then measured 3 Cords 2 Levels 14 feet which reached the 64th
Mile Post.
At 6h 30m P.M.   {B = 2}   Shorter
Thermometer 59°   {D = 8}
Measured since 2h 30m P.M. 19 Cords.
Measured in all this day 43 Cords.

12   At 8h A.M.   {B = 2.5 Longer} Mr. Dixon has   {B = 2.5   Shorter
Thermometer 47°   {D = 4.5 Shorter}   {D = 4.5   Longer
At 6 Cords 3 Levels 11 Feet the 63rd Mile Post.
At 3h P.M.   {B = 3}   Shorter
Thermometer 70°   {D = 11}
Measured since 8h A.M. 29 Cords.
At 6h P.M.   {B = 3   Longer
Thermometer 60°   {D = 6   Shorter
Measured since 3h P.M. 13 Cords.
Measured in all this day 42 Cords.

                                                          345

1768
April

13   At 9h A.M.   B = 0
        Thermometer 64°   D = 8   Shorter
        At 8 Cords 5 Levels 4.5 feet the 61 Mile Post.
        At 1h P.M.   B = 1.5   Shorter
        Thermometer 76°   D = 9
        Since 9h A.M. measured 20 Cords.
        At 30 Cords 6 Levels 1 foot the 60th Mile Post.
        Since 1h P.M. measured 13 Cords.
        At 6h P.M.   B = 0   Shorter
        Thermometer 64°   D = 7
        Measured in all this day 33 Cords.

14   At 8h 45m A.M.   B = 3   Longer
        Thermometer 53°   D = 5   Shorter
        At 19 Cords 6 Levels 16.5 feet the 59th Mile Post.
        Since 8h A.M. measured 33 Cords.
        At 4h 30m P.M.   B = 4   Longer
        Thermometer 53°   D = 4   Shorter
        Measured in all this day 33 Cords.

15   At 9h A.M.   B = 12   Longer
        Thermometer 45°   D = 6
        At 8 Cords 7 Levels 13 feet the 58th Mile Post.
        Measured in all this day 22 Cords.
        Note: This reached all most the South side of Esquire Delany's Fields.
        Did not measure the Levels again it raining very fast. This day
        we passed through swamps two feet deep in water nearly half the way.   346

16   At 8h A.M.   B = 15   Longer
        Thermometer 46°   D = 5
        At 8 Cords 8 Levels 7.5 feet the 57th Mile Post.
        At 30 Cords 9 Levels 2.5 feet the 56th Ditto.
        Measured since 8h A.M. 33 Cords.
        At 4h P.M.   B = 13   Longer
        Thermometer 56°   D = 7.5
        Measured in all this day 33 Cords.

17 Sun.   At Mr. Bucks.

18   At 8h 15m A.M.   B = 2.5   Longer
        Thermometer 52°   D = 9
        At 19 Cords 9 Levels 15.5 feet, the 55th Mile Post.
        At Noon   B = 2   Longer   Since 8h 15m measured
          Thermometer 67°   D = 4   Shorter   22 Cords.

        At 6h 30m P.M.   B = 2   Longer
        Thermometer 58°   D = 3   Shorter.   Since Noon measured 16 Cords.
        Measured in all this day 38 Cords.
        Found one joint when the Levels were exactly
        Plumbed did not quite correspond: Corrected it.

19   At 8h 30m A.M.   B = 1   Longer
        Thermometer 53°   D = 0
        At 3 Cords 10 Levels 8 Feet, the 54th Mile Post.
        At 25 Cords 10 Levels 18.5 Feet, the 53rd Mile Post.
        Measured since 8h 30m A.M. 37 Cords.
        At 3h P.M.   B = 1   Shorter
        Thermometer 74°   D = 6.5
        At 47 Cords 11 Levels 11 feet the 52nd Mile Post.
        After 3h P.M. measured 11 Cords.
        Measured in all this day 48 Cords.   347

20   At 8h 30m A.M.   B = 5   Longer
        Thermometer 57°   D = 2.5   Shorter
        At 22 Cords and two feet the 51 Mile Post.
        Since 8h 30m A.M. measured 26 Cords.
        At 2h 30m P.M.   B = 1.5   Shorter
        Thermometer 78°   D = 5
        At 6h 30m P.M.   B = 4   Longer
        Thermometer 61°   D = 6   Shorter   Since 2h 30m P.M. measured 18 Cords.
        At 44 Cords and 15 feet the 50th Mile Post.
        Measured in all this day 44 Cords.

21   At 8h 30m A. M.   ⌠B = 7   Longer
     Thermometer 52⁰   ⌡D = 1   Shorter
     At 1h 30m P. M.   ⌠B = 5   Longer
     Thermometer 75⁰   ⌡D = 3   Shorter   Since 8h 30m A. M. measured 22 Cords.
     At 22 Cords 1 Level 6 feet the 49th Mile Post.
     Measured 11 Cords after 1h 30m P. M.; and left off in a Swamp of Water 18 Inches deep.
     Measured in all this day 33 Cords.

22 ⌉
23 ⌋   At Mr. Bostock's. Rain day and night.

24 Sun.   Rain until 11h A. M.

25 ⌉
26 ⌋   Swamps so full of Water we couldn't proceed.

27   At 10h A. M.   ⌠B = 3   Longer
     Thermometer 73⁰   ⌡D = 3   Shorter
     At 11 Cords 1 Level 15.5 feet the 48th Mile Post.
     At 33 Cords 2 Levels 5 feet the 47th Mile Post.
     At 5h 30m P. M.   ⌠B = 1.5   Longer
     Thermometer 72⁰   ⌡D = 5   Shorter
     Since 10h A. M. measured 35 Cords.
     Measured in all this day 35 Cords.   348

28   At 8h 30m A. M.   ⌠B = 2   Longer
     Thermometer 54⁰   ⌡D = 5   Shorter

     At 6h P. M.   ⌠B = 1   Longer
     Thermometer 61.5⁰   ⌡D = 3   Shorter   Since 8h 30m A. M. measured 33 Cords.
     Measured in all this day 33 Cords.

29   _____
30   At 7h A. M.   ⌠B = 12.5 ⌉ Longer
     Thermometer 60⁰   ⌡D = 6.5 ⌋
     At 9 Cords 3 Levels 2.5 feet the 45th Mile Post.
     At 2h P. M.   ⌠B = 7 ⌉   Longer
     Thermometer 76⁰   ⌡D = 4 ⌋
     Since 7h A. M. measured 28 Cords.
     At 31 Cords 3 Levels 9.5 feet the 44th Mile Post.
     At 6h P. M.   ⌠B = 7 ⌉   Longer
     Thermometer 73⁰   ⌡D = 4 ⌋   Since 2h P. M. measured 9 Cords.
     Measured in all this day 37 Cords.
     The last 11 Cords passed through a Swamp near the Head of the River Choptank:
     The Water near two feet deep.

May

1 Sun.   At Mr. West's, late Mr. Robinson's.
2   At 8h 30m A. M.   ⌠B = 6   Longer
     Thermometer 54⁰   ⌡D = 1   Shorter
     At 16 Cords 3 Levels 19 feet the 43rd Mile Post.
     At 6h 30m P. M.   ⌠B = 7 ⌉   Longer
     Thermometer 56⁰   ⌡D = 2 ⌋   Since 8h 30m A. M. measured 32 Cords.
     Measured in all this day 32 Cords.
     N. B. The last 3 or 4 Cords passed across a Mill Pond in Choptank which I did not
     attend: The Water about 4 feet deep.   349

3   At 10h A. M.   ⌠B = 7.5 ⌉ Long.
     Thermometer 61⁰   ⌡D = 4   ⌋
     At 6 Cords 7 Levels 13 feet the 42nd Mile Post.
     At 3h P. M.   ⌠B = 2 ⌉   Longer
     Thermometer 82⁰   ⌡D = 0 ⌋
     Since 10h A. M. measured 24 Cords.
     At 6h 15m P. M.   ⌠B = 5.5 ⌉ Longer
     Thermometer 75⁰.5   ⌡D = 2   ⌋
     Since 3h P. M. measured 9 Cords.
     Measured in all this day 33 Cords.
     Note: There appears to be an error of one chain in the former measurement: For
     the 43rd Mile Post at   3 Levels 19 feet
     Common difference about   + 8
     the 42nd should have been at   4 Levels 7 feet
     but was at   7   13
     Difference = 66 ft. = 1 chain =   3 Levels 6 feet   That the Mile between the 42nd and 43rd is too great.

4 At 11h 30m A. M. $\lbrace$B = 7.5$\rbrace$ Long.
    Thermometer 79° $\lbrace$D = 4 $\rbrace$ Thunder storm all the morning.
    At 17 Cords 8 Levels 9 feet the 40th Mile Post.
    Measured in all this day 19 Cords.
    This passed the South Bank of the Main Branch of the Choptank one Level. This Branch was about
    4 Levels wide and 3.5 feet deep.

5 At 8h A. M. $\lbrace$B = 5.5$\rbrace$ Long.
    Thermometer 70°5 $\lbrace$D = 6 $\rbrace$
    At 20 Cords 8 Levels 17 feet the 39th Mile Post.
    At 2h P. M. $\lbrace$B = 2 $\rbrace$ Longer
    Thermometer 86° $\lbrace$D = 0 $\rbrace$
    Since 8h A. M. measured 22 Cords.
    At 5h 30m P. M. B = 6 Longer
    Thermometer 72° D = 3
    Since 2h P. M. Measured 11 Cords.
    Measured in all this day 33 Cords.

350

6 At 9h 30m A. M. $\lbrace$B = 11$\rbrace$ Long.
    Thermometer 66° $\lbrace$D = 3$\rbrace$
    At 9 Cords 9 Levels 11 feet the 38th Mile Post.
    At 4h P. M. $\lbrace$B = 8 $\rbrace$ Longer
    Thermometer 63° $\lbrace$D = 7.5$\rbrace$
    Since 9h 30m A. M. measured 27 Cords.
    At 31 Cords 10 Levels 5 feet the 37th Mile Post:
    After 4h P. M. we measured 6 Cords.
    Measured in all this day 33 Cords.

7 At 8h A. M. $\lbrace$B = 9.5$\rbrace$ Longer
    Thermometer 60° $\lbrace$D = 9 $\rbrace$
    At 20 Cords 10 Levels 19.5 feet, the 36th Mile Post.
    At 3h P. M. $\lbrace$B = 3.5$\rbrace$ Long.
    Thermometer 74° $\lbrace$D = 3 $\rbrace$
    Since 8h A. M. measured 34 Cords.
    Measured in all this day 34 Cords.

8 Sun. In the Golden Grove.

9 At 7h 30m A. M. $\lbrace$B = 3 Longer
    Thermometer 63° $\lbrace$D = 0
    At 8 Cords 11 Levels 13.5 feet the 35th Mile Post.
     31 Cords 0 Levels 8 feet the 34th Mile Post.
    At 4h 30m P. M. $\lbrace$B = 1.5 Shorter
    Thermometer = 85° $\lbrace$D = 8
    Since 7h 30m A. M. measured 44 Cords.
    Measured in all this day 44 Cords.

10 At 8h 30m A. M. $\lbrace$B = 3   Longer
    Thermometer 61° $\lbrace$D = 2.5 Shorter
    At 9 Cords 1 Level 2.5 feet the 33rd Mile Post.
    At 7h P. M. $\lbrace$B = 0
    Thermometer 68° $\lbrace$D = 1 Longer
    Since 8h 30m measured 31 Cords.
    Measured in all this day 31 Cords.
    N. B. Corrected the Ends of the Levels, which were a little out of Perpendicular. 351

11 At 9h 15m A. M. $\lbrace$B = 7.5 Longer
    Thermometer 70° $\lbrace$D = 3.5
    Rain in the Night and Morning.
    At 6h 30m P. M. $\lbrace$B = 3   Long.
    Thermometer 72° $\lbrace$D = 3
    Since 9h 30m A. M. measured 44 Cords.
    Measured in all this day 44 Cords.
    At 7h A. M. $\lbrace$B = 12   Longer
    Thermometer 54°5 $\lbrace$D = 11
    Rain in the Night.
    At 2h P. M. $\lbrace$B = 2 $\rbrace$ Longer
    Thermometer 67° $\lbrace$D = 1$\rbrace$
    Since 7h A. M. measured 22 Cords.
    At 44 Cords 5 Levels 2 feet the 28th Mile Post.
    At 6h 30m P. M. $\lbrace$B = 1.5 Long.
    Thermometer 68° $\lbrace$D = 0
    Since 2h P. M. Measured 23 Cords.
    Measured in all this day 45 Cords.

13   At 8h 30m A. M.   { B = 8 }   Longer
Thermometer 68°   { D = 2 }
At 21 Cords 5 Levels 17 feet the 27th Mile Post.
At 3h P. M.   { B = 0
Thermometer 75°   { D = 2.5   Shorter
Since 8h 30m A. M. Measured 25 Cords.
After 3h P. M. measured 8 Cords.
Measured in all this day 33 Cords.

14   At 10h 30m A. M.   { B = 4   Longer
Thermometer 66°   { D = 10.5

At 3h P. M.   { B = 8 }   Longer
Thermometer 74.°5   { D = 6 }
Since 10h 30m measured 22 Cords.
Measured in all this day 22 Cords.   352

15 Sun. At Kemuel Godwin's.
16   At 7h 30m A. M.   { B = 10 }   Long.
Thermometer 57°   { D = 9 }
At 10 Cords 7 Levels 9 feet, the 25th Mile Post.
At 3h 15m P. M.   { B = 0 }
Thermometer 81°   { D = 2 }   Shorter
Since 7h 30m A. M. Measured 32 Cords.
At 32 Cords 8 Levels 9.5 feet the 24th Mile Post.
After 3h 30m measured 12 Cords.
Measured in all this day 44 Cords.

17   At 8h 30m A. M.   { B = 7 }   Longer
 Thermometer 66°   { D = 5 }
At 10 Cords 9 Levels 3.5 feet the hole where the 23rd Mile Post stood; the Post
                        Lying by it.
At 3h P. M.   { B = 4.5 } Shorter. Since 8h 30m A. M. Measured 32 Cords.
Thermometer 87°   { D = 4 }
At 32 Cords 9 Levels 15 feet, the 22nd Mile Post.
After 3h P. M. measured 12 Cords.
Measured in all this day 44 Cords.

18   At 8h 30m A. M.   { B = 5.5 } Long.
Thermometer 67°   { D = 3 }
At 10 Cords 10 Levels 7.5 feet the 21st Mile Post.
At 1h P. M.   { B = 10 } Longer, measured my self
Thermometer 90°   { D = 4 }
Since 8h 30m A. M. measured 12 Cords.
The last 4 Cords passed through Marshy-Hope: The Water 4 and some places 5 feet
deep: this I did not attend.
Measured in all this day 12 Cords.
NOTE: The Brass Standard was wet, nearly all the time coming through
        the water.   353

19   At 9h 30m A. M.   { B = 10 } Long.
Thermometer 69°   { D = 5 }

At 3h P. M.   { B = 6 }   Long.
Thermometer 86°   { D = 1.5 }
Since 9h 30m A. M. Measured 22 Cords.
Measured in all this day 22 Cords.

20   At 8h A. M.   { B = 10 } Long.
Thermometer 69°   { D = 7 }
Great dews for 4 mornings past.
At 20 Cords 11 Levels 9.5 feet the 19th Mile Post.
At 3h P. M.   { B = 3 }   Longer
Thermometer 93°   { D = 1 }
Since 8h A. M. Measured 23 Cords.
After 3h P. M. Measured 14 Cords   At 6h P. M.
Measured in all this day 37 Cords.

1768
May

21   At 9h A.M.   )B = 5(Longer
           Thermometer 73°   )D = 3(Great dew.
           At 6 Cords and four feet, the 18th Mile Post.
           At 4h P.M.   )B = 2(Longer
           Thermometer 86°   )D = 3(Shorter
           Since 9h A.M. measured 30 Cords.
           Measured in all this day 30 Cords.

22 Sun. At Mr. Brown's.

23   Rain.

24   At 7h A.M.   )B = 19(Longer
           Thermometer 50°   )D = 16(
           At 3h P.M.   )B = 11(Longer
           Thermometer 75°   )D = 10(
           Since 9h A.M. measured 40 Cords.
           At 42 Cords 1 Level 13 feet the 15th Mile Post.
           After 3h P.M. Measured 15 Cords.
           Measured in all this day 55 Cords.   354

25   At 9h 30m A.M.   )B = 16(Longer
           Thermometer 59°   )D = 12(
           At 31 Cords 2 Levels 7.5 feet, the Hole or place where the 13th Mile Post stood.
           At 4h P.M.   )B = 19(Long.
           Thermometer 56°   )D = 15(
           Since 9h 30m A.M. Measured 33 Cords.
           Measured in all this day 33 Cords.
           Rain last Night and this Morning: Passed this Morning half a mile
           through water about 18 Inches deep.

26   At 9h 30m A.M.   )B = 21(Long.
           Thermometer 58°   )D = 17(
           At 20 Cords 2 Levels 12.5 feet, the place where the
           12th Mile Post stood. And at 42 Cords 2 Levels 19.5 feet
                         Ditto, the 11th Mile Post.
           At 5h 30m P.M.   )B = 21(Long.
           Thermometer 53°   )D = 15(
           Since 9h 30m A.M. Measured 44 Cords.
           Measured in all this day 44 Cords.
           Rain last night and part of this day; the
           Levels continually wet.

27   At 8h A.M.   )B = 11(Long.
           Thermometer 65°   )D = 7(
                 9 Cords 8 Levels 8.5 feet
           At   19 Cords 9 Levels 4 feet   The Points from which we laid off the
                42 Cords 2 Levels 16 feet   Offsets (in 1764) for the true Tangent Line.
           At 20 Cords 3 Levels 4 feet the 10th Mile Post.
           At 3h 15m P.M.   )B = 8(Long.
           Thermometer 79°   )D = 6(
           Since 8h A.M. Measured 33 Cords.
           At 42 Cords 3 Levels 12 feet the 9th Mile Post.
           After 3h 15m measured 22 Cords. (At 7h P.M. finished).
           Measured in all this day 55 Cords.
           Dry weather.   355

28   ———

29 Sun. At Mr. John Twiford's on the Banks of the River Nanticoke.

30   ———

31   At 8h 15m A.M.   )B = 1(Long.
           Thermometer 79°   )D = 0(
           At 9 Cords 3 Levels 19.5 feet, the 8th Mile Post.
           At 3h 30m P.M.   )B = 4(Shorter
           Thermometer 90°   )D = 8(
           Since 8h 15m A.M. Measured 31 Cords 4 Levels which
           reached to the River Nanticoke; High Water.
           Measured in all this day 31 Cords and 4 Levels.
           N.B. Very dry weather for 3 days past: The Levels
           did not pass through any water this day.
           At 31 Cords 4 Levels 13.5 feet, the 7th Mile Post.
           This was found by squaring off to
           the Post in our second Line, for it was removed out
           of this Line at Right Angles in 1764.

Began at the 6th Mile Post at 8h A.M. $\begin{cases} B = 7.5 \\ D = 0 \end{cases}$ Long.

                                               Thermometer 84°

At 2h 30m P.M.   B = 7   Long.
Thermometer 74°   D = 1
Since 8h A.M. measured 25 Cords.
After 2h 30m P.M. Measured 19 Cords.
Measured in all this day 44 Cords.

3   At 9h A.M. $\begin{cases} B = 10.5 \\ D = 5 \end{cases}$ Long.
Thermometer 76°

At 0 Cords 1 Level 3 feet, the 4th Mile Post.
At 3h P.M. $\begin{cases} B = 2.5 \\ D = 0.5 \end{cases}$ Long.
Thermometer 85°   Short
Since 9h A.M. Measured 33 Cords.
At 44 Cords 1 Level 16 feet the second Mile Post.
After 3h P.M. Measured 22 Cords.
Measured in all this day 55 Cords.

4   At 6h 15m A.M. $\begin{cases} B = 14 \\ D = 7+ \end{cases}$ Long.
Thermometer 64°

At 1h P.M. $\begin{cases} B = 2 \\ D = 2 \end{cases}$ Longer than the Standard
Thermometer 82°   Shorter
Since 6h 15m Measured 33 Cords 2 Levels 17.5 feet.
Measured in all this day 33 Cords 2 Levels 17.5 feet which reached the
Middle Point.
Note: This day we left a Mark in the ground (in a swamp) 12 Cords
before we came to the Middle Point; when we came to the 1st
Middle Point we measured back again to the Mark; and we fell
short of the said Mark about 4 Inches.

5 Sun. At Mr. Twiford's.
6   Began at the 6th Mile Post and measured Northward through the
Cripple of Nanticoke.
At 7h 30m A.M. $\begin{cases} B = 8 \\ D = 4 \end{cases}$ Long.
Thermometer 67°

At 2h P.M. $\begin{cases} B = 5.5 \\ D = 0 \end{cases}$ Long.
Thermometer 77°

Since 7h 30m A.M. we have measured 19 Cords 2 Levels which reached
to a Mark on the South Side of the River Nanticoke.
Passed over the River and began at the Point left off at on the
31st of May viz at 31 Cords 4 Levels; and measured three Levels South
and there placed a Mark: We then measured a Base from this
last Mark (westward) of 24 Levels; and there placed Mark; and
then took the Angles as by the Figure.
Here AB the River. AC = 24 Levels.
Angles taken with a Hadley's Quadrant
as by the Figure. This Quadrant had an Ivory
Arch, divided as Mr. Bird's but the makers
name was not upon it.
Hence the Breadth of the River AB = 31.67 Levels.
Measured in all this day 19 Cords 5 Levels besides the distance
between the Marks placed near the Banks of the River.
N.B. Since March the 12th Inclusive. Each Cord has been
equal to 12 Levels. The Level B always beginning the Cord,
and D ending it; so that except the Cord lengthened or
shortened more than one-half a Level no error of 2 Levels could arise
which was never the case; the Cord was often daily proved, and when
down was not taken up till the Level D was brought to
its place.
One Man was constantly employed to stretch the Cord, who also
kept the Reckoning besides Mr. Dixon and myself; so that no
error of a Cord could arise: Even the Mile Posts were sufficient
for that purpose as the Lines had been measured so often before.

356

Figure
357

358

9   Left Mr. Twiford's. Situated on the most Rural and delightful
Banks of River Nanticoke. Here is the most pleasing Contemplative
View I've ever seen in America; the River makes a turn from
the Southward to the Eastward nearly at Right Angles and not one House
to be seen on either side of the River, though the whole in
View for 4 Miles: But Nature's genuine produce of
Pine and Cedar on both sides its rural Banks, for
which Ships resort from all parts to supply distant
Climes destitute of so great a blessing.

10   At Dover.

11   At Mount Pleasant.

12 Sun.   At Ditto.

13   At Newark.

14   Discharged all Hands.

16   At Brandywine.

20   At Philadelphia.

21   Informed the Commissioners we had finished the mensuration
of a Degree of Latitude for the Royal Society; and that we
were now ready for returning Home.
Were informed by the Reverend Mr. Peters and Mr. Chew, that a meeting
of the Commissioners of both Provinces was necessary
before we left the Continent; and that before this meeting, they desired
to have the Plan of the Lines Engraved.

26 Sun.   Returned to the Forks of Brandywine.

29   At Philadelphia.

Moon Eclipsed

At 8h 48m by the Watch, the Moon entered the Cloud; the Eclipse
not begun, Clouds continued etc.

July

8   Compared the 5 feet brass Rod (which we used on measuring
the Lines for the Royal Society) with the brass Yard belonging
to the 6 foot Sector; and found it one Division and a half of
those divisions at the End of the Brass Rod (that is .015
of an Inch) shorter than the Yard in 5 feet. - Thermometer 70°; two
of them agreeing, one of which we used on the Line.
We compared the measures by taking the whole Yard and
two feet, and also by taking 2.5 feet on the Yard twice, it always
by many trials appearing that the Rod is not 5 feet according to the Yard;
it wanting .015 of an Inch

$$
\begin{array}{r}
.015 \\
4 \\
\hline
.060 \text{ in one Level} \\
264 \text{ Levels in one Mile} \\
\hline
240 \\
360 \\
120 \\
\hline
15.840 = \text{Inches in a Mile}
\end{array}
$$

difference between the
measures: therefore our measurements by the Levels should
be 15.84 Inches in a Mile more than by the Chain Measure; that is;
the distance between the Mile Posts should be one Mile
and 15.84 Inches.
N.B. We have marked the length of the Yard from one End of the Rod by making
a point between two scratches thus 1 · 1 on the Rod.

18   Acquainted Mr. Chew that Mr. Dawkins who had undertaken
(by an agreement with the Reverend Mr. Ewen, one of the Gentlemen Commissioners) to
Engrave a Plan of the Lines (and had about half finished it);
would not proceed farther in the work.

19   Mr. Smither engaged to finish the Engraving the said Plans
by an agreement with Mr. Chew.

August

16   Two Hundred copies of the Plans of the Lines Printed off.

(Editorial Note: Certificate of Admission to membership in the American Philosophical Society.)

Mr. Charles Mason
        is duly admitted a corresponding Member of the
        American Society held at Philadelphia for
        promoting useful knowledge. Dated 15 Day of
        April AD 1768.

                        Signed by order of the Society
                            Cha. Thomson
                                Corresponding Secretary   361

1768
August
  17   The Rev. Mr. Peters informed us there was a Meeting of the
            Gentlemen Commissioners of both Provinces to be held at Newtown
            on Chester River in Maryland, the 25th Instant; where we
            were desired to attend.
  25   Attended the Gentlemen Commissioners at New Town,
  26   where our accounts were settled. Certificates given us
  27   of the same: and the whole work of our part relating
            to the Business we had been engaged in for the Honorable
            Proprietors of Maryland and Pennsylvania, was entirely finished.
  31   At Philadelphia.

September
  8   Left Ditto and proceeded for New York.
  9   At Ditto.
  10   At Ditto.
  11   At 11h 30m A. M. went on Board the Halifax Packet Boat for
            Falmouth. Thus ends my restless progress
            in America.
                                    C. Mason   362

(Undated   An envelope addressed to Messrs. Mason and Dixon
            in the handwriting of Thomas Penn.)

        To
            Mr. Charles Mason and Jeremiah
            Dixon at the Prince of Wales's Arms
            the Corner of
                    Leicester Fields
                        London

                WINDSOR
                (Rubber Stamp)   363

Gentlemen:
            I have received your letter and account and shall
    be in Town on Thursday about three o'clock. I am by appointment to
    dine with Mr. Wilmot Friday and would meet Mr. Hemessley an hour before dinner
    there or if he will tell you what time will best suit him and you inform
    me of it Thursday at three o'clock I will endeavour to make it suit me,
    and will see Mr. Wilmot the same morning at the House of Lords, I am

                        Your very humble Servant

                        Thomas Penn

    Hope House near Windsor
    November 14, 1768   364

FIGURE 21a

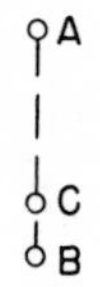

FIGURE 21b

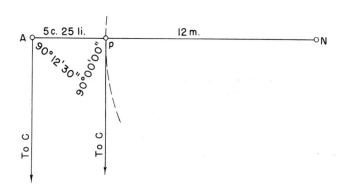

FIGURE 23

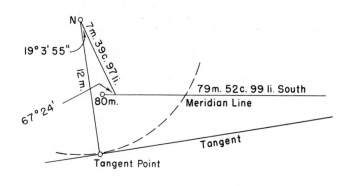

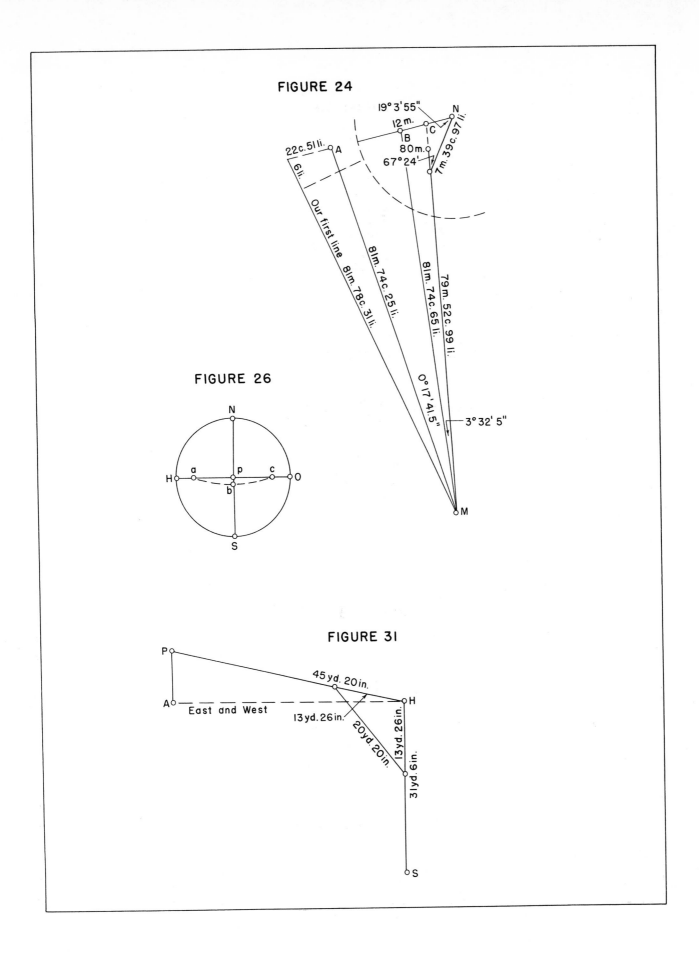

FIGURE 24

19° 3' 55"

12 m.
B C

22c. 51 li. A

6 li.

80 m.
67° 24'

7m. 39c. 97 li.

N

79m. 52c. 99 li.

81m. 74c. 25 li.

81m. 74c. 65 li.

Our first line 81m. 78c. 31 li.

0° 17' 41.5"

3° 32' 5"

M

FIGURE 26

N

H a p c O
b

S

FIGURE 31

P

A East and West

45 yd. 20 in.

13 yd. 26 in.

20 yd. 20 in.

13 yd. 26 in.

31 yd. 6 in.

H

S

213

FIGURE 69

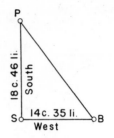

FIGURE 72

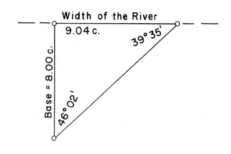

FIGURE 73

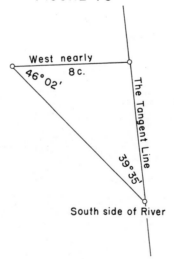

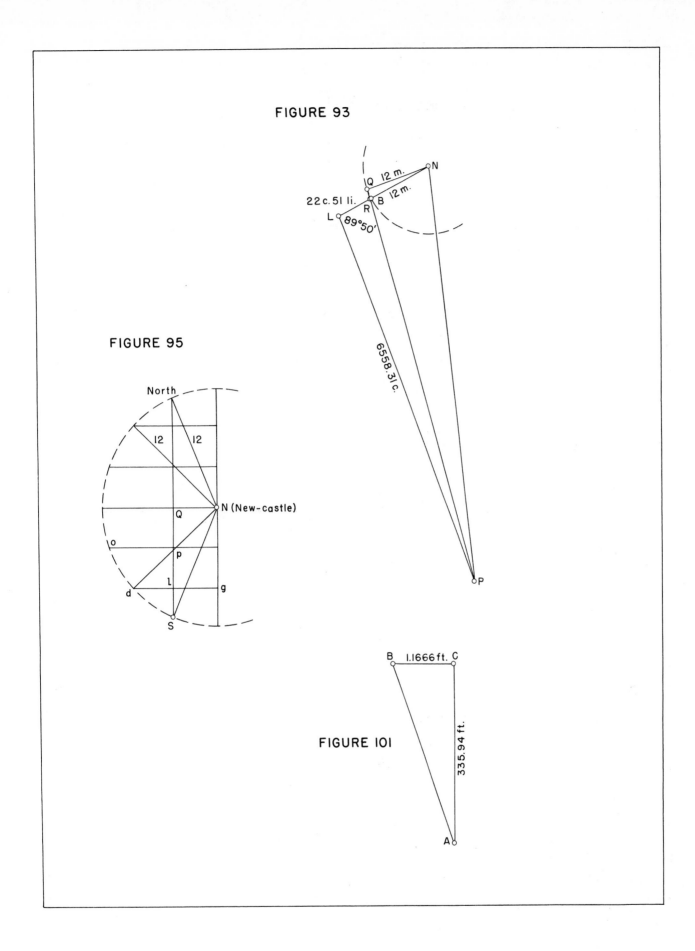

FIGURE 93

FIGURE 95

FIGURE 101

215

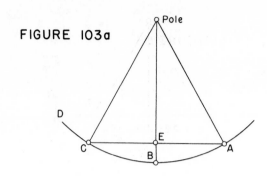

FIGURE 103a

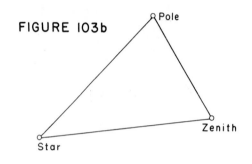

FIGURE 103b

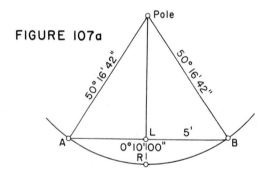

FIGURE 107a

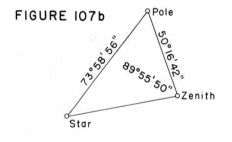

FIGURE 107b

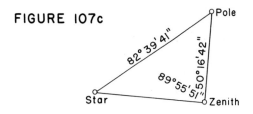

FIGURE 107c

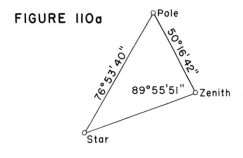

FIGURE 110a

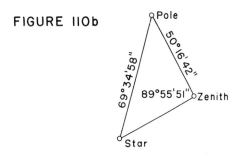

FIGURE 110b

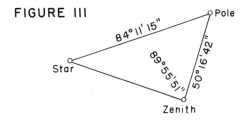

FIGURE 111

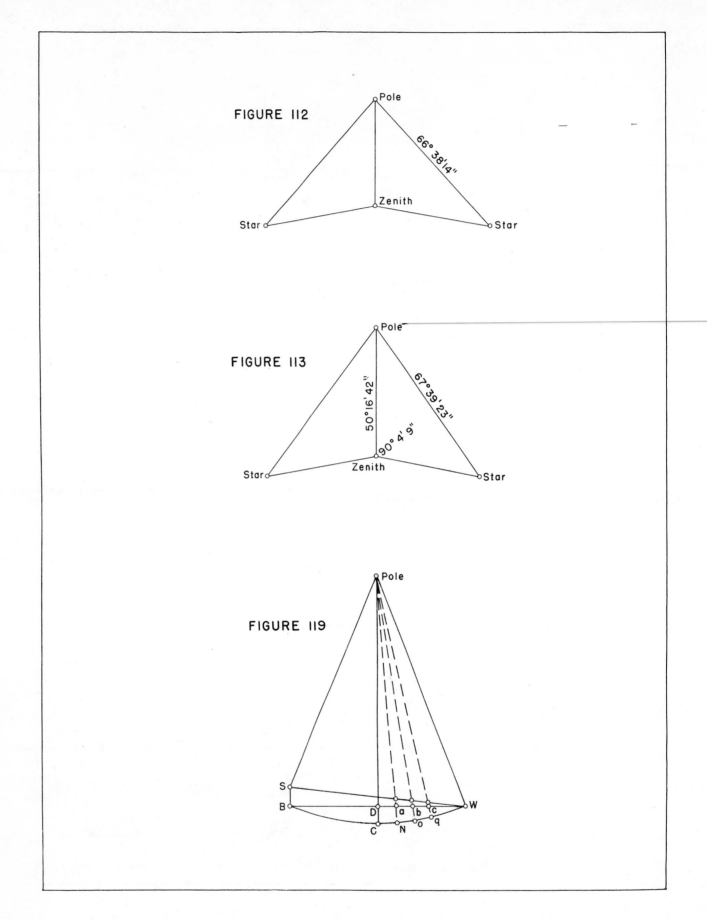

FIGURE 112

66° 38' 4"

Pole

Zenith

Star

Star

FIGURE 113

50° 16' 42"

67° 39' 23"

90° 4' 9"

Pole

Zenith

Star

Star

FIGURE 119

Pole

S

B

D   a   b   c

W

C   N   o   q

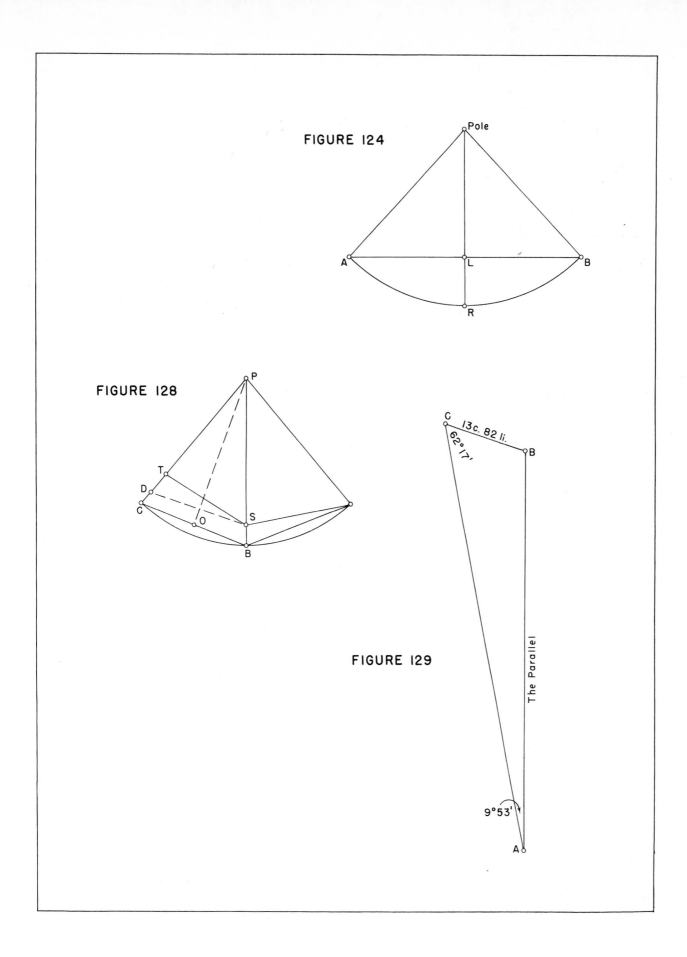

FIGURE 124

FIGURE 128

FIGURE 129

C   13c. 82 li.   B

62°17'

The Parallel

9°53'

A

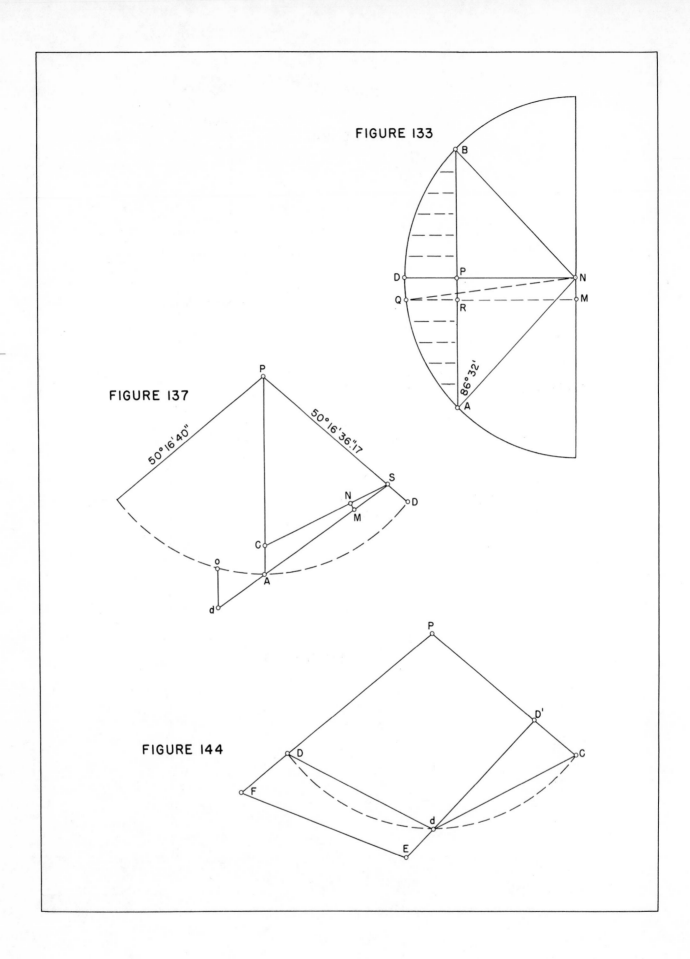

FIGURE 133

FIGURE 137

FIGURE 144

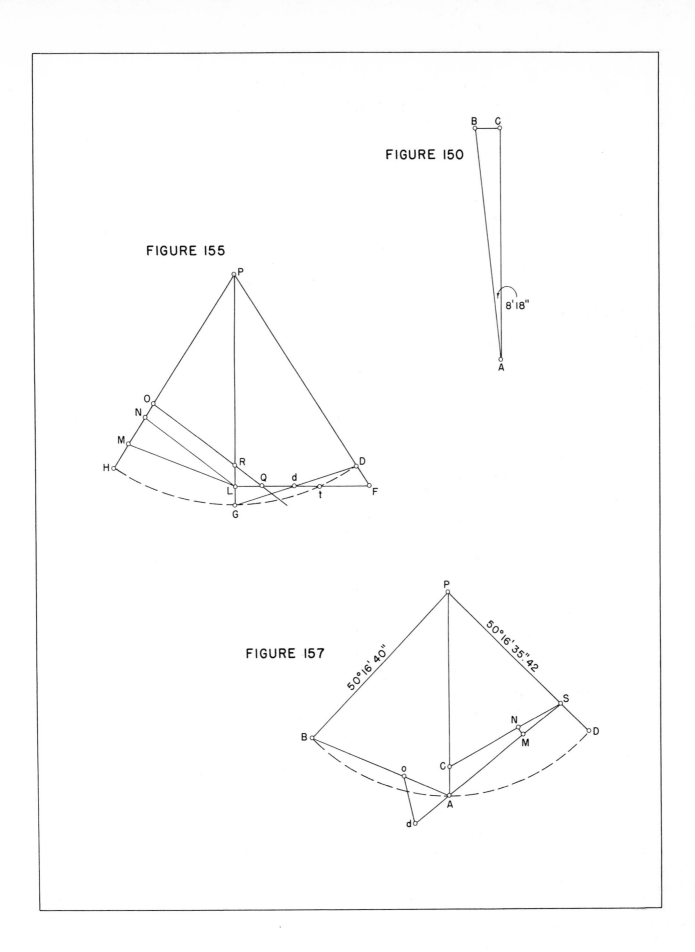

FIGURE 150

FIGURE 155

FIGURE 157

221

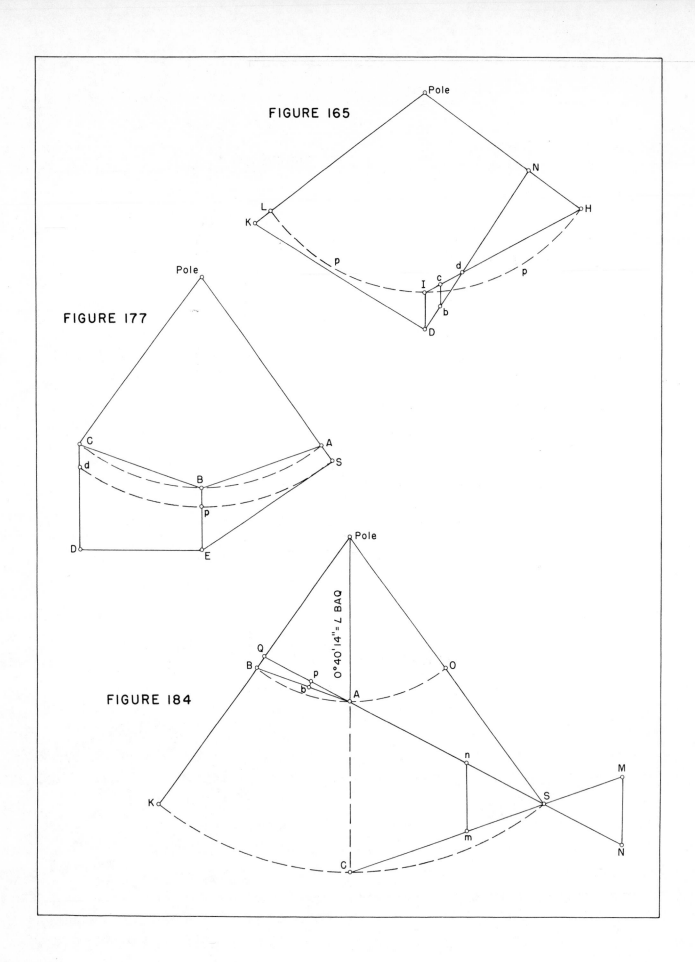

FIGURE 165

FIGURE 177

FIGURE 184

0°40'14" = ∠ BAQ

222

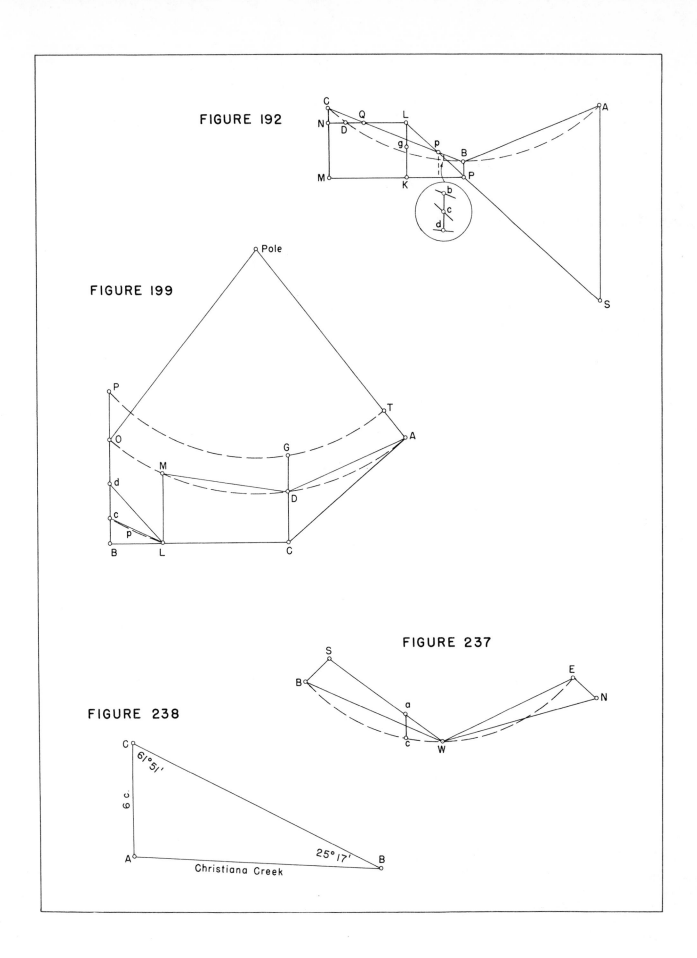

FIGURE 192

FIGURE 199

FIGURE 237

FIGURE 238

Christiana Creek

61°51'

6 c.

25°17'

223

FIGURE 239

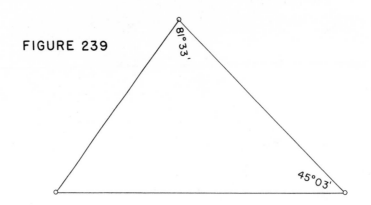

FIGURE 266a

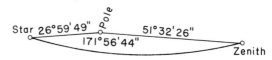

FIGURE 266b

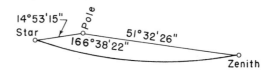

FIGURE 267

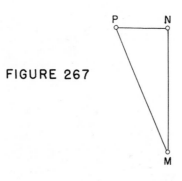

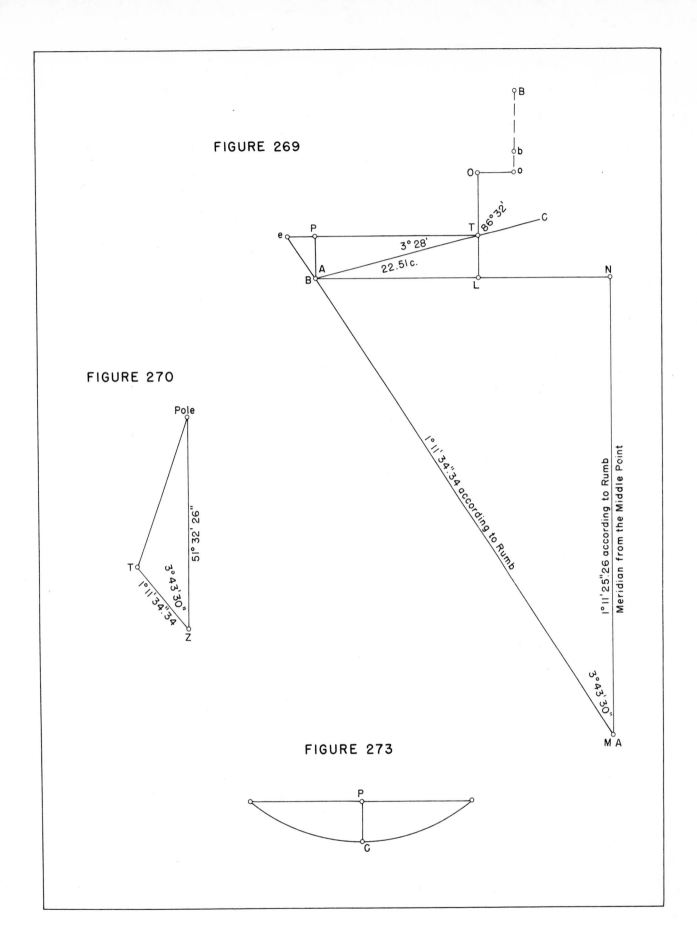

FIGURE 269

FIGURE 270

FIGURE 273

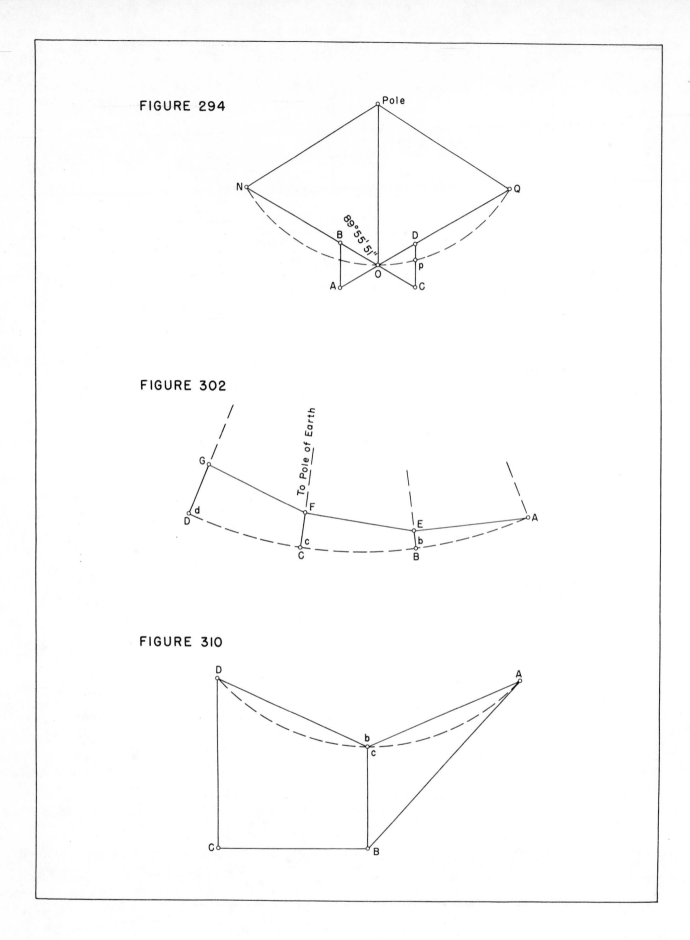

FIGURE 294

FIGURE 302

To Pole of Earth

FIGURE 310

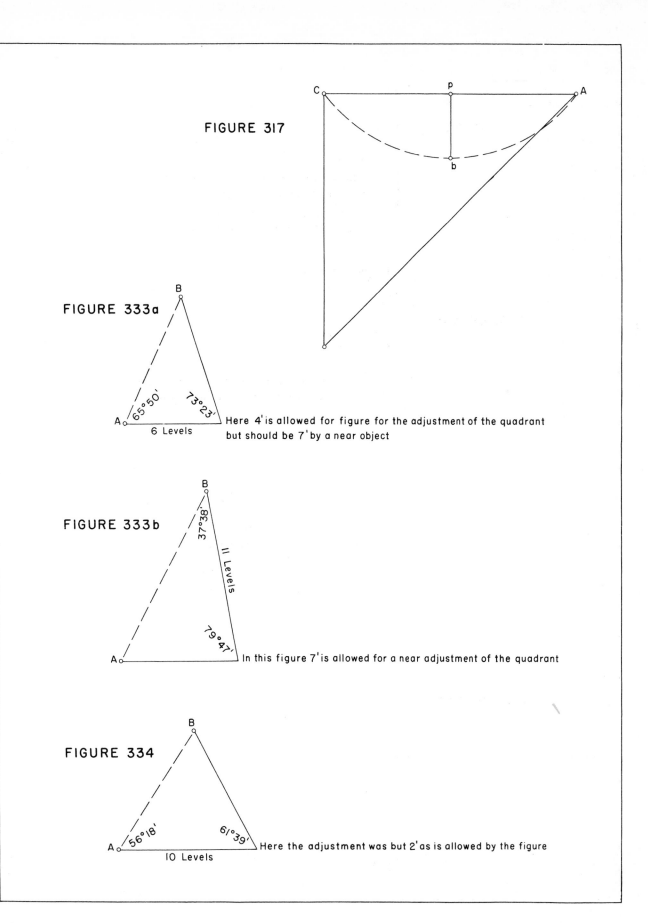

FIGURE 317

FIGURE 333a

65°50' 73°23'
A 6 Levels Here 4' is allowed for figure for the adjustment of the quadrant
but should be 7' by a near object

FIGURE 333b

37°38'
11 Levels
79°47'
A In this figure 7' is allowed for a near adjustment of the quadrant

FIGURE 334

56°18' 61°39'
A 10 Levels Here the adjustment was but 2' as is allowed by the figure

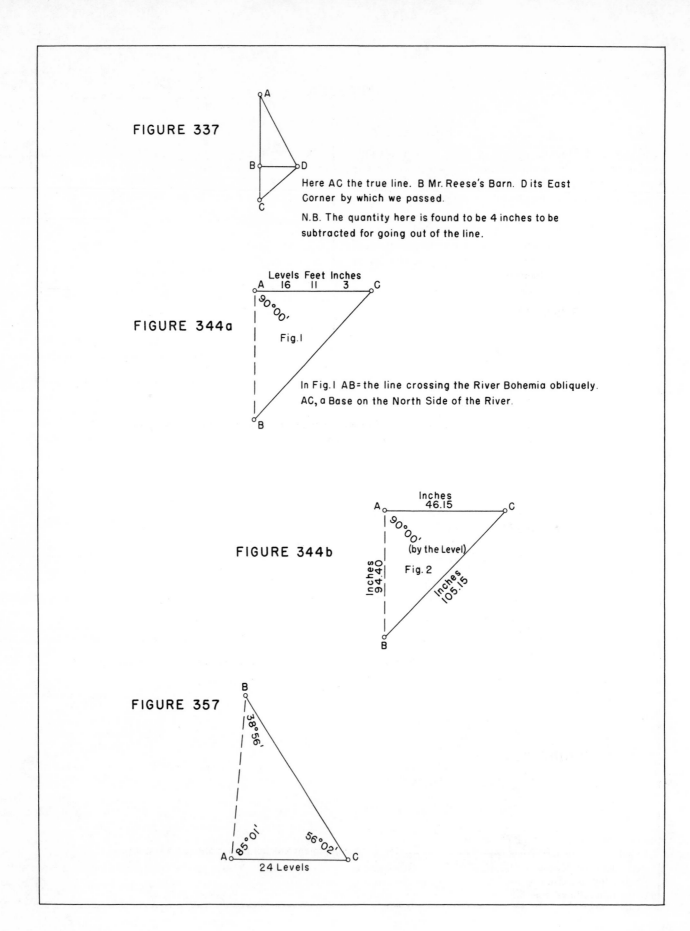

FIGURE 337

Here AC the true line. B Mr. Reese's Barn. D its East Corner by which we passed.

N.B. The quantity here is found to be 4 inches to be subtracted for going out of the line.

FIGURE 344a

Levels Feet Inches
A   16   11   3   C
90°00'
Fig.1

In Fig.1 AB= the line crossing the River Bohemia obliquely. AC, a Base on the North Side of the River.

FIGURE 344b

Inches 46.15
90°00'
(by the Level)
Inches 94.40
Fig. 2
Inches 105.15

FIGURE 357

38°56'
85°01'
56°02'
24 Levels

228

APPENDIX

ENTRIES PRECEDING THE JOURNAL

Mason and Dixon's record of their survey actually begins on page 25 of the manuscript Journal as it has come down to us. The first 24 pages contain material which is extraneous, incidental, or misplaced as follows:

Pages 1-4. Explanatory introduction added when the manuscript was in possession of the Department of State. Its contents are utilized in the first chapter of the editorial Introduction.

Pages 5-12. Correspondence regarding the acquisition of the manuscript by the Department of State:

Department of State.
Washington, November 2, 1876.
George W. Childs, Esquire,
Philadelphia, Pennsylvania.
Sir:

On September 3rd. a Mr. S. P. Mayberry addressed the Secretary of the Interior from the Elm Avenue Hotel, Philadelphia, stating that the original journal of the Commissioners who located Mason and Dixon's line, giving a full and complete account relative to the proceedings each day, was on exhibition at the Centennial Exhibition, and belonged to a gentleman in Halifax; and the writer suggested that the journal be bought, if possible.

The matter has been referred to me, and as I have no acquaintance with the writer himself, and as it is not at all likely that he can now be found near Philadelphia, I take the liberty of addressing you, to ask whether you will oblige me by causing the proper inquiries to be cautiously made—probably in the Canadian Department, as the owner was said to reside at Halifax, to ascertain whether such journal actually exists, and if so, to find out, confidentially, whether it can be purchased, and for what sum.

I may add that the funds at the control of this Department for any such purpose are really small, and that no considerable price could be paid; at the same time it is believed that the notes of survey are valuable and desirable to the Government.

I am, Sir,
Your obedient servant,
Hamilton Fish.

Office of the Public Ledger.
Philadelphia, February 12, 1877

Mr dear Mr. Fish:

I enclose a letter my friend Mr. Dreer has just received in regard to the Mason & Dixon matter. Mr. D. says it is the best copy in existence and has matter connected with it that the others have not.

The owner has no idea who wants it, nor are we in any way committed.

With high esteem,
very truly your friend
Geo. W. Childs

Hon. Hamilton Fish

Department of State.
Washington, February 17th, 1877.
George W. Childs, Esq.
Philadelphia, Pa.
My dear Sir:

I have to acknowledge the receipt of your note of the 12th instant enclosing a letter to Mr. Dreer from the owner of the manuscripts relating to the Mason and Dixon line.

I will take advantage of the interest you have shown in securing the manuscripts to this Department; by requesting you to conclude the purchase of them at the price named by their owner, five hundred dollars in gold; and I will thank you to inform me when and by what means I shall remit a draft for the same.

I return herewith Mr. James' letter.

I am, my dear Sir,
Your obedient servant.
Hamilton Fish.

Halifax, Nova Scotia
Provincial Museum.
Feb. 26, / '77.

Secy. Hamilton Fish
Sir:

We have just received a letter from Mr. Dreer of Phili. in which he says that you desired him to request (Judge) A. James to send the Mason & Dixon Journal to your address, and that you would remit to him a *Draft for Five Hundred Dollars in Gold.*

I am instructed accordingly by Judge James to forward to you the said Journal.

I have the honor to be
Your obedient servant,
D. Honeyman

Judge
Alexander James
(of the Supreme Court of Nova Scotia)
P.S. Some of the members of the Nova Scotia Government have a wish to retain it in N.S. but the proper place for it is in the Archives of the Government of the United States.

D. H.

Halifax, Nova Scotia
March 8, 1877

Hon. Secretary
   Hamilton Fish
      State Department, Washington.
Sir:

I forwarded to you as instructed by Mr. Dreer of Philadelphia a *registered Package* containing the Mason & Dixon Journal. As I am responsible to Judge James, the owner of the said Journal, for the Journal or its value $500 (Five Hundred Dollars in Gold) you will favor me by remitting to me the cheque for the above amount in terms of the agreement with Mr. Dreer. It was committed to my care as the *Representative of Nova Scotia in the Canadian Department of the Centennial Exhibition* and exhibited in our Department where it came to Mr. Dreer's notice.

I have the honor to be
Your obedient servant
D. Honeyman

Address
   Rev. Dr. David Honeyman
      Director of the Provincial Museum,
         Halifax, Nova Scotia.

If you wish any information regarding your correspondent, apply to my personal friends Dr. F. V. Hayden & Prof. Baird.

Department of State.
Washington, D.C.
March 8th, 1877.

George W. Childs, Esq.
   Philadelphia, Pa.
Sir:

Referring to previous correspondence on the subject, I have to enclose the Disbursing Clerk's com check, No. 1483, for $500, in payment of the original copy of the Field notes of the survey of Mason & Dixon line; purchased of Dr. Honeyman & also a voucher therefor, which I will thank you to have signed by him and returned to this Department at your earliest convenience.

I am, Sir, Your obedient servant.
Hamilton Fish.

Pages 13-16. Rough notes of observations, not printed here because they appear in more finished style in the Journal as indicated here:

P. 13. Observations reported as of 20 and 21 December, 1763.

P. 14. Observations reported as of 30 and 31 December, 1763, and 1 and 2 January, 1764.

P. 15. Observations reported as of 28, 29, and 30 December, 1763.

P. 16. Observations reported as of 25 and 27 December, 1763.

Page 17 is blank except for the word "London."

Pages 18-18a: Eclipse of the Moon, March, 1764:

The Eclipse of the Moon ended in the Forks of the Brandywine the 17th of March 1764 at 8h 04m 10s by the watch.

Equal Altitudes of Regulus by the watch thus

8h	58m	46s	10h	27m	30s	(very dubious)
9h	01m	16s	10h	29m	41s	
9h	04m	05s	10h	32m	09s	

Hence Regulus passed the Meridian

by the watch	9h	45m	28s
Right Ascension of Regulus	9h	55m	48s
Watch slow for Sidereal Time	0h	10m	20s

Note: Air was very clear and eclipse observed with a magnifying power of about 50. The earth's shadow on the disk was the best defined I ever saw. The watch moved very regular Sidereal Time.

19h	30m	57s	
19h	30m	55s	
19h	30m	56s	(Mean)
9h	45m	28s	Regulus passed according to the watch
9h	55m	48s	Right ascension of Regulus
0h	10m	20s	Watch slow for Sidereal Time
8h	04m	10s	Eclipse of the Moon ended
8h	14m	30s	Right Ascension of the Mid Heaven at time of Eclipse
23h	31m	27s	Right Ascension of the Sun
8h	23m	03s	Apparent time, Evening Estimate
1h	36m	40s	At Paris, morning of 18th
5h	13m	37s	Difference, Meridian at Paris by Estimate
23h	52m	31s	Right Ascension of Sun at the End of the Eclipse seen at Brandywine
8h	14m	30s	Right Ascension of Mid-Heaven
8h	28m	59s	Apparent Time precisely
1h	36m	40s	At Paris
5h	14m	41s	Time Difference from Paris

Pages 19-20. Observations made in 1764:

This we finished the 20th of March, when we began to run a Visto in the Meridian Southward. We measured the horizontal distance twice over, dividing the distance into five parts and any part that there was the least doubt of an error we measured a third time; and the result was that two measurements differed not quite three yards. All the Hills were measured with levels having Plummets to shew when they were Horizontal.—The Reckoning kept by each of us and a Surveyor all separate. We have finished a (Datum) for Running the Western Boundary; and have set up a post Marked West.

Received your letter of Thursday and we shall exert our utmost endeavor to completely answer its contents. The beginning of the winter was very favourable for observations, but the Spring has been almost entirely cloudy.— Your Instrument, the Sector, Returns to itself with such accuracy that we hope our journal will bear the nicest examination of any Practical Astronomer.

The Latitude of the Southernmost point of the City of Philadelphia; from the mean of 32 observations the extreme of which differed only 3."5 is 39°56′29."1 North. At this point we settled the Zenith Distances of 8 stars from the Mean of 52 observations. On the (blank) of January we left Philadelphia and Set up the Sector in the Forks of

Brandywine (31 miles west) where we made about the same number of observations of the (stars).

Page 21. Observations reported in 1763 but of dubious dating as Mason and Dixon did not arrive in Philadelphia until late that year.

81 Miles	AB = 80 chains in an
81 miles 74 chains 25 links according to the Book = CA the Tangent when the radius was continued, 5 chains 25 links West of the 12 miles from Newcastle	Inch
	AC + 81 miles = the length of the last tangent line to the Radius of the circle from Newcastle.

100 :80 : :97 :78.60 = 78 chains and 60 links according to (indistinct) = length of the Tangent CA

19 August 1763

The Angle CAN = 90°12′30″ measured, Then went to the post p (12 miles from N) and set off 89°55′43″ with the Line pN, and extended a line northerly 157 feet 8 inches where we found in the earth a square white oak post marked $\frac{T}{XII}$ after fixing of which we took the angles and distances from thence to several trees to determine if should it want to be moved. 19 August 1763

The 20th August 1763 proceeded to make calculations to find the situation of the point that would be in the Periphery of the circle which would be the Tangent point by the Data mentioned yesterday and find that the course of the Tangent line should be 2′45″ Eastward of the line last run and that the Radius from Newcastle should be 15′15″ more Northerly than the 12 mile Line or Radius formerly run from thence and that the post in our Instructions to be marked TP should be set off by an angle of 89°52′22.″30 with the said radius by a line extended Northerly from the post marked $\frac{M}{XII}$ in length, two hundred and 81 feet and 8 tenths part of an inch but it proved too late to fix the post The 21st August 1763

This morning I went to the post marked $\frac{M}{XII}$ and set off the angle 89°52′22.″30 with the radius formerly run and extended a line therefrom 281 feet 8 inches where we fixed firmly in the earth a square white post marked TP and after we had fixed the same we took the bearings and distances of several trees, etc. to know if it wanted to be moved; next proceeded to go back and mark off the offsets from each 5 mile post agreeable to calculation.

Figures 21a and b

Page 22. Miscellaneous notes dated between 1762 and 1767:

From the Meridian first run they were to lay off an angle of 3°32′5″ westerly by a meeting of the Commissioners held at New Castle the 30th of April 1762. The 25th of May 1762 the Surveyors began at Midpoint and ended Sept. 9th 1762, when they say from the 81 Milepost they continued the line 60 chains, where they placed a squared white post, and then continued it 14 chains 65 links to another white oak post set in the intersection of the said line and 12 mile line or radius run from the center of Newcastle last winter, the said post being 33 chains 76 links Eastward of the post fixed at the extremity of the radius. They afterwards by Lord Baltimores large Theodolite took the angle included between the now finished line and the 12 mile line run from the center of New Castle last winter and judged the same to be somewhat more than 90°26′ which excess could not be exactly determined by the said Instrument.

On the 17th September 1762, The Commissioners gave the surveyors the following instructions. You are to go to the post marked Middle point and set off an angle from the line last run Northwesterly of 16′40″. Agreeable to this they met at the Middle point 18th September 1762 and proceeded to run a third line which they ended the 19th August 1763, which ran 5 chains 25 links west of the Periphery of the circle, see the other side of this paper.

Note: In April 1767 William Lukins (Surveyor General of the Province of Pennsylvania) told me that our statute yard was the thickness of a piece of Parchment shorter than theirs, with which they measured the Tangent Line.

Pages 23-24 contain only diagrams which are reproduced in original or transcribed from elsewhere in the present volume (figs. 5, 23, 24).